Name ______________________________

CARNEGIE LEARNING

D1473801

High School Math Solution

MATHbook

ALGEBRA I • VOL. 1 STUDENT EDITION

4th Edition

AUTHORING TEAM

Sandy Bartle Finocchi | Amy Jones Lewis

Josh Fisher | Janet Sinopoli | Victoria Fisher | Sarah Galasso

501 Grant Street, Suite 1075
Pittsburgh, PA 15219
Phone: 888-851-7094
Customer Service Phone: 412-690-2444

www.carnegielearning.com

Foundation Authors (2010)

William S. Hadley,
Algebra and Proportional Reasoning

Mary Lou Metz,
Data Analysis and Probability

Mary Lynn Raith,
Number and Operations

Janet Sinopoli,
Algebra

Jaclyn Snyder,
Geometry and Measurement

Acknowledgments

- The members of the Carnegie Learning Production Team—Sara Kozelnik, Sara Schmidt Boldon, Laura Norris, Mary Travis, Jaana Bykonich, Michelle Rohm, and Bob Dreas
- The members of Carnegie Learning Cognitive Scientist Team—John Connelly, Bob Hausmann, and Martina Pavelko—for their insight in learning science and collaboration on MATHia Software.
- **Primary Design:** Abbe Eckstein
- **Design Support:** Madison Kalo, Douglas Fuchs, and Heather Greenwood
- Production Vendors: Paul Leveno, BizeeWorks, LLC, Lumina Datamatics, LTD, and Trivium Education Services

Credits: Art and Photo Credits follow the Index.

ISBN: 978-1-68459-742-0

Student Edition

Printed in the United States of America

3 4 5 6 7 8 9 B&B 26 25 24 23 22

Cover Design by Anne Milliron and Moncur (thinkmoncur.com)

LONG + LIVE + MATH

Mathematics is so much more than memorizing rules. It is learning to reason, to make connections, and to make sense of the world. Focus on the journey and the process.

No matter where you are starting from, your effort will lead to improvement.

We believe in Learning by Doing™ — and we believe in YOU!

Introducing Carnegie Learning's High School Math Solution

You will develop a deep understanding of key mathematical ideas by actively engaging with them in various ways — in print and online, together and individually, through concept and application.

60/40

LEARN
TOGETHER WITH

MATHbook

When you work in this textbook, you'll collaborate, create, communicate, and problem-solve together with your peers.

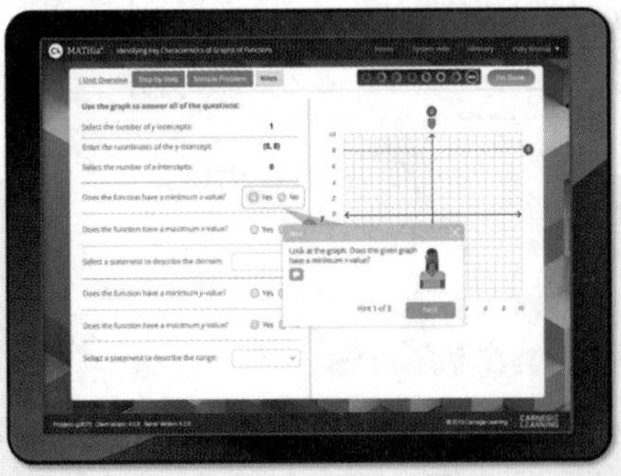

LEARN
INDIVIDUALLY WITH

MATHia

When you work in this software, you'll work at your own pace and receive 1-to-1 coaching that adapts to your needs as you go.

EXPLORE FAMILY RESOURCES ONLINE

www.carnegielearning.com/home-connection/

Download MATHia progress trackers!
www.carnegielearning.com/login

TOPIC 3 Linear Regressions

MATHbook

MATHia

ALGEBRA I • VOL. 1

MODULE 2 Exploring Constant Change

TOPIC 1 Linear Functions

MATHbook

MATHia

TOPIC 2 Solving Linear Equations and Inequalities

TOPIC 3 Systems of Equations and Inequalities

TOPIC 4 Functions Derived from Linear Relationships

ALGEBRA I • VOL. 2

MODULE 3 Investigating Growth and Decay

TOPIC 1 Introduction to Exponential Functions

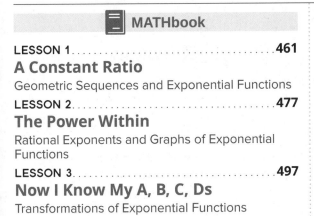

MATHbook

MATHia

TOPIC 2 Using Exponential Equations

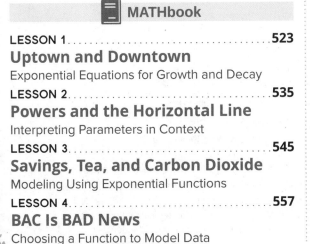

MATHbook

MATHia

ALGEBRA I • VOL. 2

MODULE 4 Describing Distributions

TOPIC 1 One-Variable Statistics

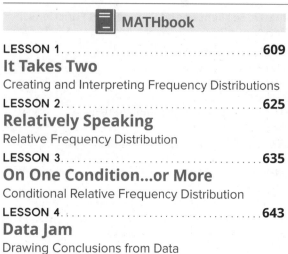

TOPIC 2 Two-Variable Categorical Data

ALGEBRA I • VOL. 2

MODULE 5 Maximizing and Minimizing

TOPIC 1 Introduction to Quadratic Functions

TOPIC 2 Solving Quadratic Equations

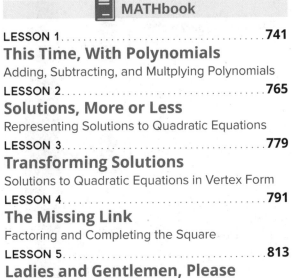

MATHbook

MATHia

TOPIC 3 Applications of Quadratics

MATHbook

MATHia

Let's Get Started!

Hi! We're the Content Design Team. We are the people at Carnegie Learning that created MATHbook.

Hi! Where should I begin?

We're going to start with a sample lesson so you know what to expect from MATHbook.

What if I need help?

Great question! Don't worry—you won't be working alone. You'll work in pairs or groups so you can talk and learn with other students in your class. #teamworkmakesthedreamwork

And TutorBot is always around with online help. TutorBot, say hi!

Hi, I'm TutorBot, the LiveHint chatbot. You can use me for help with your assignments.

How do I get good at this?

First, have confidence that you will get good at this. You will have plenty of opportunities to investigate and practice throughout the year.

The reality is that learning something new means being clumsy, making mistakes, accepting feedback, trying again, and practicing over time. Remember, effort matters!

Read on to get started with the sample lesson!

Let's do it!

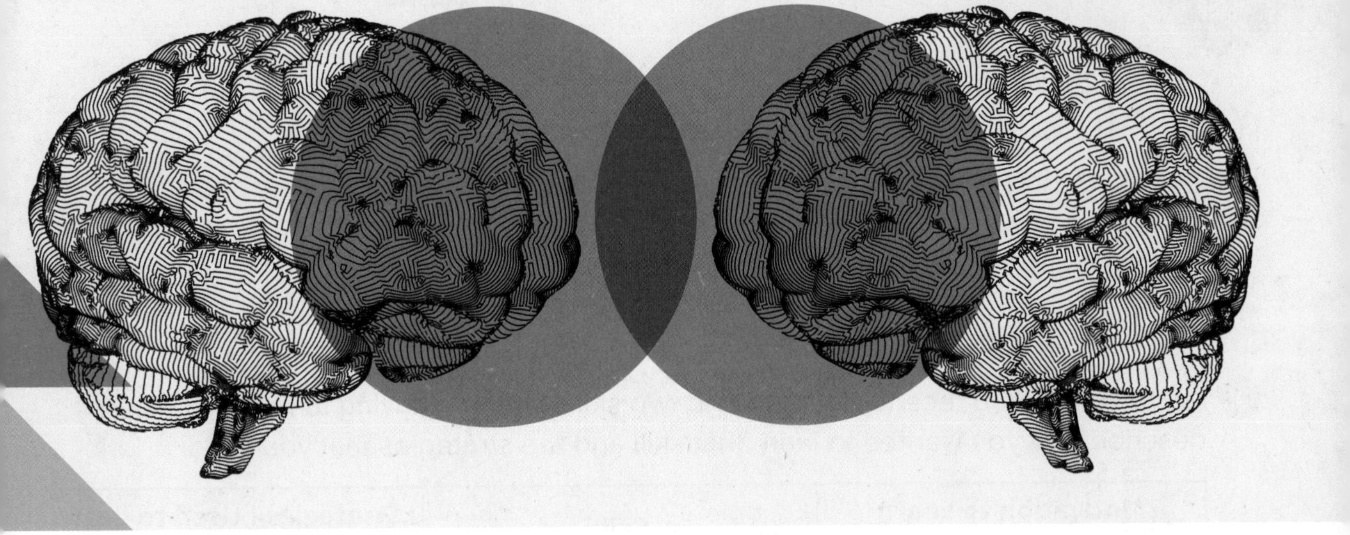

A Meeting of the Minds

An Introduction to MATHbook and Your Learning Resources

KEY TERMS
yet

Learning Goals

- Establish a community of learners.
- Preview the contents of MATHbook.
- Consider how you will interact with MATHbook to make your learning visible.
- Understand how MATHia software supports each MATHbook Topic.
- Set personal goals to take ownership of your learning.

REVIEW (1–2 minutes)

The questions in this section review a skill you will need in the lesson.

> Consider each question. Be prepared to share your strategies, conclusions, and questions.

1. Why is it helpful to review what you already know before learning something new?

TAKE NOTE . . .
Each lesson opens with a statement that connects what you have learned with a question to ponder.

In previous math classes, you explored transformations, analyzed patterns and relationships, learned about functions, operations with real numbers, probability and statistics, and geometry.

How can you use MATHbook and MATHia software to meet the goals of this course?

You Already Know A Lot

Each Lesson in this book begins with a Getting Started that gives you the opportunity to use what you know about the world and what you have learned in previous math classes. You know a lot from a variety of learning experiences.

> Think about how you learn.

1. List two skills you recently learned and two skills you are striving to improve. Then, describe why you wanted to learn that skill and the strategies that you used.

Motivation to Learn or Improve the Skill	Skill	Strategies I Used to Learn or Improve This Skill

One learning strategy is to talk with your peers. In this course, you will work with your classmates to solve problems, discuss strategies, and learn together.

> Compare and discuss your list with a classmate.

2. Which strategies do you have in common? Which strategies does your classmate have that you did not think of on your own?

ASK YOURSELF . . .
How do your strategies change based on what you are learning and what you already know about it?

THINK ABOUT . . .
Listening well, cooperating with others, and appreciating different perspectives are essential life skills.

> Be prepared to share your list of learning strategies with the class.

Learning Together with MATHbook

In this course, you will learn new math concepts by exploring and investigating ideas, reading, writing, and talking to your classmates. You will even learn by making mistakes with concepts you haven't mastered yet.

HABITS OF MIND

- Make sense of problems and persevere in solving them.

> Flip through the first Module of your MATHbook.

1. What do you find interesting? Does anything look familiar?

THINK ABOUT . . .
Using the word **yet** should remind you that the process is more important than answer-getting. So, take risks!

2. Compare the title and subtitle of several lessons. **What do you notice?**

3. Describe the icons you see within the lessons.

You will encounter different problem types as you work through activities.

Worked Example	Thumbs Up	Thumbs Down	Who's Correct
WORKED EXAMPLE			

When you see one of these problem types, take your time and read through it. Question your own understanding, think about the connections between steps, consider why the method is correct, or analyze what error was made.

> Search through the different Activities in Module 1 and locate a Worked Example, Thumbs Up, Thumbs Down, or Who's Correct.

4. What Topic, Lesson, and Activity are you in? **How do you know?**

5. How do you see these problem types helping you learn?

In MATHbook, you can mark up the pages in any way that is helpful to you as you take ownership of your learning.

> Analyze a page from Brody's MATHbook.

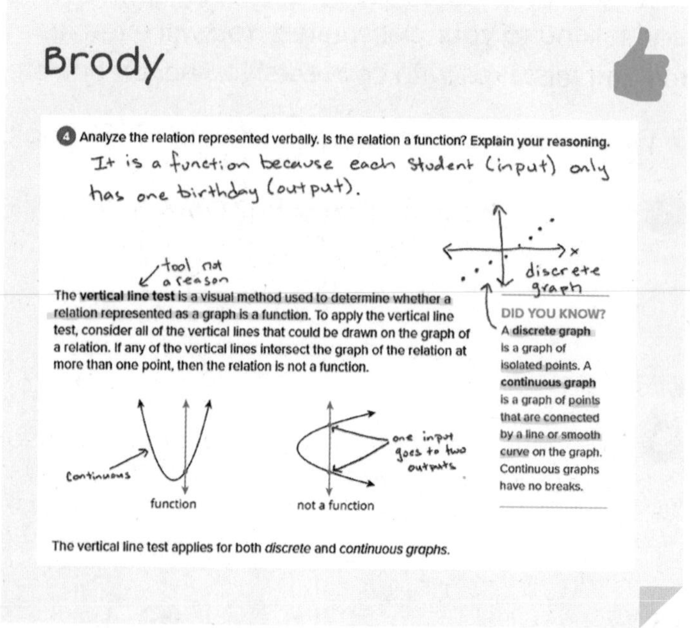

Brody

4 Analyze the relation represented verbally. Is the relation a function? Explain your reasoning.

It is a function because each student (input) only has one birthday (output).

discrete graph

tool not a reason

The **vertical line test** is a visual method used to determine whether a relation represented as a graph is a function. To apply the vertical line test, consider all of the vertical lines that could be drawn on the graph of a relation. If any of the vertical lines intersect the graph of the relation at more than one point, then the relation is not a function.

continuous

function

one input goes to two outputs

not a function

The vertical line test applies for both *discrete* and *continuous graphs.*

DID YOU KNOW?

A **discrete graph** is a graph of isolated points. A **continuous graph** is a graph of points that are connected by a line or smooth curve on the graph. Continuous graphs have no breaks.

6 What strategies did Brody use to make sense of the key term and diagrams?

7 Locate the term **discrete graph** in the glossary. What page is it on?

Through the process of writing, you clarify your understanding and improve your communication skills. The Academic Glossary on Page FM-20 is your guide as you engage with the kind of thinking you do as you are learning the content.

DID YOU KNOW . . .

Colleges and employers highly value candidates with strong verbal communication skills.

8 Locate the phrase **explain your reasoning** in the Academic Glossary. Which of the Ask Yourself questions might Brody have asked himself?

It is not just about what mathematical content you are learning, but how you are learning it. Did you notice the Habits of Mind beside each Activity title? You can locate the full list on Page FM-19.

9 What is the Habit of Mind for this **Using MATHbook** activity? **How will developing this habit help you?**

10 How will Learning Together help you learn math?

MATHia CONNECTION
- Pre-Launch Protocol

Learning Individually with MATHia

To learn the concepts in each topic, you will work with your classmates to complete the lessons within MATHbook, and you will work individually to complete workspaces in the MATHia software.

HABITS OF MIND
- Look for and make use of structure.
- Look for and express regularity in repeated reasoning.

> Watch the animation about MATHia.

1 How are supports included to help you solve problems within MATHia?

You will notice that there are MATHia Connections at the start of some Activities.

> Analyze this worked example.

WORKED EXAMPLE

ACTIVITY 2

MATHia CONNECTION
- Identifying Quantities

The MATHia Connection indicates the workspaces that have similar content to this activity. In the workspaces listed, you will practice the skills you are developing in a lesson.

TAKE NOTE . . .
If you are without access to MATHia, a Skills Practice workbook is available for you to practice each topic's skills and mathematical concepts.

2 How many workspaces are associated with Topic 1 *Quantities and Relationships*?

3 How will Learning Individually support your mathematical understanding?

So, Give It a Shot!

The Talk the Talk activity is your opportunity to reflect on the main ideas of the lesson.

- Be honest with yourself.
- Ask questions to clarify anything you don't understand yet.
- Show what you know!

REMEMBER . . .
Revisit the question posed on the lesson opening page to gauge your understanding.

1. Why is it important to take time to reflect on your progress?

2. Describe the different ways you will learn math this year.

3. It is important to set personal and academic goals for the year. List three goals for this school year.

- ______________________________
- ______________________________
- ______________________________

There are resources to assist you as you review the concepts in each topic. See Page FM-18 for *Your Tools for Review*.

4. Where do you locate a Topic Summary? How can you use this resource to prepare for an assessment?

INTRO LESSON ASSIGNMENT

> Use a separate piece of paper for your Journal entry.

JOURNAL

If how you felt about learning math this year were a meme, what would the meme be? Sketch or include your meme and explain your reasoning.

REMEMBER

In this course, you will build on your work with solving equations, systems of equations, statistics, and recognizing functions. You will apply your knowledge of transformations to explore a variety of function families. You will investigate non-linear functions such as exponential and quadratic functions.

PRACTICE

> Share the Family Guide for Topic 1 *Quantities and Relationships* with an adult.

1. Follow this QR code or URL to access the digital file.

ONLINE RESOURCES FOR FAMILIES
www.carnegielearning.com/home-connection/

2. What information does the Family Guide provide?

As you complete the Practice section of each Assignment, LiveHint is your textbook assistant. LiveHint allows you to obtain real-time hints from any device on questions through the TutorBot. With LiveHint, you never have to navigate through assignments on your own.

LiveHint™

> Go to **LiveHint.com**.

3. Follow the instructions to access hints to this question.

- First hint: ______________________
- Second hint: ______________________
- Third hint: ______________________

STRETCH Optional

Why do you think Module 1 is titled *Searching for Patterns*?

Your Tools for Review

There are topic-level resources to assist you as you review the concepts and prepare for an assessment.

MIXED PRACTICE

At the end of each topic, a **Mixed Practice** worksheet provides practice with skills from previous topics and this topic.

Spaced Review
Fluency and problem solving from previous topics

End of Topic Review
Review problems from this topic

Log in to MyCL for a version with **additional space** for you to write your answers.

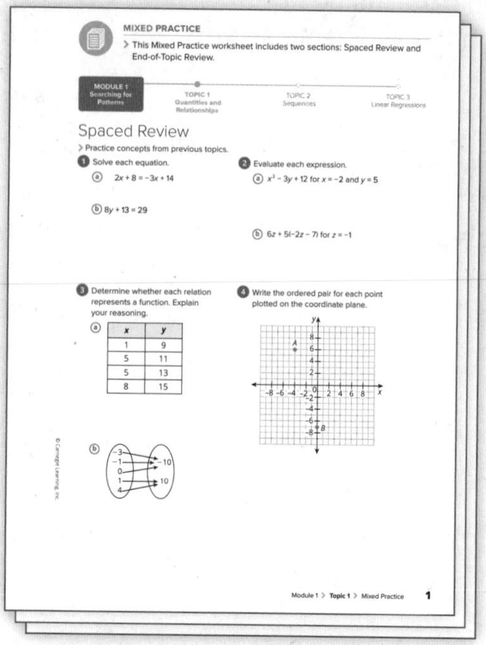

TOPIC SUMMARY

A **Topic Summary** is available online for review of the key terms and main ideas of each lesson.

ASK YOURSELF . . .

- Do I know the meaning of each key term?
- Do I remember the main concepts of each lesson?
- Do I understand the strategy used to solve the worked example?

Log in to MyCL to download the **Topic Summary**.

Watch a video of each **Worked Example**.

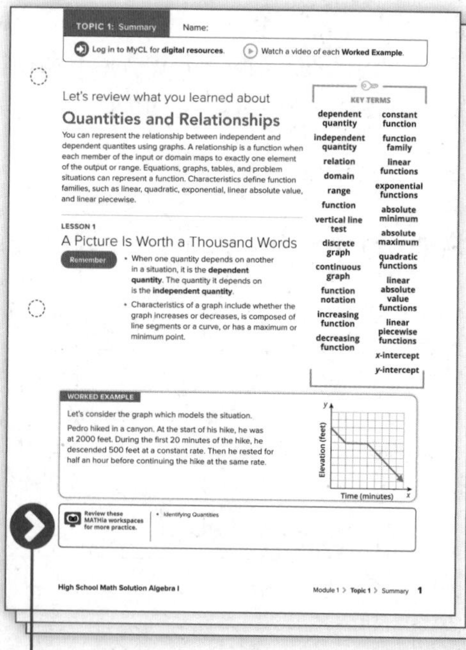

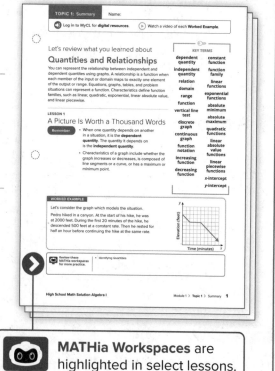

MATHia Workspaces are highlighted in select lessons.

HABITS OF MIND

> Tear out this page and use it as a guide as you engage with the the kind of thinking you do as you are learning the content.

Mathematical Practices

The types of activities within this book require you to make sense of mathematics and to demonstrate your reasoning through problem solving, writing, discussing, and presenting.

FOR ALL LESSONS . . .

Make sense of problems and persevere in solving them.

ASK YOURSELF . . .

- What is this problem asking and what is my plan for answering it?
- What tools do I need to solve this problem?
- Does my answer make sense?

TAKE NOTE . . .

To help develop these habits of mind ask yourself the types of questions listed as you work.

Each activity denotes the practice or pair of practices intentionally being developed. With practice you can develop the habits of mind of a productive mathematical thinker.

WHEN YOU SEE . . .	ASK YOURSELF . . .	WHAT DOES THIS MEAN FOR YOU?
HABITS OF MIND • Reason abstractly and quantitatively. • Construct viable arguments and critique the reasoning of others.	• What representation can I use to solve this problem? • How can this problem be represented with symbols and numbers? • How can I explain my thinking? • How does my strategy compare to my partner's?	
HABITS OF MIND • Model with Mathematics. • Use appropriate tools strategically.	• What expression or equation could represent this situation? • What tools would help me solve this problem? • What representations best show my thinking? • How does this answer make sense in the context of the original problem?	
HABITS OF MIND • Attend to precision.	• Is my answer accurate? • Did I use the correct units or labels? • Is there a more efficient way to solve this problem? • Is there more sophisticated vocabulary that I could use in my explanation?	
HABITS OF MIND • Look for and make use of structure. • Look for and express regularity in repeated reasoning.	• What characteristics of this expression or equation are made clear through this representation? • How can I use what I know to explain why this works? • Can I develop a more efficient method? • How could this problem help me to solve another problem?	

ACADEMIC GLOSSARY

There are important terms you will encounter throughout this book.

Knowing what is meant by these terms and using these terms will help you think, reason, and communicate your ideas. You will often see these phrases in highlighted questions throughout each activity.

TERM	DEFINITION	ASK YOURSELF	RELATED PHRASES
Analyze	To study or look closely for patterns. Analyzing can involve examining or breaking a concept down into smaller parts to gain a better understanding of it.	• Do I see any patterns? • Have I seen something like this before? • What happens if the shape, representation, or numbers change?	**Examine** **Evaluate** **Determine** **Observe** **Consider** **Investigate** **What do you notice?** **What do you think?** **Sort and match**
Explain Your Reasoning	To give details or describe how to determine an answer or solution. Explaining your reasoning helps justify conclusions.	• How should I organize my thoughts? • Is my explanation logical? • Does my reasoning make sense? • How can I justify my answer to others?	**Show your work** **Explain your calculation** **Justify** **Why or why not?**
Represent	To display information in various ways. Representing mathematics can be done using words, tables, graphs, or symbols.	• How should I organize my thoughts? • How do I use this model to show a concept or idea? • What does this representation tell me? • Is my representation accurate?	**Show** **Sketch** **Draw** **Create** **Plot** **Graph** **Write an equation** **Complete the table**
Estimate	To make an educated guess based on the analysis of given data. Estimating first helps inform reasoning.	• Does my reasoning make sense? • Is my solution close to my estimation?	**Predict** **Approximate** **Expect** **About how much?**
Describe	To represent or give an account of in words. Describing communicates mathematical ideas to others.	• How should I organize my thoughts? • Is my explanation logical? • Did I consider the context of the situation? • Does my reasoning make sense?	**Demonstrate** **Label** **Display** **Compare** **Determine** **Define** **What are the advantages?** **What are the disadvantages?** **What is similar?** **What is different?**

Searching for Patterns

Getting Ready for Module 1

Searching for Patterns

You will investigate a variety of function families, recognizing their key characteristics. You will build on your work with numeric patterns to explore sequences as functions. You will expand your knowledge of lines of best fit to determine whether it is appropriate to use a linear model and differentiate between correlation and causation.

The lessons in this module build on your prior experiences with functions, numeric patterns, and writing linear equations.

Review these key terms and writing linear equations to get ready to search for patterns.

KEY TERMS

function

A function maps each element from the domain, or input, to one and only one element from the range, or output.

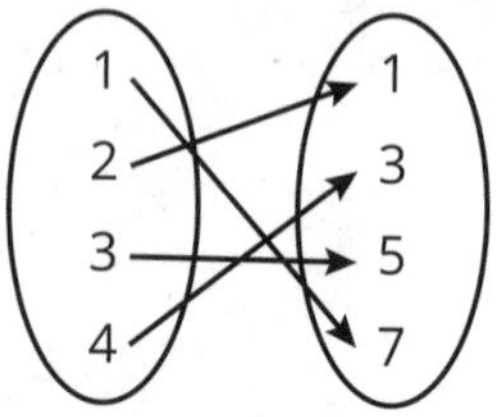

This mapping represents a function.

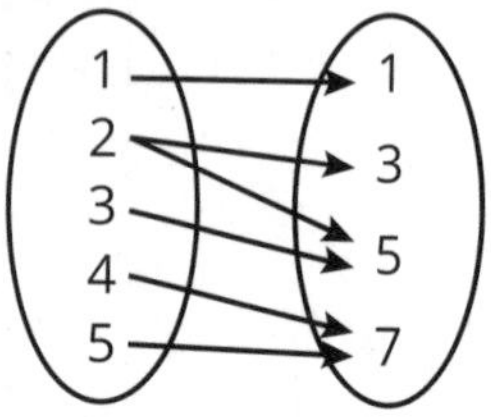

This mapping does NOT represents a function.

numeric pattern

A numeric pattern is a sequence, or ordered set, of numbers you create by following a given rule.

RULE: Multiply by 2 and add 1

Input	1	2	3
Output	3	5	7

MATHia

Brush up on your skills.
If you need more practice with these skills, ask your teacher for access to corresponding workspaces in MATHia.

SKILLS YOU WILL NEED

Writing Linear Equations

You can use the slope formula to write the equation of the line given two points.

Consider the points (3, 10) and (2, 7).

Determine the slope.

$$m = \frac{y_2 - y_1}{x_2 - x_1}$$
$$= \frac{10 - 7}{3 - 2} = \frac{3}{1} = 3$$

Substitute the slope, $m = 3$, a point, (3, 10), and $(0, y)$ into the slope formula and solve for the y-intercept.

$$3 = \frac{y - 10}{0 - 3}$$
$$3 = \frac{y - 10}{-3}$$
$$-9 = y - 10$$
$$1 = y$$

Use what you know to write the equation. $m = 3$ and (0, 1).

$$y = mx + b$$
$$y = 3x + 1$$

The equation for the line containing the points (3, 10) and (2, 7) is $y = 3x + 1$.

REVIEW

> Evaluate each expression for $x = 7$.

1. $x - 15$
2. $2x + 3.1$
3. $3(x - 5)$
4. $\frac{2}{3}(x + 2) - 2x$

See Appendix on page 457 for answers.

LESSON 1

A Picture Is Worth a Thousand Words

Understanding Quantities and Their Relationships

KEY TERMS

dependent quantity

independent quantity

Learning Goals

- Understand quantities and their relationships with each other.
- Identify the independent and dependent quantities for a scenario.
- Use a reasonable scale for a graph modeling a scenario.
- Identify key characteristics of graphs.
- Describe similarities and differences between pairs of graphs and scenarios.

REVIEW (1–2 minutes)

> Emma bought a new video game. The graph shown describes the number of hours Emma spent playing the game over a period of 7 days.

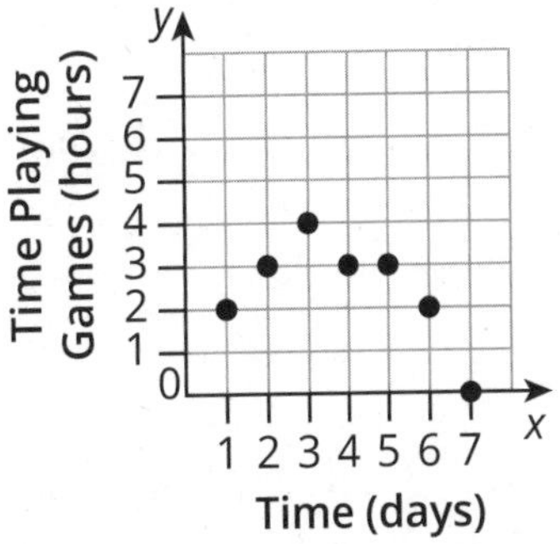

1 What does the highest point on the graph represent with respect to the scenario? The lowest point?

You have analyzed graphs of relationships and identified important features such as intercepts and slopes.

How can the key characteristics of a graph tell a story?

What Comes First?

Have you ever planned a party? You may have purchased ice, gone grocery shopping, selected music, made food, or even cleaned in preparation. Many times, these tasks depend on doing another task first. For example, you wouldn't make food before grocery shopping, now would you?

> Consider the two quantities that are changing in each relationship.

- the number of movie tickets purchased and the total cost
- the number of eggs used and the numbers of cakes baked
- the number of students in attendance at school and the number of lunches served
- the number of hours driven and the number of miles to a vacation destination
- the number of minutes a swimming pool is filled with water and the number of gallons of water in the swimming pool

1 Circle the *independent quantity* and underline the *dependent quantity* in each relationship.

2 Describe how you can determine which quantity is independent and which quantity is dependent in any problem situation.

REMEMBER...
When one quantity depends on another in a problem situation, it is the **dependent quantity**. The quantity it depends upon is the **independent quantity**.

Connecting Scenarios and Their Graphs

HABITS OF MIND
- Model with mathematics.
- Use appropriate tools strategically.

While a person can describe the monthly cost to operate a business, or talk about a marathon pace a runner ran to break a world record, graphs on a coordinate plane enable people to see the data. Graphs relay information about relationships in a visual way.

You can use lines or smooth curves to represent relationships between points on a graph. In some problem situations, all the points on the line will make sense. In other problem situations, not all the points will make sense. So, when you model a relationship with a line or a curve, it is up to you to consider the situation and interpret the meaning of the data values shown.

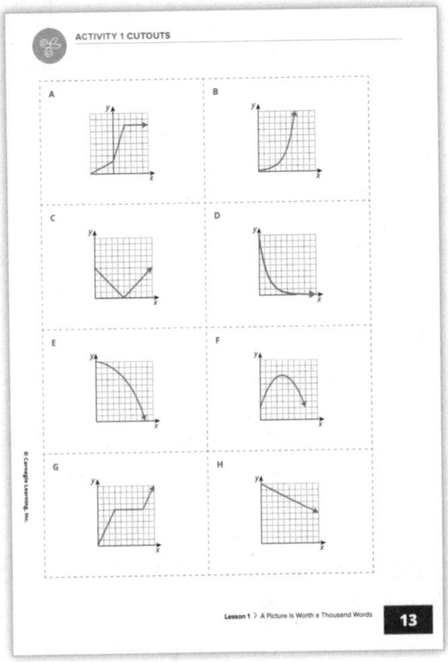

> Cut out the graphs located on page 13. Then, read each of the eight scenarios in this activity.

- Determine the independent and dependent quantities.
- Match each scenario to its corresponding graph. Glue the graph next to the scenario.
- For each graph, label the *x*- and *y*-axis with the appropriate quantity and a reasonable scale, and then interpret the meaning of the origin.

Daredevil

Greyson completes a dive from a cliff 100-feet above a river. It takes him only 1.7 seconds to hit the water.

- independent quantity:
- dependent quantity:

THINK ABOUT...
Be sure to include the appropriate units of measure for each quantity.

Something's Fishy

Candice is cleaning the office building's 200-gallon aquarium. For cleaning, she must remove the fish from the aquarium and drain the water. The water drains at a constant rate of 10 gallons per minute.

ASK YOURSELF...
What strategies will you use to match each graph with one of the eight scenarios?

- independent quantity:

- dependent quantity:

Smart Phone, but Is It a Smart Deal?

You have your eye on an upgraded smart phone. However, you currently do not have the money to purchase it. Your cousin will provide the funding, as long as you pay him back with interest. He tells you that you only need to pay $1 in interest initially, and then the interest will double each week after that. You consider his offer and wonder if this *really* is a good deal.

- independent quantity:

- dependent quantity:

Can't Wait to Hit the Slopes!

Andrew loves skiing—he just hates the ski lift. To make matters worse, the ski lift has been acting up today. Andrew is using the GPS on his phone to track the ski lift's progress as it travels up the mountain. It moves at a steady rate of 400 feet per minute until it stops suddenly. Andrew calls his friends to tell them that he is stuck. They talk on the phone for 10 minutes until finally the ski lift begins moving again.

- independent quantity:

- dependent quantity:

It's Magic

The Amazing Aloysius is practicing one of his tricks. As part of this trick, he cuts a rope into many pieces and then magically puts the pieces of rope back together. He begins the trick with a 20-foot rope and then cuts it in half. He then takes one of the halves and cuts that piece in half. He repeats this process until he is left with a piece so small he can no longer cut it.

- independent quantity:

- dependent quantity:

Baton Twirling

Jill is a drum major for the Altadena High School marching band. For the finale of the halftime performance, Jill tosses her baton in the air so that it reaches a maximum height of 22 feet. This gives her 2 seconds to twirl around twice and catch the baton when it comes back down.

- independent quantity:

- dependent quantity:

Cold Weather

The number of guests at a ski resort on any given day is related to the day's high temperature. When the high temperature is −20°F or below, no one comes to the resort. As the temperature increases, so does the number of guests. Once the temperature reaches 0°F and increases through the single digits, the number of guests soars. When the temperature is 10°F or higher, the ski resort is at full capacity with 400 guests.

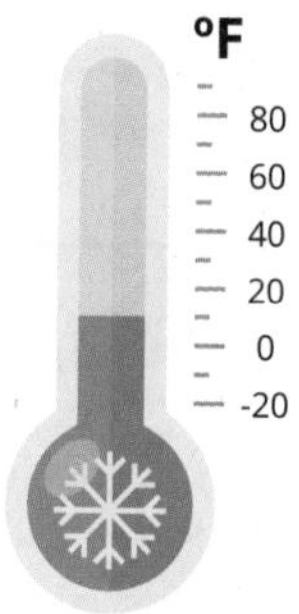

- independent quantity:

- dependent quantity:

Jelly Bean Challenge

Mr. Wright judges the annual Jelly Bean Challenge at the summer fair. Every year, he encourages the citizens in his town to guess the number of jelly beans in a jar. He records all the possible guesses and the number of jelly beans that each guess was off by.

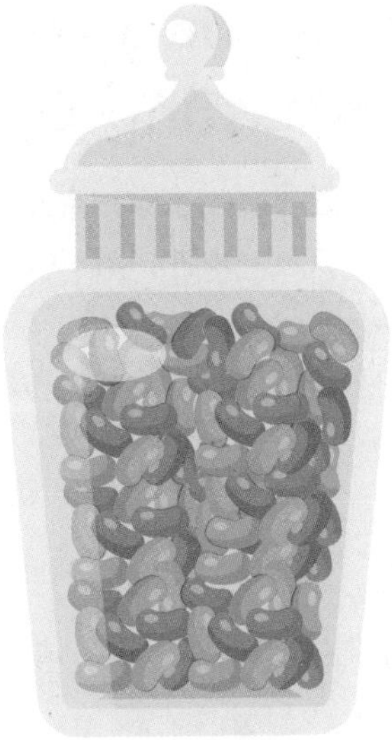

- independent quantity:

- dependent quantity:

Comparing and Contrasting Graphs

HABITS OF MIND
- Look for and make use of structure.
- Look for and express regularity in repeated reasoning.

Now that you have matched a graph with the appropriate problem situation, let's go back and examine all the graphs.

1. What similarities do you notice in the graphs?

THINK ABOUT...
Look closely when analyzing the graphs. What do you see?

2. What differences do you notice in the graphs?

3. How did you label the independent and dependent quantities in each graph?

4. Analyze each graph from left to right. **Describe any graphical characteristics you notice.**

5 Compare the graphs for each pair of scenarios given. **Describe any similarities and differences you notice.**

(a) *Smart Phone, but Is It a Smart Deal?* and *Cold Weather*

(b) *Something's Fishy* and *It's Magic*

(c) *Baton Twirling* and *Jelly Bean Challenge*

A Writer and a Mathematician

1. Write a scenario and sketch a graph to describe a possible trip to school.

Scenario

____

____

____

____

____

____

Graph

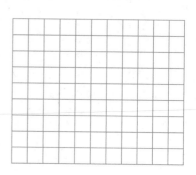

2. Describe the meaning of the points, or smooth curve, represented by your graph.

3. Compare your scenario and sketch with your classmates' scenarios and sketches. **What similarities do you notice? What differences do you notice?**

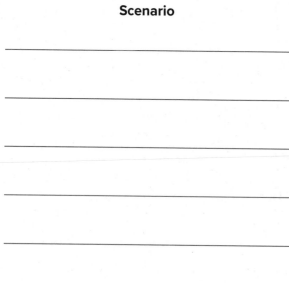

A

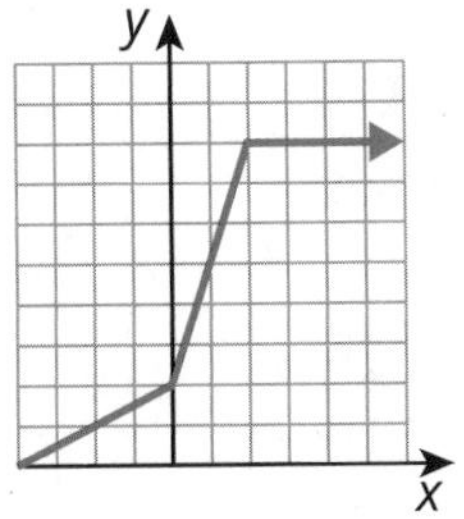

B

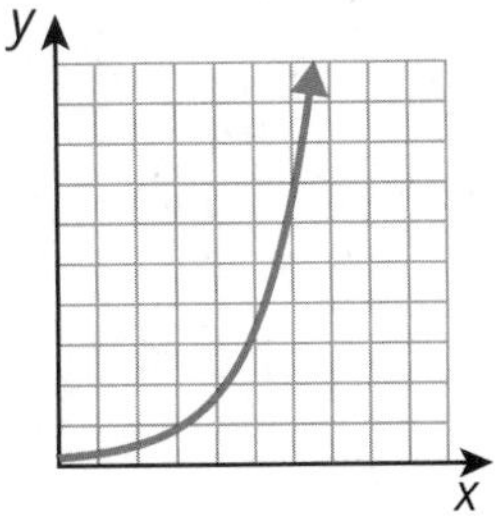

C

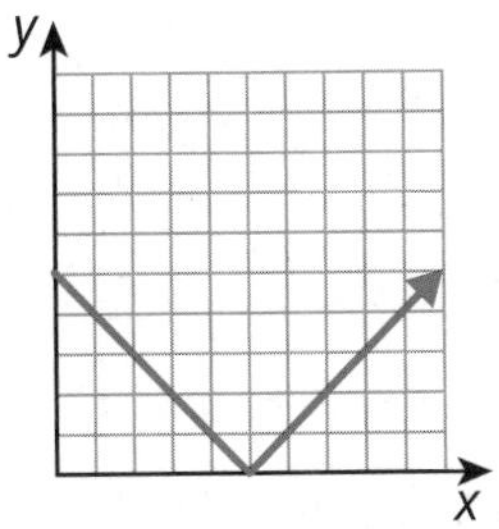

D

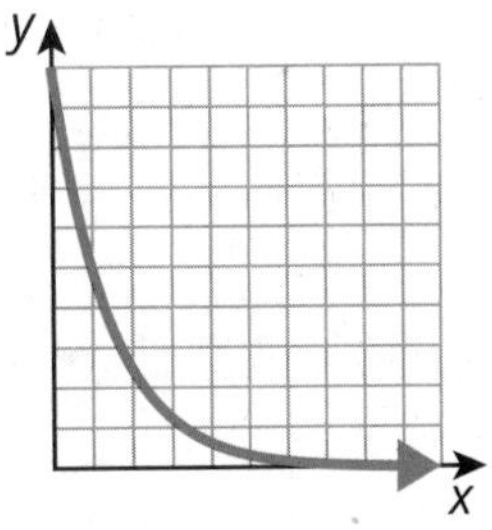

E

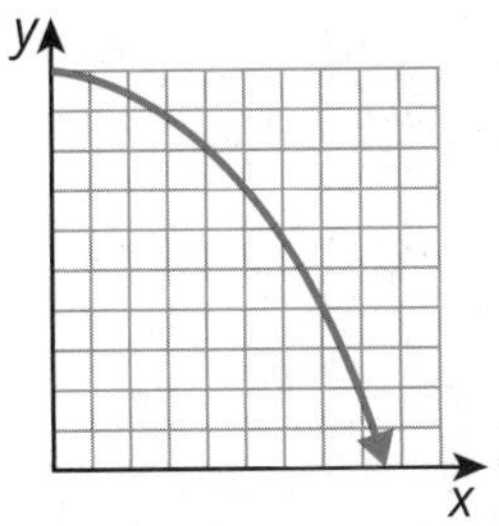

F

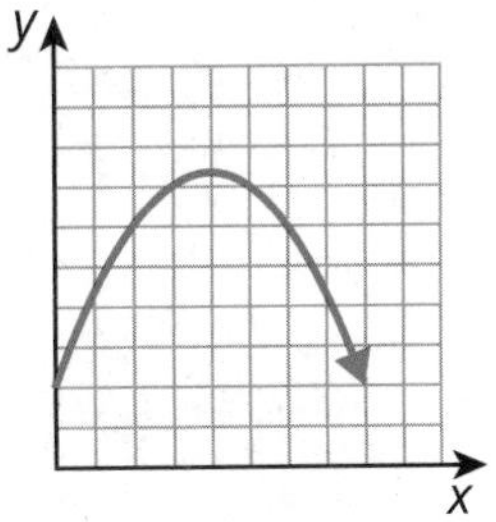

G

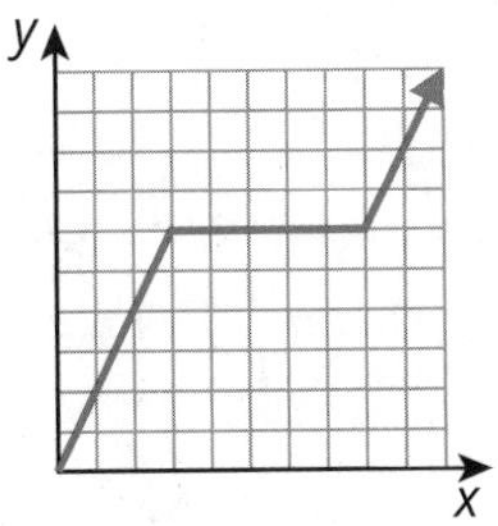

H

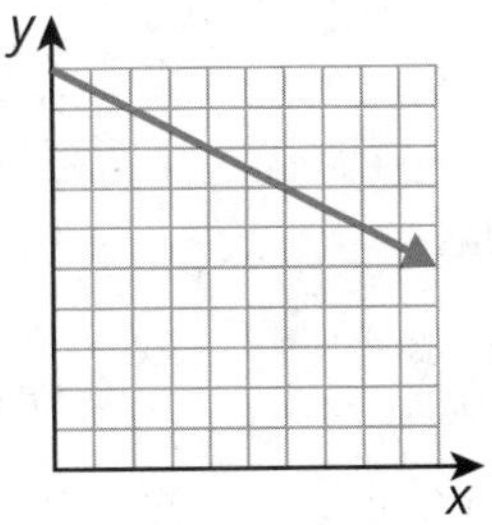

Why is this page blank?

So you can cut out the graphs on the other side.

LESSON 1 ASSIGNMENT

> Use a separate piece of paper for your Journal entry.

JOURNAL

Describe how you can distinguish between an independent quantity and a dependent quantity. Use an example in your description.

REMEMBER

When one quantity depends on another in a problem situation, it is the dependent quantity. The quantity it depends upon is the independent quantity. You represent the independent quantity on the *x*-axis and the dependent quantity on the *y*-axis.

PRACTICE

1 Read each scenario and identify the independent and dependent quantities. Be sure to include the appropriate units of measure. Then determine which graph models the scenario.

(a) Endangered Species

The initial population of 450 endangered turtles tripled each year for the past five years.

(b) Video Games

Gillian starts with $40 and is playing games that cost 50 cents per game.

(c) Sales Commission

Julian receives $3000 per month and a 10% commission on the amount of sales.

(d) Cooling Tea

A cup of tea cools rapidly from 180°F, and then slows down gradually as it nears room temperature.

A

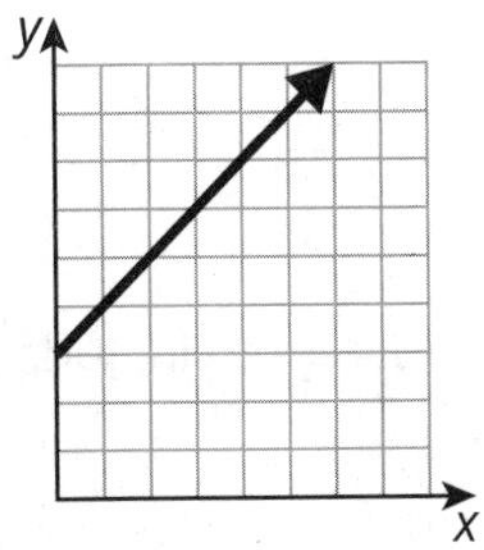

B

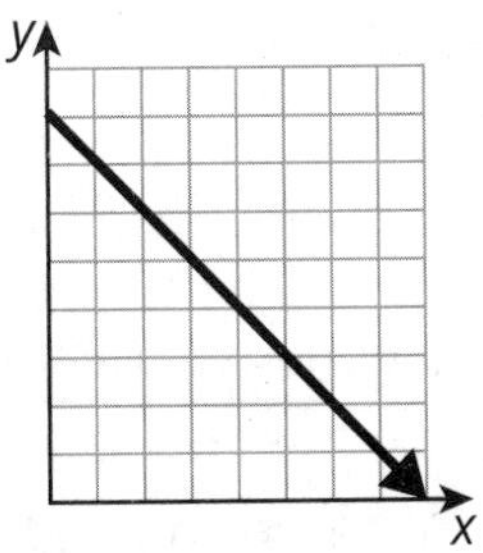

C

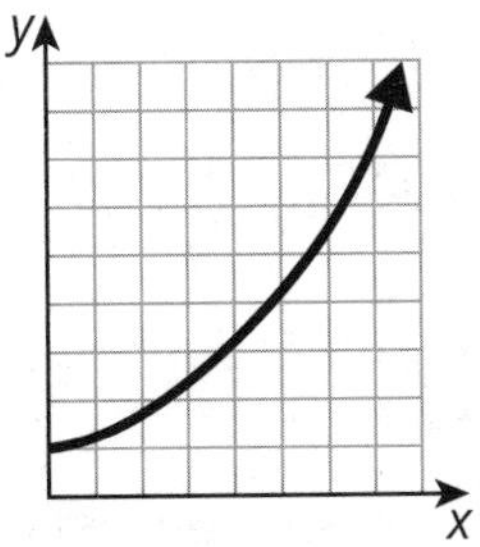

D

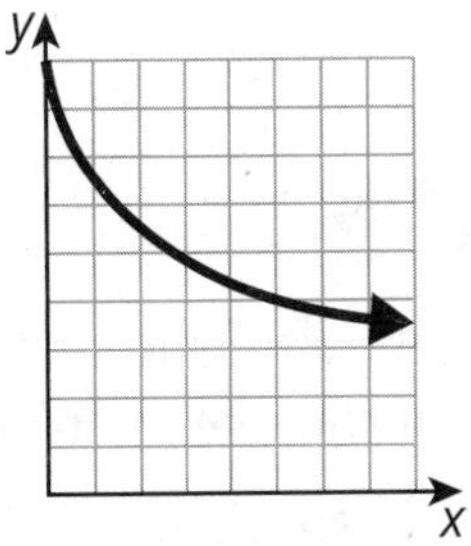

Go to LiveHint.com for help on the PRACTICE questions.

2 Compare each pair of graphs and describe any similarities and differences you notice.

ⓐ

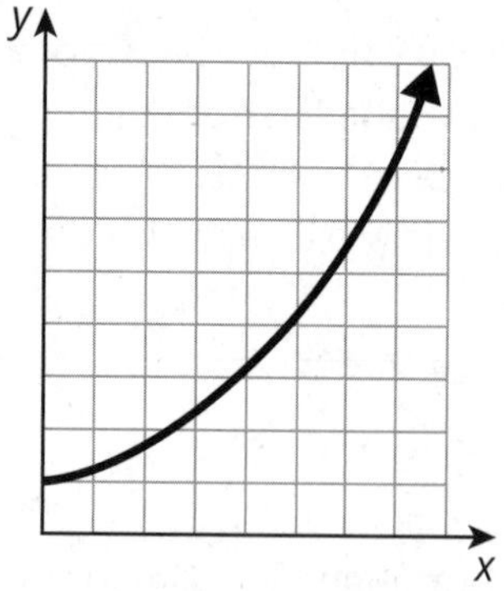

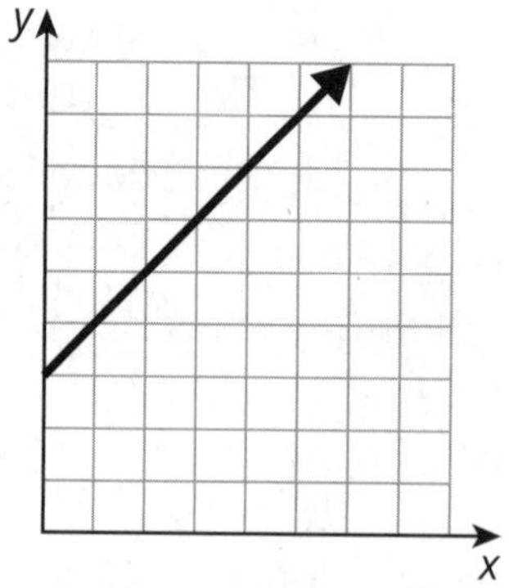

ⓑ

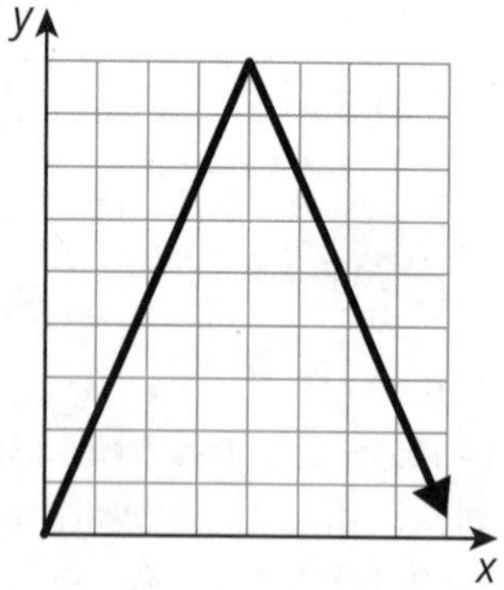

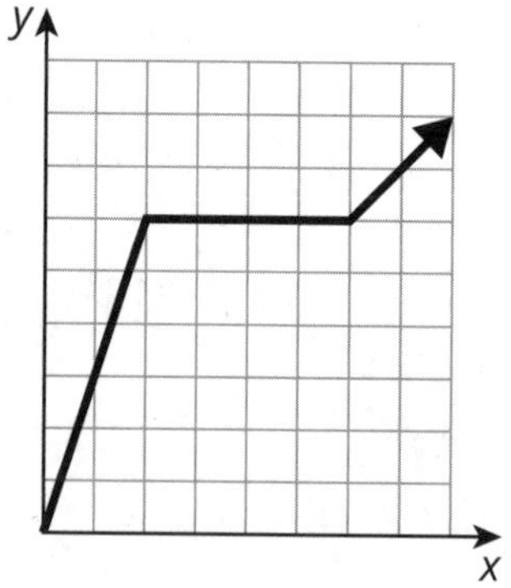

STRETCH Optional

> Read the scenario and identify the independent and dependent quantities. Be sure to include the appropriate units of measure.

1 A student performs several experiments in which he swings a pendulum for a 20-second duration. He uses a string that is 27 cm long, and he tests pendulum masses of different sizes, varying from 2 to 12 grams. He records the number of swings each pendulum makes in 20 seconds.

2 The student then decides to make a second graph showing the string length (in cm) as the independent quantity. What changes must the student make to his experiment?

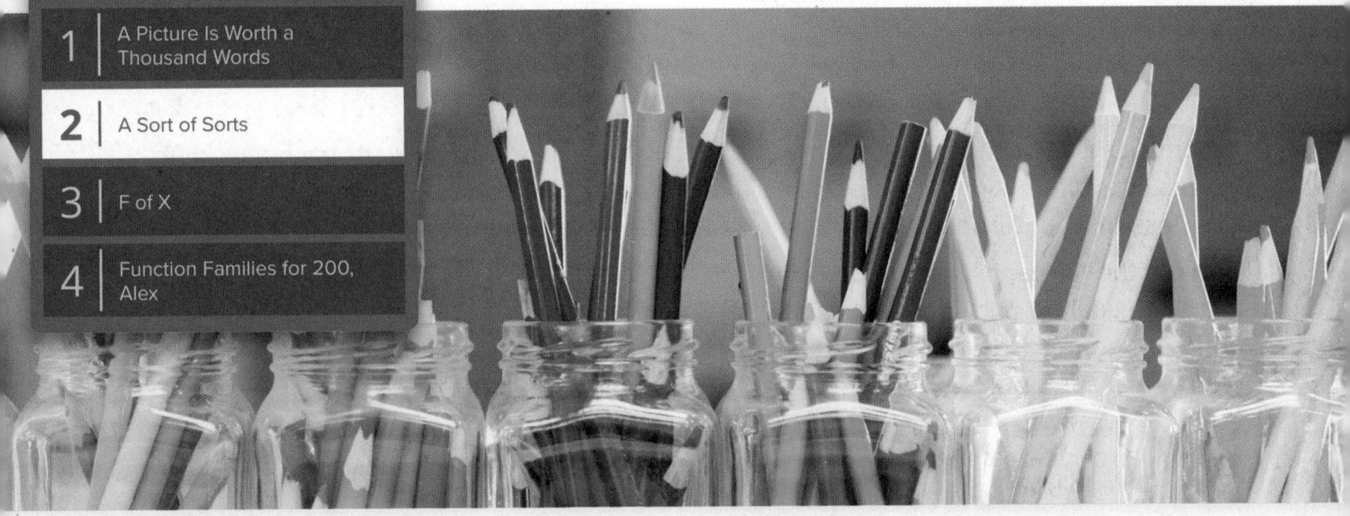

LESSON 2

A Sort of Sorts

Analyzing and Sorting Graphs

Learning Goals

- Review and analyze graphs and graphical behavior.
- Determine similarities and differences among various graphs.
- Sort graphs and give reasons for the similarities and differences between the groups of graphs.

REVIEW (1–2 minutes)

> Write the coordinates of each point and name the quadrant it is in or the axis on which it lies.

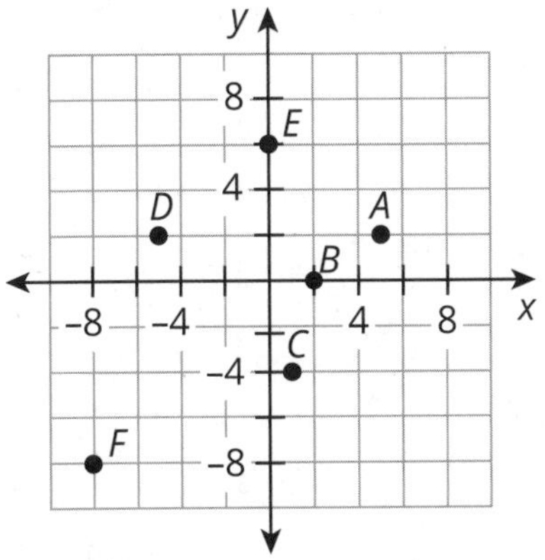

You have used graphs to analyze the relationship between independent and dependent quantities.

Do the graphs of certain types of relationships share any characteristics?

Let's Sort Some Graphs

Mathematics is the science of patterns and relationships. Looking for patterns and sorting patterns into different groups based on similarities and differences can provide valuable insights. In this lesson, you will analyze many different graphs and sort them into various groups.

> Cut out the 18 graphs located on pages 23, 25, and 27. Then analyze and sort the graphs into at least two different groups. You may group the graphs in any way you feel is appropriate.

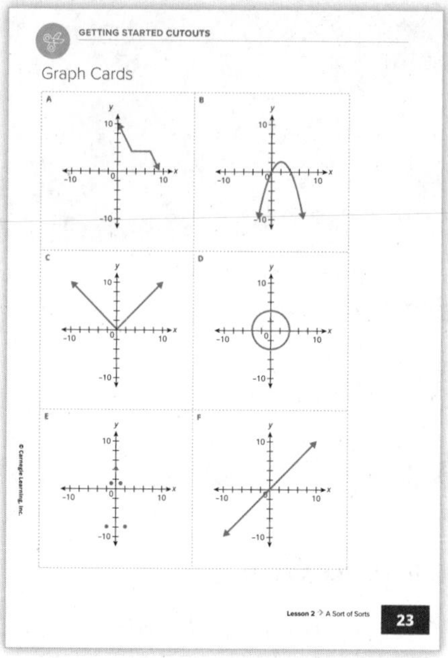

Record the following information for each of your groups.

- Name each group of graphs.
- List the letters of the graphs in each group.
- **Provide a rationale for why you created each group.**

TAKE NOTE...
Keep your graphs. You will need them in the next lesson.

Identifying Graphical Behaviors

In this activity, you will consider different ways to group the graphs.

HABITS OF MIND

- Reason abstractly and quantitatively.
- Construct viable arguments and critique the reasoning of others.

1 Matthew grouped these graphs together. Why do you think he put these graphs in the same group?

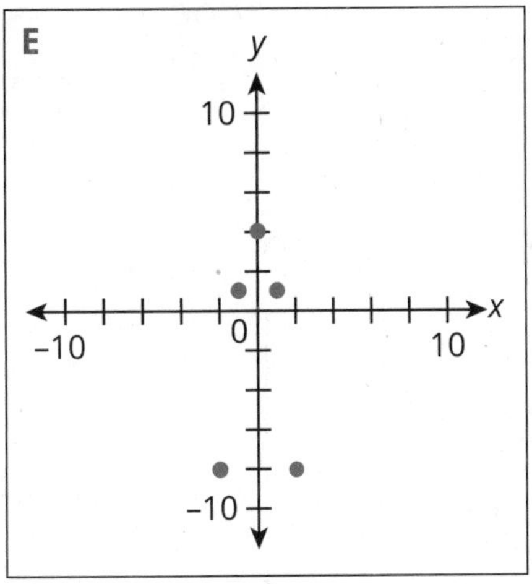

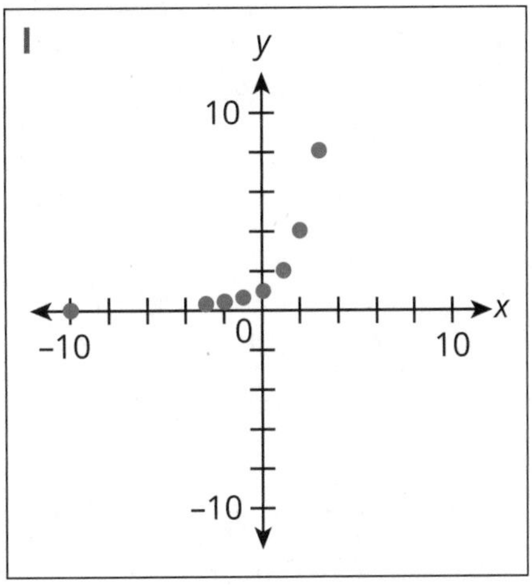

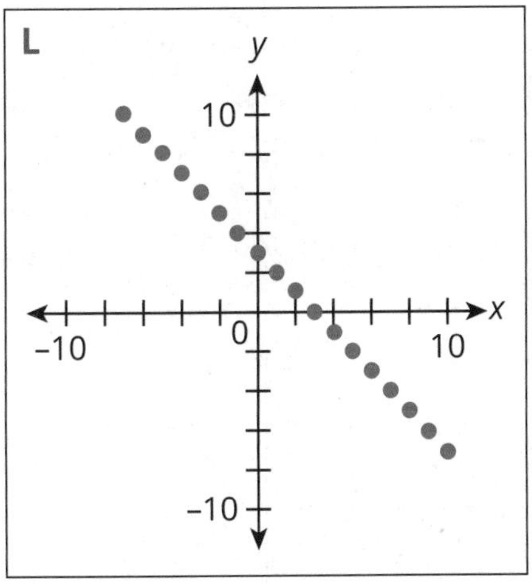

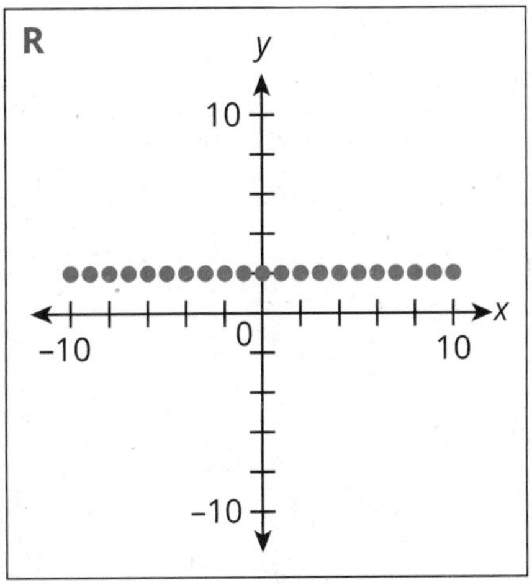

2 Consider Ashley's correct grouping.

Ashley

I grouped these graphs together because they all have a vertical line of symmetry. If I draw a vertical line through the middle of the graph, the image is the same on both sides.

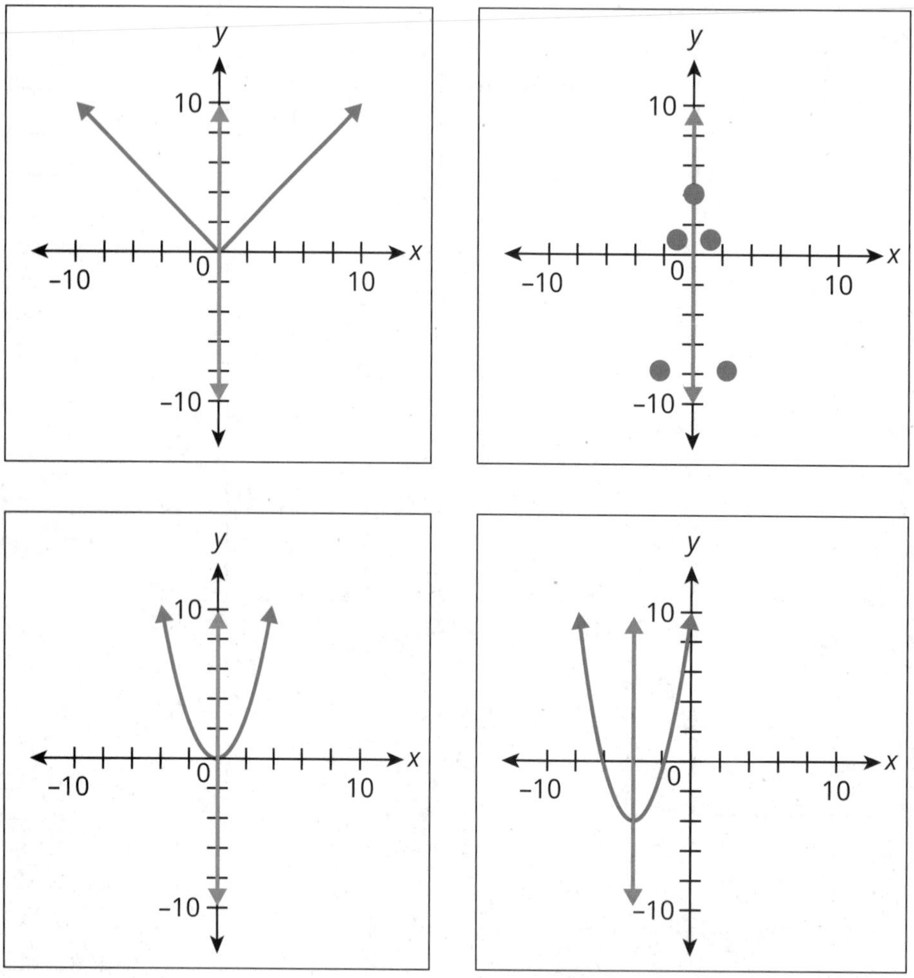

(a) Show why Ashley's reasoning is correct.

(b) If possible, identify other graphs that have a vertical line of symmetry.

3 Judy grouped these graphs together, but did not provide any rationale.

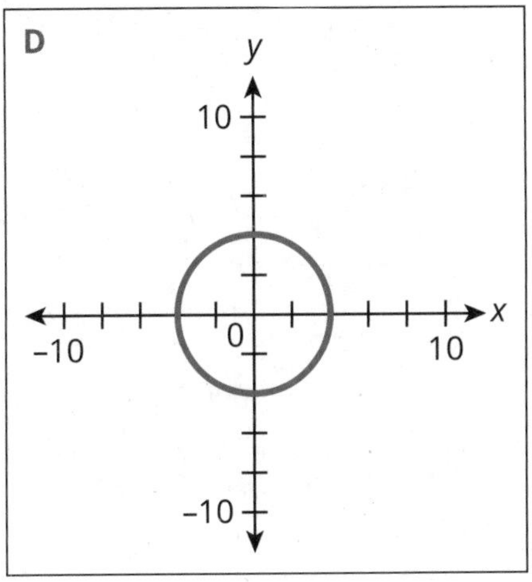

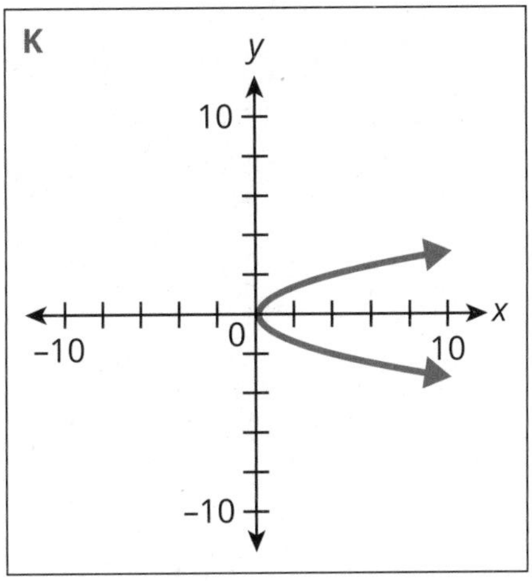

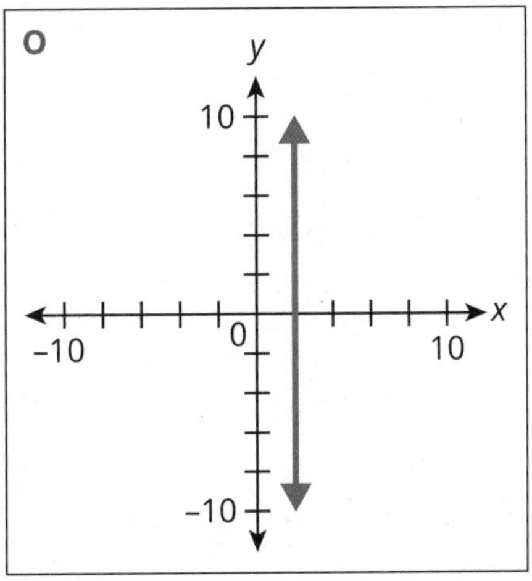

(a) What do you notice about the graphs?

(b) What rationale could Judy have provided?

Compare and Contrast

> Compare your groups with your classmates' groups.

1. Create a list of the different graphical behaviors you noticed.

ASK YOURSELF...
Are any of the graphical behaviors shared among your groups? Or, are they unique to each group?

Graph Cards

A

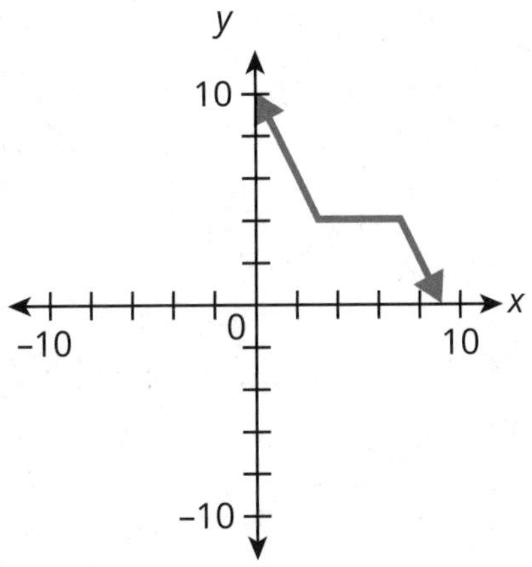

B

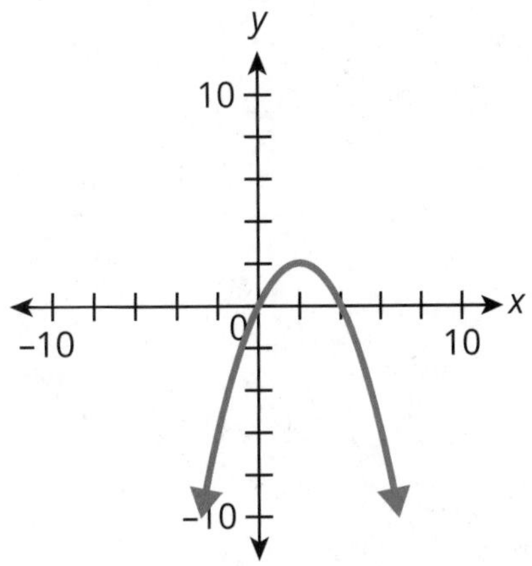

C

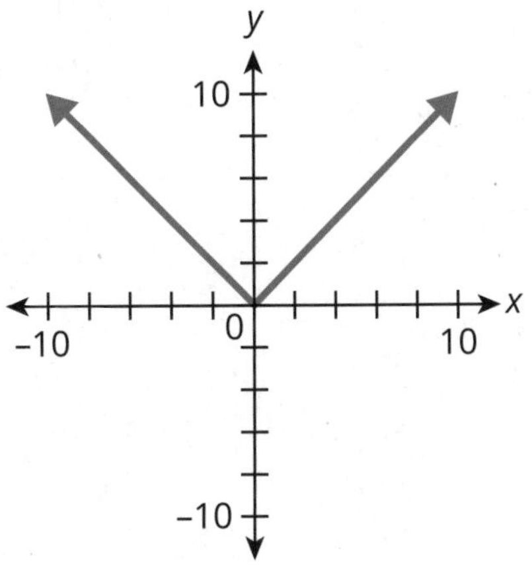

D

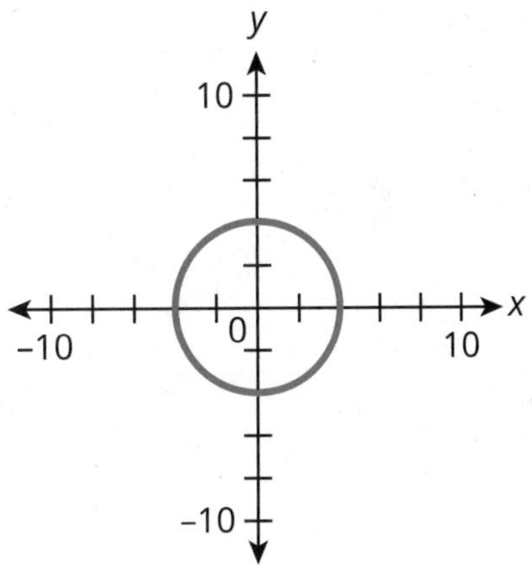

E

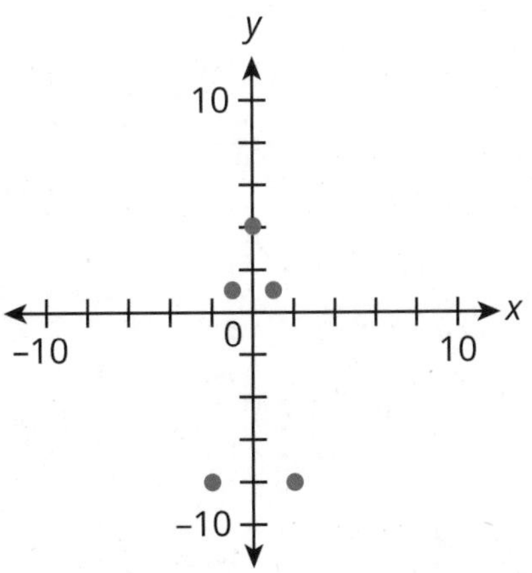

F

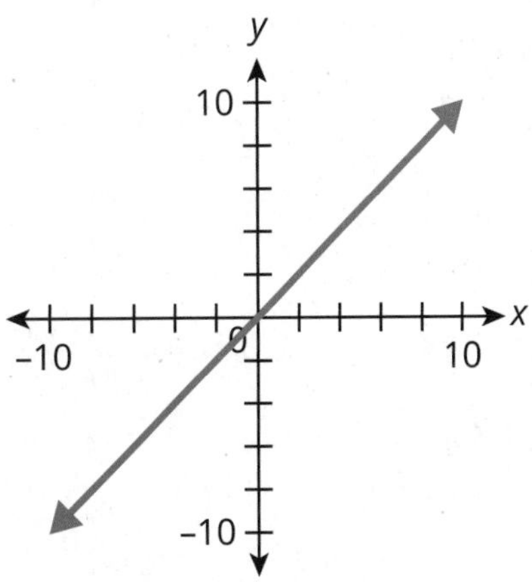

Why is this page blank?

So you can cut out the graphs on the other side.

G

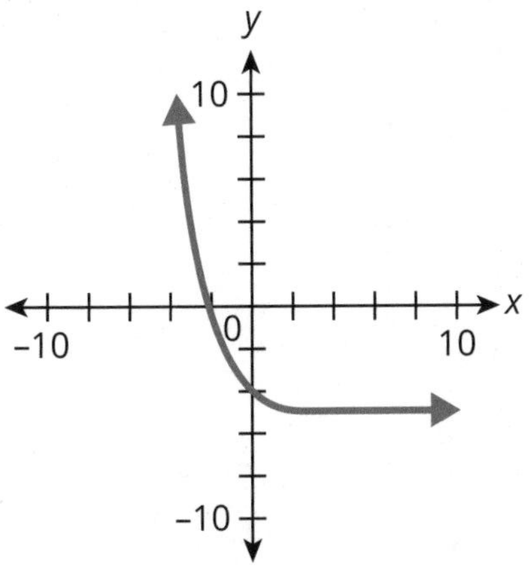
y
x
10
0
−10
10
−10

H

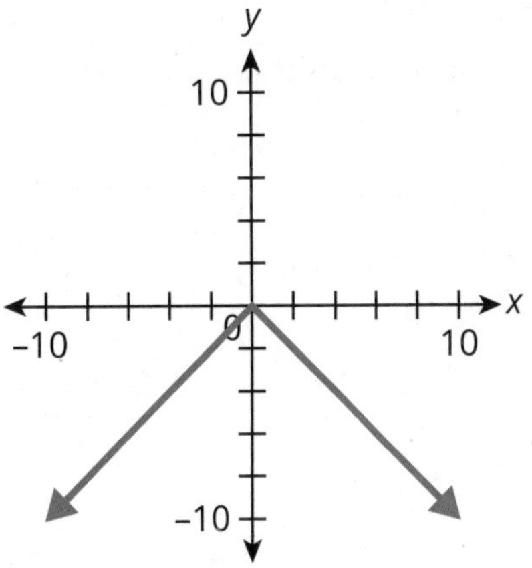
y
x
10
0
−10
10
−10

I

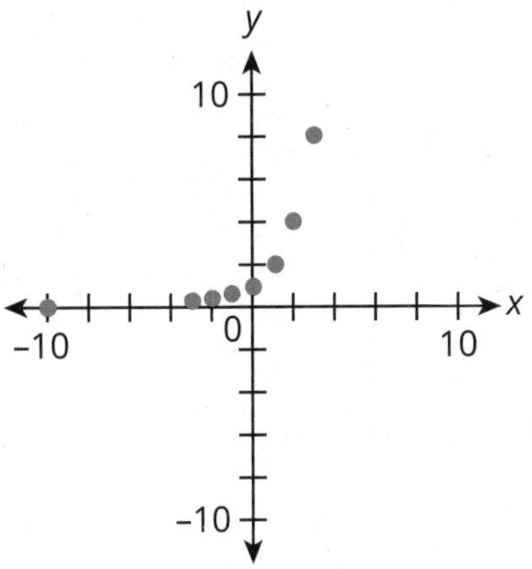
y
x
10
0
−10
10
−10

J

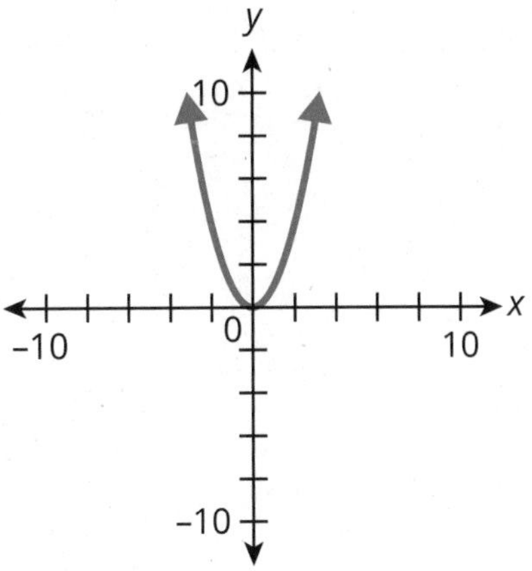
y
x
10
0
−10
10
−10

K

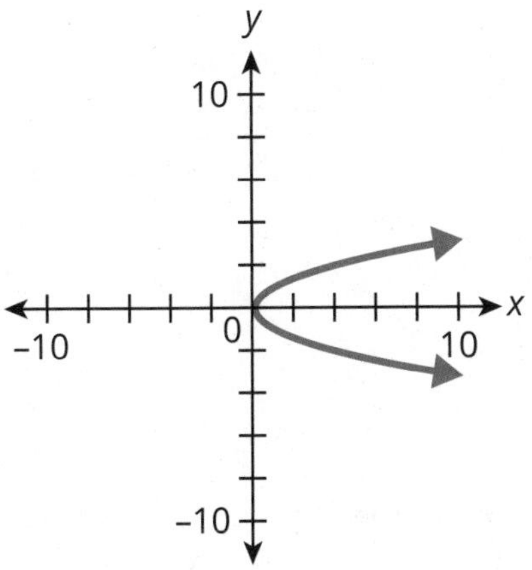
y
x
10
0
−10
10
−10

L

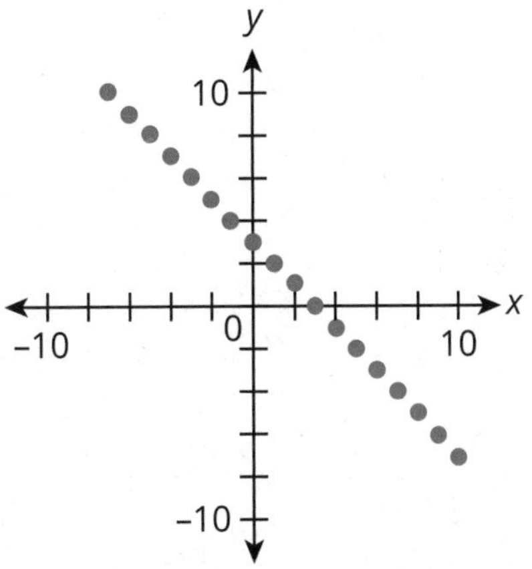
y
x
10
0
−10
10
−10

Why is this page blank?

So you can cut out the graphs on the other side.

M

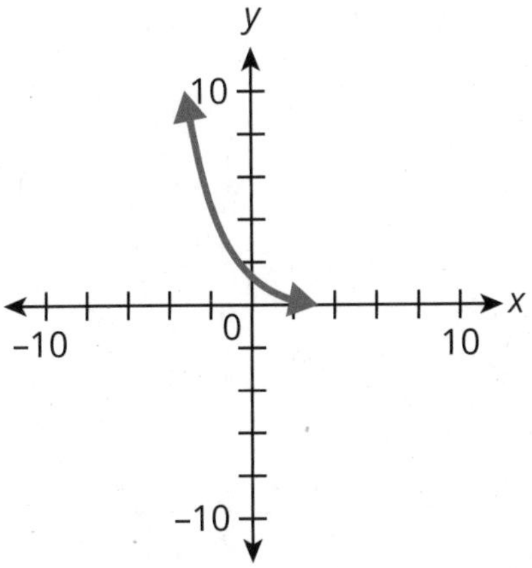
y
10
-10
0
10
x
-10

N

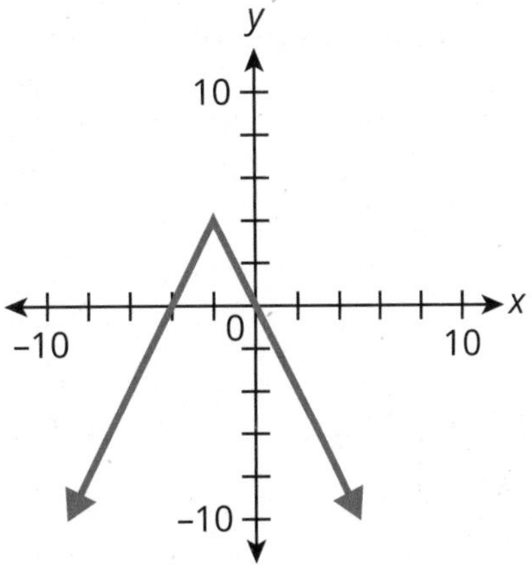
y
10
-10
0
10
x
-10

O

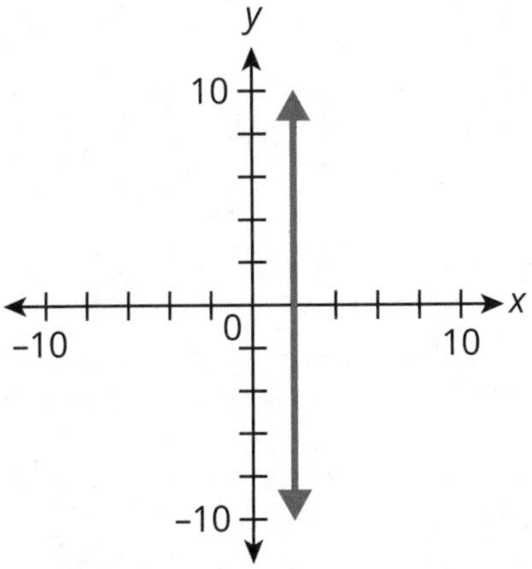
y
10
-10
0
10
x
-10

P

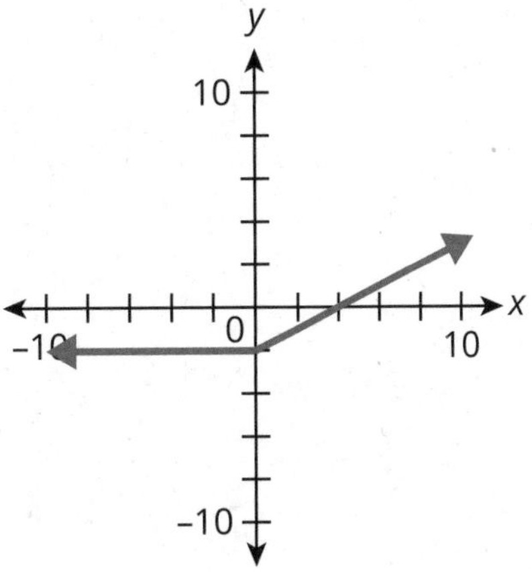
y
10
0
10
x
-10

Q

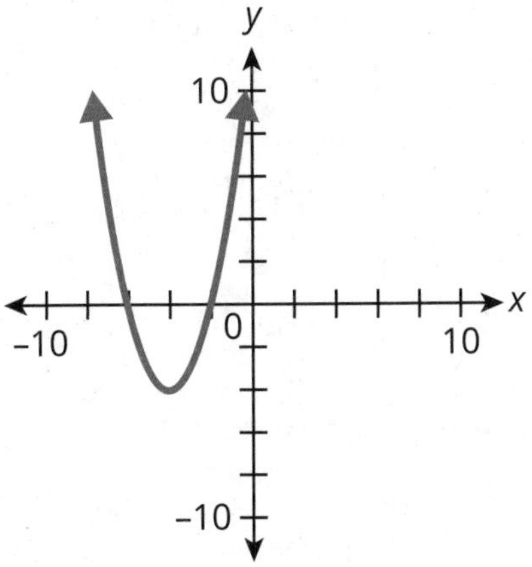
y
10
-10
0
10
x
-10

R

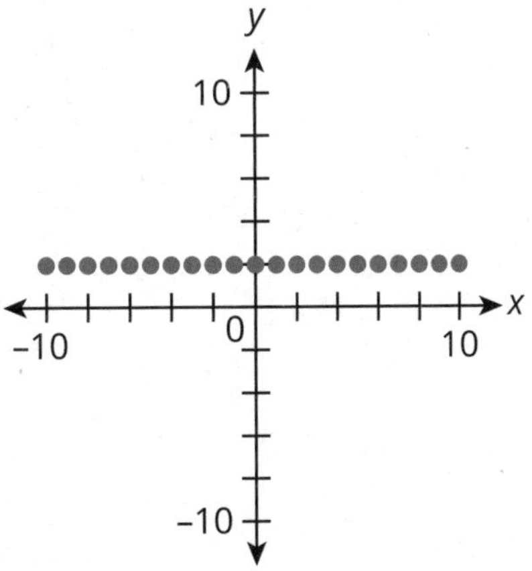
y
10
-10
0
10
x
-10

Why is this page blank?

So you can cut out the graphs on the other side.

LESSON 2 ASSIGNMENT

> Use a separate piece of paper for your Journal entry.

JOURNAL

Describe the importance of graphical representations.

REMEMBER

Graphs of relationships between quantities have characteristics that can give you essential information about the relationship. For example, a graph can increase, decrease, neither increase nor decrease, or both increase and decrease. A graph can have straight lines or smooth curves, a maximum or minimum, or no maximum or minimum.

PRACTICE

1 Record the letter of each graph with the given characteristic.

(a) Has a vertical line of symmetry

(b) Has a horizontal line of symmetry

(c) Passes through exactly 1 quadrant

(d) Passes through all 4 quadrants

A

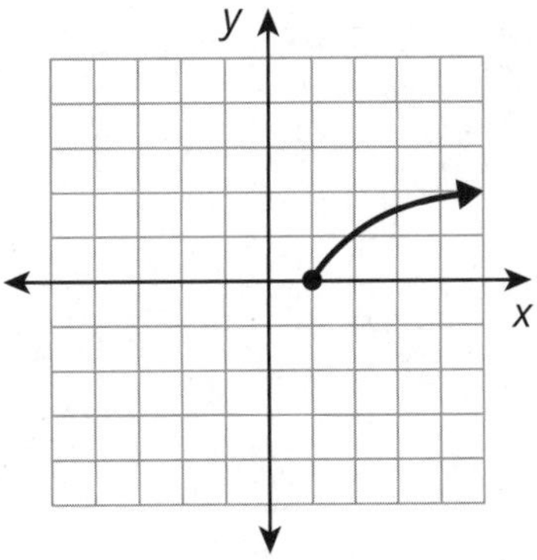

B

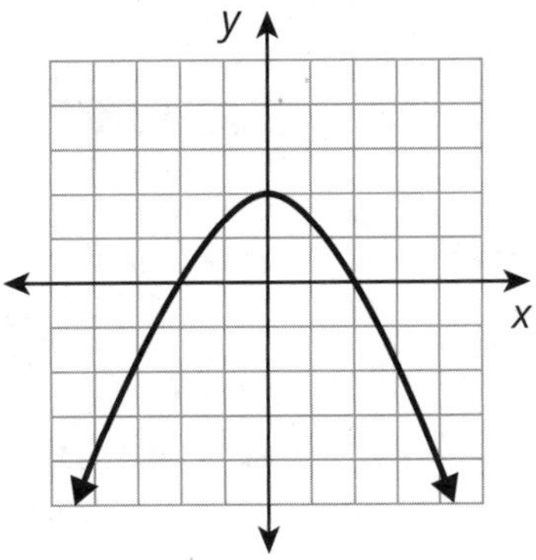

C

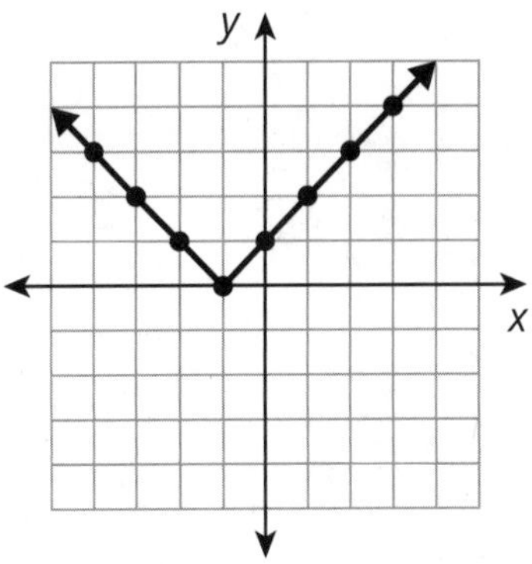

D

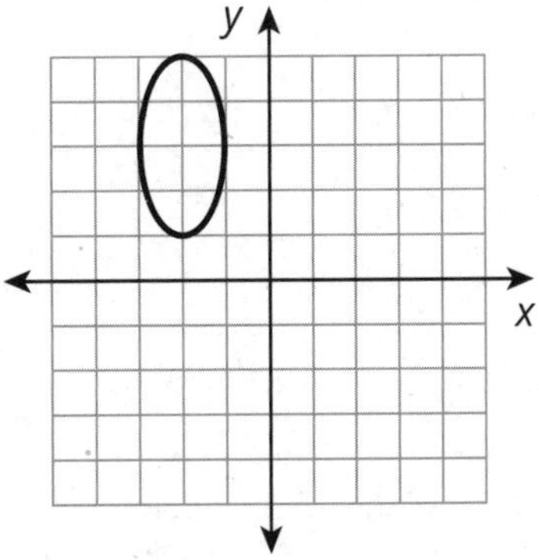

E

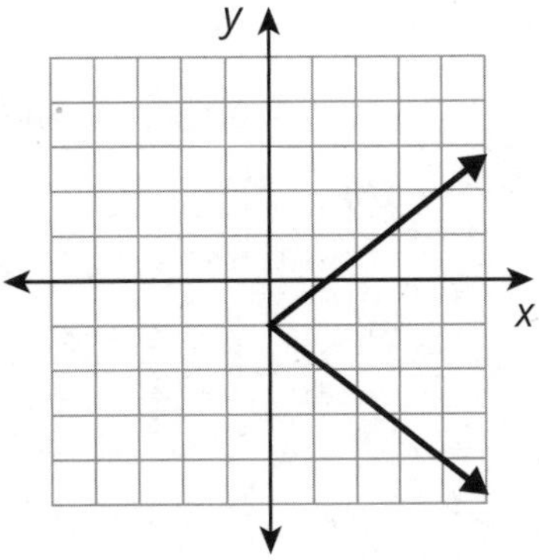

F

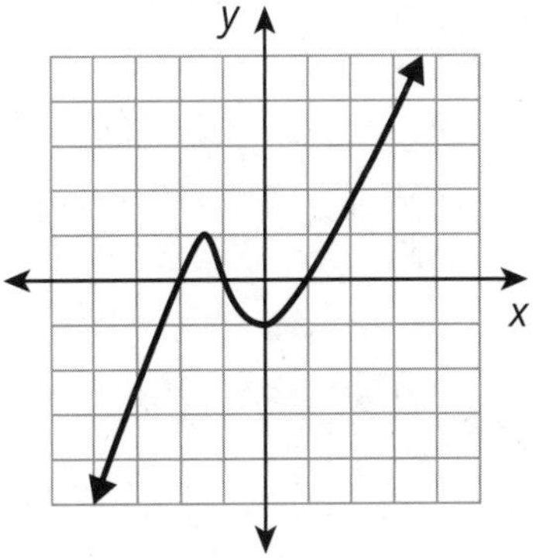

Go to LiveHint.com for help on the PRACTICE questions.

STRETCH Optional

> Describe characteristics of each graph, including whether or not it has a vertical or horizontal line of symmetry and the number of quadrants it passes through.

1. Diagonal line through the origin that increases from left to right
2. Diagonal line through the origin that decreases from left to right
3. Diagonal line that does not pass through the origin
4. Horizontal line below the origin
5. Vertical line to the right of the origin

LESSON 3

F of X

Recognizing Functions and Function Families

Learning Goals

- Define a function.
- Write equations using function notation.
- Recognize multiple representations of functions.
- Determine and recognize characteristics of functions and function families.

KEY TERMS

- relation
- domain
- range
- function
- vertical line test
- discrete graph
- continuous graph
- function notation
- increasing function
- decreasing function
- constant function
- function family
- linear functions
- exponential functions
- absolute minimum
- absolute maximum
- quadratic functions
- linear absolute value functions
- linear piecewise functions
- *x*-intercept
- *y*-intercept

REVIEW (1–2 minutes)

> Match each equation with its graph.

1 $y = \frac{1}{2}x$

2 $y = 2x + 1$

3 $y = -2x + 1$

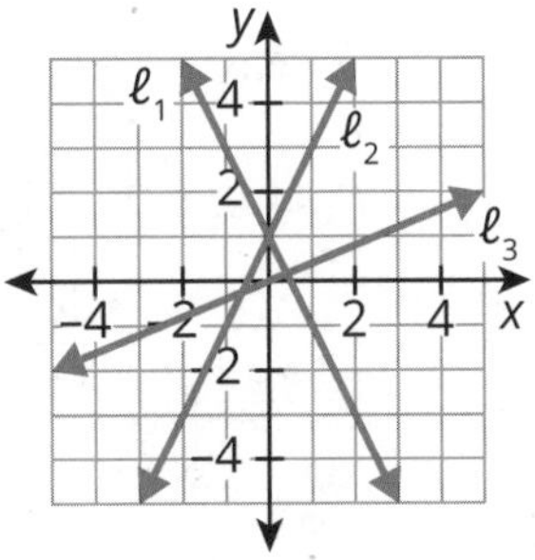

You have sorted graphs by their graphical behaviors.

How can you describe the common characteristics of the graphs of the functions?

Odd One Out

> Consider the graphs.

1 Which of the graphs does not belong with the others? **Explain your reasoning.**

Graph A

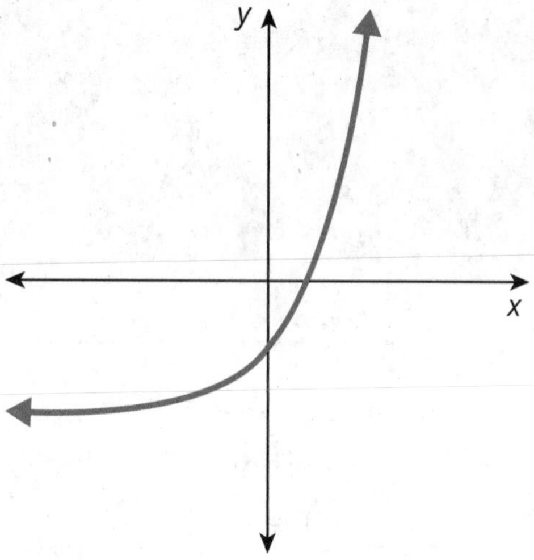

Graph B

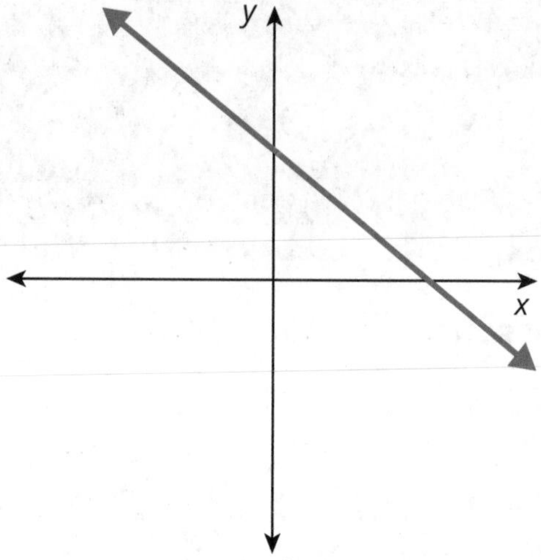

Graph C

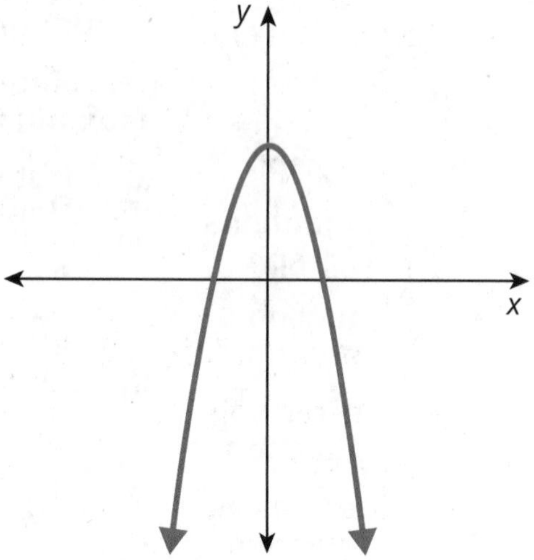

Graph D

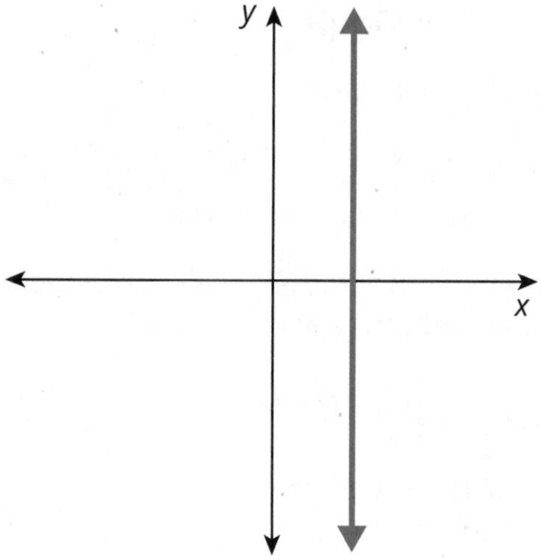

MATHia CONNECTION
- Interpreting Function Notation
- Identifying Domain and Range

Functions and Non-Functions

HABITS OF MIND
- Attend to precision.

You can represent a *relation* in the following ways.

A **relation** is the mapping between a set of input values called the **domain** and a set of output values called the **range**.

Ordered Pairs

$\{(-2,2), (0,2), (3, -4), (3,5)\}$

Equation

$y = \frac{2}{3}x - 1$

Verbal

The relation between students in your school and each student's birthday.

Mapping

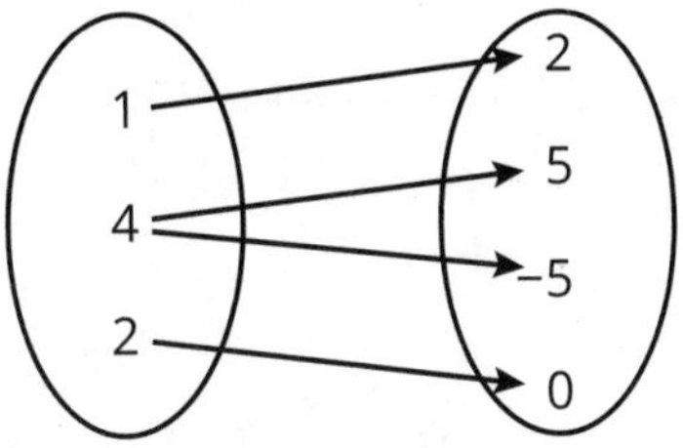

Graph

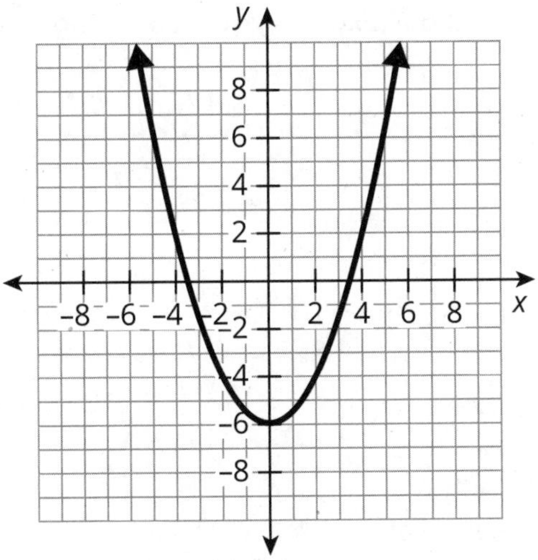

Table

x	y
−1	1
2	0
5	−5
6	−5
7	−8

1. Identify the domain and range in each representation.

A **function** is a relation that assigns to each element of the domainexactly one element of the range. You can represent a function in a number of ways.

2 Analyze the relation represented as a table. Is the relation a function? **Explain your reasoning.**

THINK ABOUT...
So all functions are relations, but only some relations arefunctions.

3 Analyze the relation represented as a mapping. Is the relation a function? **Explain your reasoning.**

4 Analyze the relation represented verbally. Is the relation a function? **Explain your reasoning.**

The **vertical line test** is a visual method used to determine whether a relation represented as a graph is a function. To apply the vertical line test, consider all of the vertical lines that could be drawn on the graph of a relation. If any of the vertical lines intersect the graph of the relation at more than one point, then the relation is not a function.

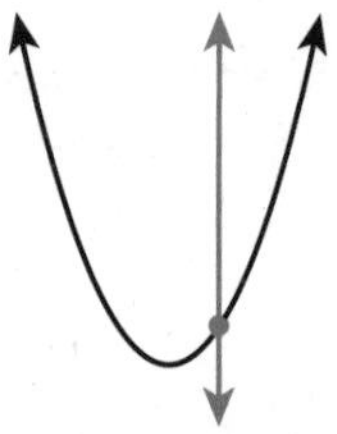

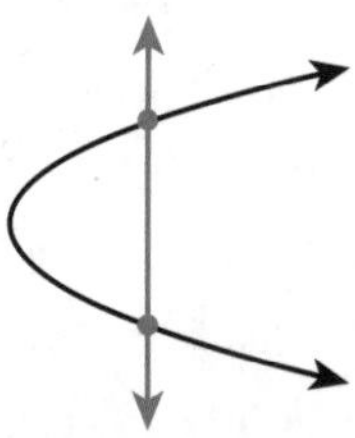

DID YOU KNOW?
A **discrete graph** is a graph of isolated points. A **continuous graph** is a graph of points that are connected by a line or smooth curve on the graph. Continuous graphs have no breaks.

The vertical line test applies for both *discrete* and *continuous graphs*.

5 How can you determine whether a relation represented as a set of ordered pairs is a function? **Explain your reasoning.**

6 How can you determine whether a relation represented as an equation is a function? **Explain your reasoning.**

7 Determine which relations represent functions. If the relation is not a function, state why not.

ⓐ $y = 3x + 4$

ⓑ For every house, there is one and only one street address.

ⓒ

Domain	Range
−1	4
0	0
3	−2
0	4

ⓓ

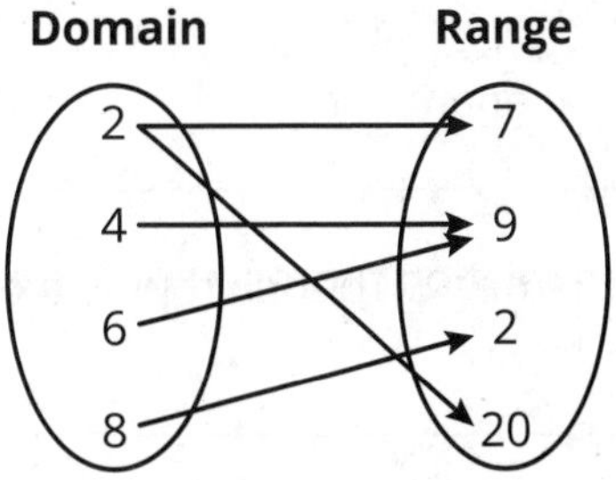

ⓔ

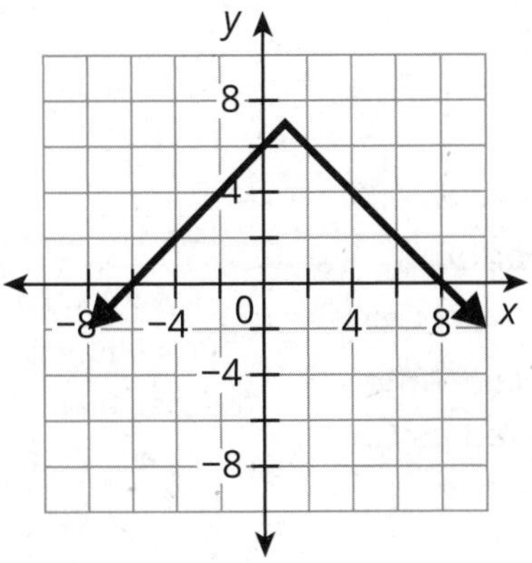

ⓕ {(−7, 5), (−5, 5), (2, −2), (3, 5)}

8 Analyze the three graphs Judy grouped together in the previous lesson, Graphs D, K, and O. Are the graphs she grouped functions? **Explain your conclusion.**

9 Use the vertical line test to sort the graphs in the previous lesson into two groups: functions and non-functions. Record your results by writing the letter of each graph in the appropriate column in the table shown.

Functions	Non-Functions

You can write an equation representing a function using *function notation*. Let's look at the relationship between an equation and function notation.

> Consider this scenario.

U.S. Shirts charges $8 per shirt plus a one-time charge of $15 to set up a T-shirt design.

TAKE NOTE...

Function notation is a way of representing functions algebraically. The function notation $f(x)$ is read as "f of x" and indicates that x is the independent variable.

You can model this situation using the equation $y = 8x + 15$. The independent variable x represents the number of shirts ordered, and the dependent variable y represents the total cost of the order, in dollars.

This is a function because for each number of shirts ordered (independent value) there is exactly one total cost (dependent value) associated with it. You can write $y = 8x + 15$ in function notation.

name of function ⟶ $f(x) = 8x + 15$

↑ independent variable

The cost, defined by f, is a function of x, defined as the number of shirts ordered.

You can write a function in a number of different ways. You could write the T-shirt cost function as $C(s) = 8s + 15$, where the cost, defined as C, is a function of s, the number of shirts ordered.

TAKE NOTE...

If f is a function and x is an element of its domain, then $f(x)$ denotes the output of f corresponding to the input x.

> Consider the U.S. Shirts function, $C(s) = 8s + 15$.

10 Identify which expression in the function equation represents each part of the function.

(a) Domain

(b) Range

11 Describe the possible domain and range for this situation.

You have identified the domain and range of a function given its equation.

12 Explain how you can identify the domain and range of a function given each representation.

(a) A verbal statement

(b) A graph

WORKED EXAMPLE

There are different ways to write the domain and range of a function given its graph.

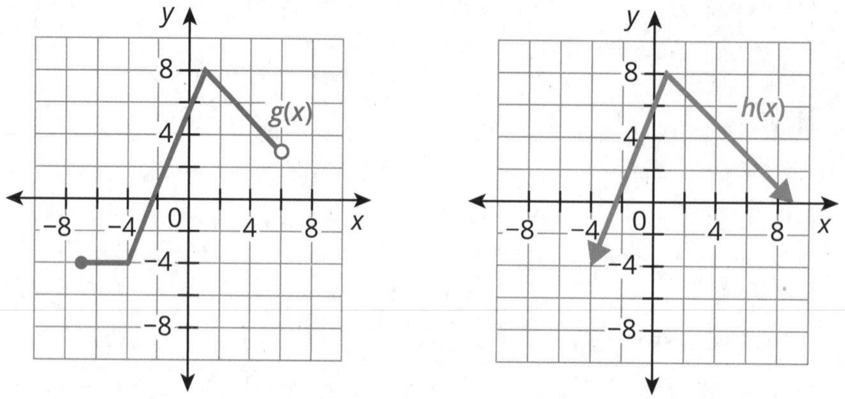

	Domain		Range	
	$g(x)$	$h(x)$	$g(x)$	$h(x)$
In Words	The domain is all real numbers greater than or equal to –7 and less than 6.	The domain is the set of all real numbers.	The range is all real numbers greater than or equal to –4 and less than or equal to 8.	The range is all real numbers less than or equal to 8.
Using Notation	$-7 \le x < 6$	$-\infty < x < \infty$	$-4 \le y \le 8$	$y \le 8$

13 Consider the Graph Cards from the previous lesson that represent continuous functions. Label each of these cards with the appropriate domain and range.

Linear and Exponential Functions

> Gather all of the graphs that you identified as functions.

You describe a function as increasing when the value of the dependent variable increases as the value of the independent variable increases. When a function increases across the entire domain, the function is an **increasing function**.

You describe a function as decreasing when the value of the dependent variable decreases as the value of the independent variable increases. When a function decreases across the entire domain, the function is a **decreasing function**.

When the value of the dependent variable of a function remains constant over the entire domain, the function is a **constant function**.

HABITS OF MIND

- Look for and make use of structure.
- Look for and express regularity in repeated reasoning.

THINK ABOUT...

When determining whether a graph is increasing or decreasing, read the graph from left to right.

1. Analyze each graph from left to right. Sort all the graphs into one of the four groups listed.

- increasing function
- decreasing function
- constant function
- a combination of increasing, decreasing, and constant

Record the function letter in the appropriate column of the table.

Increasing Function	Decreasing Function	Constant Function	Combination of Increasing, Decreasing, or Constant Function

2. Each function shown represents one of the graphs in the increasing function, decreasing function, or constant function categories. Use graphing technology to determine the shape of its graph. Then match the function to its corresponding graph by writing the function directly on the graph that it represents.

- $f(x) = x$
- $f(x) = \left(\frac{1}{2}\right)^x$
- $f(x) = \left(\frac{1}{2}\right)^x - 5$
- $f(x) = 2$, where x is an integer
- $f(x) = 2^x$, where x is an integer
- $f(x) = -x + 3$, where x is an integer

THINK ABOUT...

Be sure to correctly interpret the domain of each function. Also, remember to use parentheses when entering fractions into your calculator.

3 Consider the six graphs and functions that are increasing functions, decreasing functions, or constant functions.

(a) Sort the graphs into two groups based on the equations representing the functions and record the function letter in the table.

Group 1	Group 2

(b) What is the same about all the functions in each group?

You have just sorted the graphs into their own *function families*. A **function family** is a group of functions that share certain characteristics.

The family of **linear functions** includes functions of the form $f(x) = ax + b$, where a and b are real numbers.

The family of **exponential functions** includes functions of the form $f(x) = a \cdot b^x + c$, where a, b, and c are real numbers, and b is greater than 0 but not equal to 1.

ASK YOURSELF...
What other variables have you used to represent a linear function?

4 Go back to your table in Question 3 and identify which group represents linear and constant functions and which group represents exponential functions.

5 If $f(x) = ax + b$ represents a linear function, describe the a and b values that produce a constant function.

TAKE NOTE...
Place these two groups of graphs off to the side. You will need them again.

Quadratic and Absolute Value Functions

HABITS OF MIND

- Look for and make use of structure.
- Look for and express regularity in repeated reasoning.

A function has an **absolute minimum** when there is a point on the graph of the function that has a *y*-coordinate that is less than the *y*-coordinate of every other point on the graph. A function has an **absolute maximum** when there is a point on the graph of the function that has a *y*-coordinate that is greater than the *y*-coordinate of every other point on the graph.

1. Sort the graphs from the combination of increasing, decreasing, and constant category in the previous activity into one of the three groups listed.
   - Those that have an absolute minimum value
   - Those that have an absolute maximum value
   - Those that have no absolute minimum or maximum value

   Then record the function letter in the appropriate column of the table shown.

Absolute Minimum	Absolute Maximum	No Absolute Minimum or Absolute Maximum

2. Each function shown represents one of the graphs with an absolute maximum or an absolute minimum value. Use graphing technology to determine the shape of its graph. Then match the function to its corresponding graph by writing the function directly on the graph that it represents.
   - $f(x) = x^2 + 8x + 12$
   - $f(x) = -3x^2 + 4$, where x is an integer
   - $f(x) = -\frac{1}{2}x^2 + 2x$
   - $f(x) = -2|x + 2| + 4$
   - $f(x) = -|x|$
   - $f(x) = x^2$
   - $f(x) = |x|$

3 Consider the graphs of functions that have an absolute minimum or an absolute maximum.

(a) Sort the graphs into two groups based on the equations representing the functions and record the function letter in the table.

Group 1	Group 2

(b) What is the same about all the functions in each group?

You have just sorted functions into two more function families.

The family of **quadratic functions** includes functions of the form $f(x) = ax^2 + bx + c$, where a, b, and c are real numbers, and a is not equal to 0.

The family of **linear absolute value functions** includes functions of the form $f(x) = a|x + b| + c$, where a, b, and c are real numbers, and a is not equal to 0.

4 Go back to your table in Question 3 and identify which group represents quadratic functions and which group represents linear absolute value functions.

MATHia CONNECTION

- Identifying Key Characteristics of Graphs of Functions
- Introduction to Function Families

Linear Piecewise Functions

HABITS OF MIND

- Look for and make use of structure.
- Look for and express regularity in repeated reasoning.

Analyze the two functions shown. These functions represent the last two graphs of functions from the *no absolute minimum* or *no absolute maximum* category.

$$f(x) = \begin{cases} -2, & x < 0 \\ \frac{1}{2}x - 2, & x \geq 0 \end{cases}$$

$$f(x) = \begin{cases} -2x + 10, & x < 3 \\ 4, & 3 \leq x < 7 \\ -2x + 18, & x \geq 7 \end{cases}$$

1. Use graphing technology to determine the shapes of their graphs. Then match each function to its corresponding graph by writing the function directly on the graph that it represents.

You have just sorted the remaining functions into one more function family. The family of **linear piecewise functions** includes functions that have equation changes for different parts, or pieces, of the domain.

TAKE NOTE...

You will need these graphs again.

Graphing Functions Using Intercepts

HABITS OF MIND

- Look for and make use of structure.
- Look for and express regularity in repeated reasoning.

Recall that the ***x*-intercept** is the point where a graph crosses the *x*-axis. The ***y*-intercept** is the point where a graph crosses the *y*-axis.

1. The graphs shown represent relations with just the *x*- and *y*-intercepts plotted. If possible, draw a function that has the given intercepts. If it is not possible, explain why not.

(a)

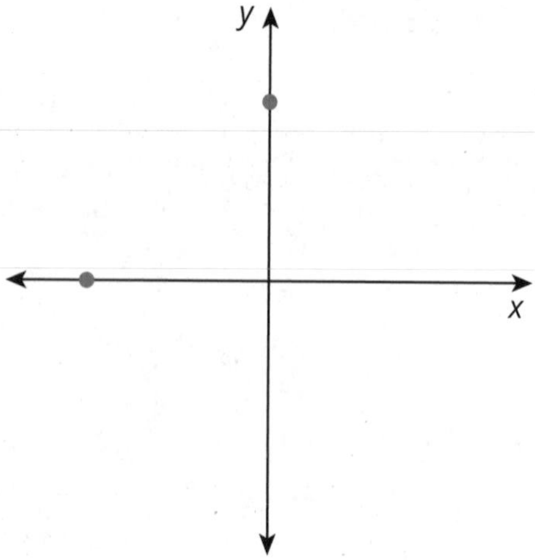

(b)

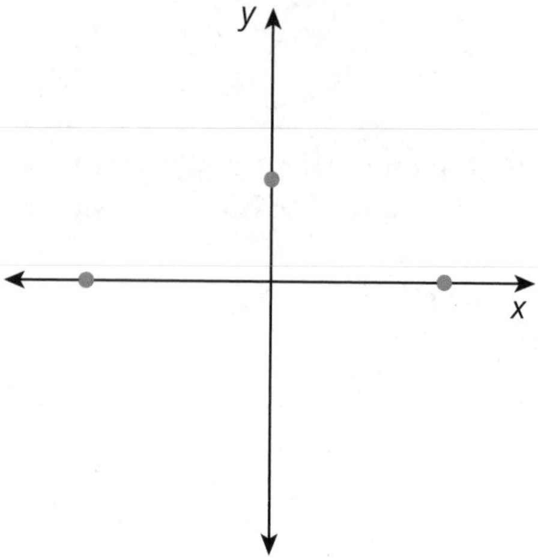

(c)

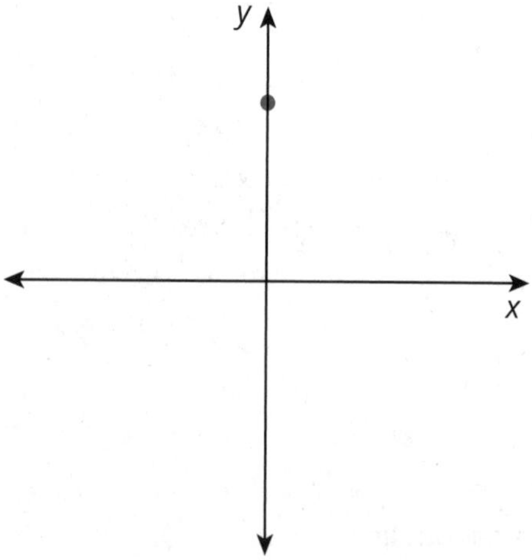

(d)

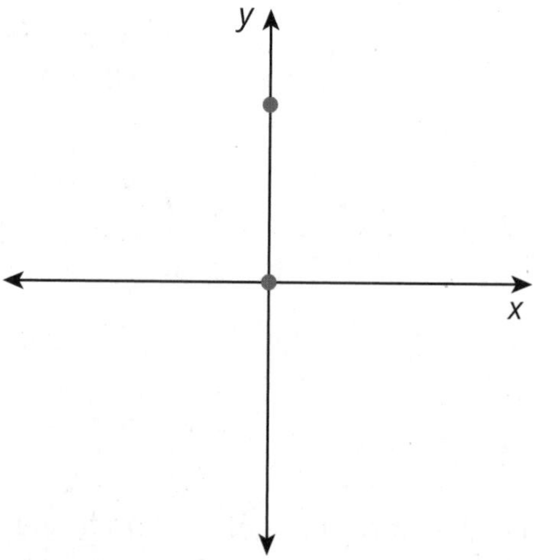

I Got All My Sisters with Me

You have now sorted each of the graphs and equations representing functions into one of five function families: linear, exponential, quadratic, linear absolute value, and linear piecewise.

1. Glue your sorted graphs and functions to the appropriate function family graphic organizer located on pages 46–50. **Write a description of the graphical behavior for each function family.**

You've done a lot of work up to this point! You've been introduced to linear, exponential, quadratic, linear absolute value, and linear piecewise functions. Don't worry—you don't need to know everything there is to know about these function families right now. As you progress through this course, you will learn more about each function family.

REMEMBER...
Hang on to your graphic organizers. They will be a great resource moving forward!

The family of **linear functions** includes functions of the form $f(x) = ax + b$, where a and b are real numbers.

Linear Functions

Graphs

Graphical Behaviors

Increasing/Decreasing/Constant:

Domain and Range:

Maximum/Minimum:

Curve/Line:

The family of **exponential functions** includes functions of the form $f(x) = a \cdot b^x + c$, where a, b, and c are real numbers, and b is greater than 0 but not equal to 1.

Exponential Functions

Graphs

Graphical Behaviors

Increasing/Decreasing/Constant:

Domain and Range:

Maximum/Minimum:

Curve/Line:

The family of **quadratic functions** includes functions of the form $f(x) = ax^2 + bx + c$ where a, b, and c are real numbers, and a is not equal to 0.

Quadratic Functions

Graphs

Graphical Behaviors

Increasing/Decreasing/Constant:

Domain and Range:

Maximum/Minimum:

Curve/Line:

The family of **linear absolute value functions** includes functions of the form $f(x) = a|x + b| + c$, where a, b, and c are real numbers, and a is not equal to 0.

Linear Absolute Value Functions

Graphs

Graphical Behaviors

Increasing/Decreasing/Constant:

Domain and Range:

Maximum/Minimum:

Curve/Line:

The family of **linear piecewise functions** includes functions that have equation changes for different parts, or pieces, of the domain.

Linear Piecewise Functions

Graphs

Graphical Behaviors

Increasing/Decreasing/Constant:

Domain and Range:

Maximum/Minimum:

Curve/Line:

LESSON 3 ASSIGNMENT

> Use a separate piece of paper for your Journal entry.

JOURNAL

Choose the term that best completes each statement.

1. __________ is a way to represent equations algebraically that makes it more efficient to recognize the independent and dependent variables.

REMEMBER

A function is a relation that assigns to each element of the domain exactly one element of the range.

Some different function families include linear functions, exponential functions, quadratic functions, linear absolute value functions, and linear piecewise functions.

2. When both the independent and dependent variables of a function increase across the entire domain, the function is a(n) __________.
3. A function has a(n) __________ if there is a point on its graph that has a *y*-coordinate that is greater than the *y*-coordinates of every other point on the graph.
4. When the dependent variable of a function decreases as the independent variable increases across the entire domain, the function is a(n) __________.
5. If the dependent variable of a function does not change or remains constant over the entire domain, then the function is a(n) __________.
6. A function has a(n) __________ if there is a point on its graph that has a *y*-coordinate that is less than the *y*-coordinate of every other point on the graph.

PRACTICE

> For each scenario, use graphing technology to determine the shape of its graph. Then identify the function family, whether it is increasing, decreasing, or a combination of both, has an absolute maximum or absolute minimum, and whether it is a smooth curve or straight line.

1. A fitness company is selling videos for one of its new cardio routines. Each video will sell for \$15. Due to fixed and variable costs, you can represent the profit that the company will see after selling x videos using the function $P(x) = 11.5x - 0.1x^2 - 150$.

2. Shari is going to put \$500 into an account with The People's Bank. The bank is offering a 3% interest rate compounded annually. You can represent the amount of money that Shari will have after x years using the function $A(x) = 500(1.03)^x$.

Go to LiveHint.com for help on the PRACTICE questions.

3 The Ace Calendar Company is going to buy a new 3D printer for $20,000. In order to plan for the future, the owners are interested in the salvage value of the printer each year. You can represent the salvage value after x years using the function $S(x) = 20{,}000 - 2000x$.

4 An underwater camera has been placed in the center of the 25-meter pool at the Grandtown Aquatic Center to take pictures of swimmers during a swim meet. The camera will go off at different times depending on the distance of the swimmer to the camera. If the swimmer is moving at a constant rate of 1.28 meters per second, then you can represent the distance the swimmer is from the camera after x seconds using the function $d(x) = 1.28|x - 9.77|$.

5 The PARK SAFE commuter lot charges different rates depending on the number of hours a car is parked during the 5-day work week. The lot charges $3 per hour for the first day, $2 per hour for the next 2 days, and will charge $1 per hour if the car is parked more than 3 days in the lot. You can represent the fees after x hours using the function shown.

$$f(x) = \begin{cases} 3x, & 0 \le x \le 24 \\ 72 + 2(x - 24), & 24 < x \le 72 \\ x + 96, & 72 < x \le 120 \end{cases}$$

STRETCH Optional

> Graph both functions on the same screen using graphing technology. Use reasoning to classify the second function as a new family. Then describe the similarities and differences between the shapes of the graphs in terms of intervals of increase and decrease, maximums or minimums, and whether they are curves or lines.

$h(x) = x^2 + 9x + 14$ $\qquad$ $p(x) = 5|x^2 + 9x| + 14$

LESSON 4

Function Families for 200, Alex

Recognizing Functions by Characteristics

Learning Goals

- Recognize similar characteristics among function families.
- Recognize different characteristics among function families.
- Determine function types given certain characteristics.

REVIEW (1–2 minutes)

> Describe characteristics of each graph.

1

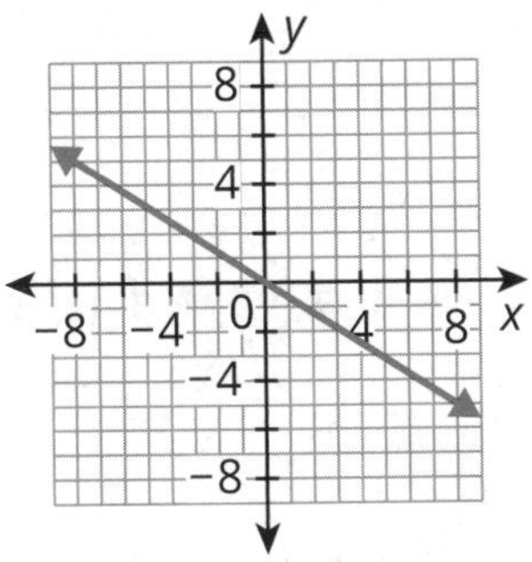

2

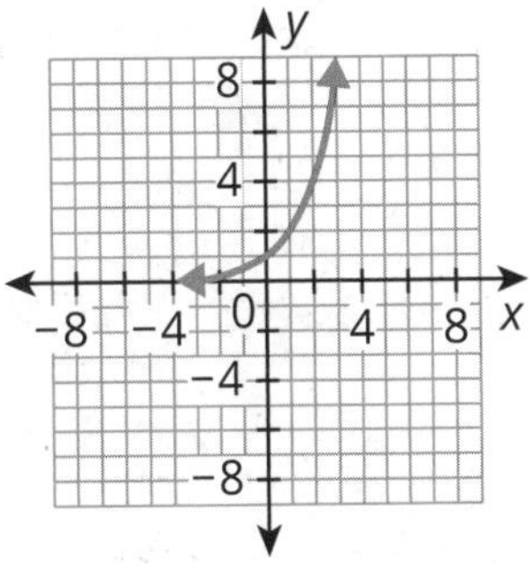

You have identified key characteristics of graphs.

How can the key characteristics help you sketch the graph of a function?

Name That Function!

You have sorted graphs according to their function family. Now, consider which function families have the given characteristics.

FUNCTION FAMILIES

linear
exponential
quadratic
linear absolute value
linear piecewise

1. Which function families can you describe using the characteristic provided?

   a) The graph is a smooth curve.

   b) The graph is made up of one or more straight lines.

   c) The graph increases or decreases over the entire domain.

   d) The graph has an absolute maximum or minimum.

2. Consider the graphical description of each function. Name the possible function families.

   a) The graph has an absolute minimum or absolute maximum and is a smooth curve.

   b) The graph either increases or decreases over the entire domain and is a straight line.

   c) The graph is a smooth curve, and either increases or decreases over the entire domain.

   d) The graph has either an absolute minimum or an absolute maximum, has symmetry, and is made up of 2 straight lines.

Each function family has certain graphical behaviors, with some behaviors common among different function families. Notice, the more specific characteristics that are given, the more specifically you can name that function!

Categorizing Scenarios into Their Function Families

HABITS OF MIND

- Look for and make use of structure.
- Look for and express regularity in repeated reasoning.

You have been introduced to several function families.

- Linear
- Exponential
- Quadratic
- Linear absolute value
- Linear piecewise

Let's revisit the first lesson **A Picture Is Worth a Thousand Words**. Each of the scenarios in that lesson represents one of these function families.

1 Describe how each scenario represents a function.

REMEMBER...
Each of the graphs representing the scenarios was drawn with either a continuous line or a continuous smooth curve to model the problem situation.

2 Complete the table on the following pages to describe each scenario.

- Identify the appropriate function family under the scenario name.
- Based on the context, identify the domain as continuous or discrete.
- Describe the graphical behavior as increasing, decreasing, constant, or a combination.

Scenario	Domain of the Real-World Situation	Graph of the Mathematical Model	Graphical Behavior
Daredevil		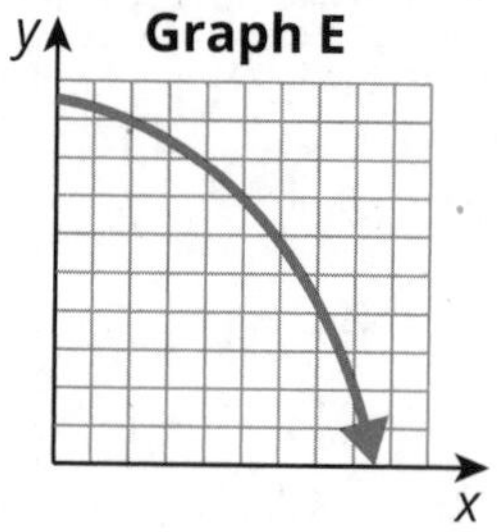	
Something's Fishy		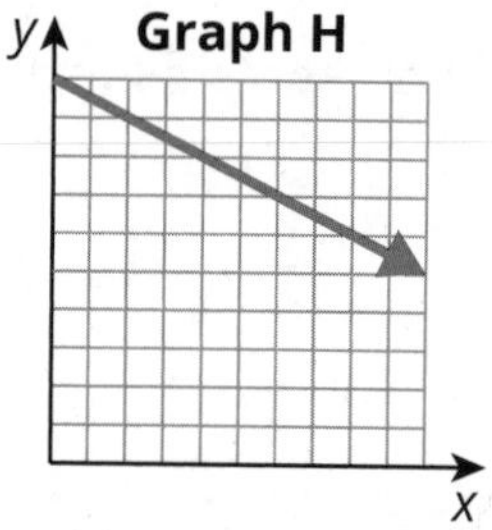	
Smart Phone, but Is It a Smart Deal?		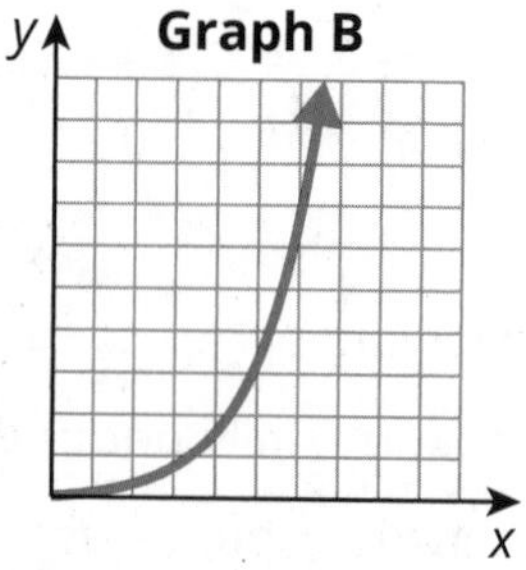	
Can't Wait to Hit the Slopes!		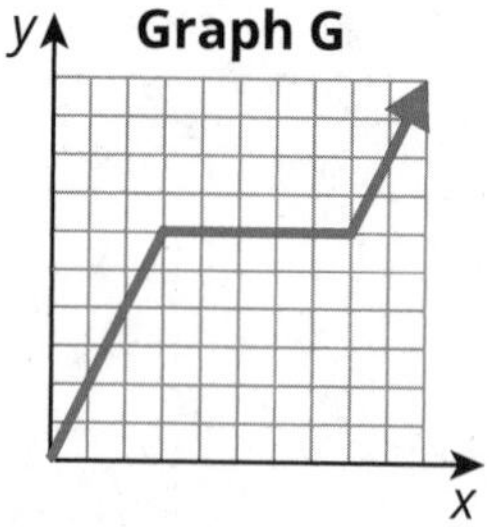	

Scenario	Domain of the Real-World Situation	Graph of the Mathematical Model	Graphical Behavior
It's Magic		Graph D 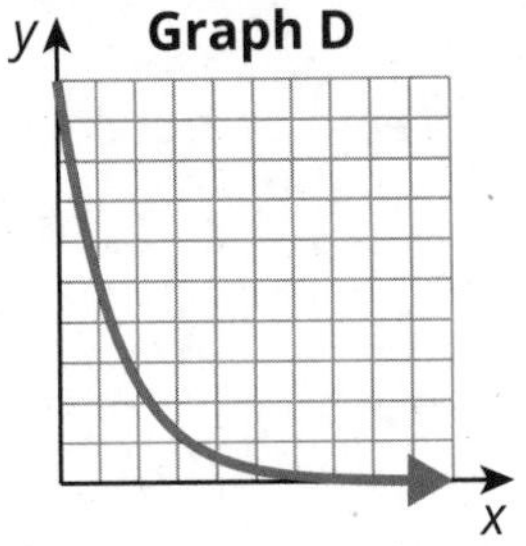	
Baton Twirling		Graph F 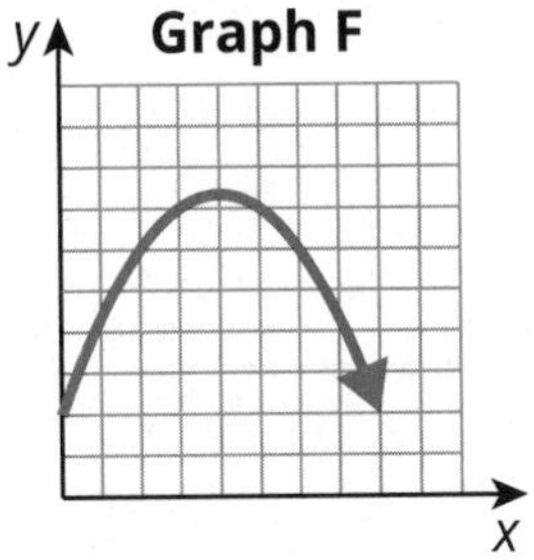	
Cold Weather		Graph A 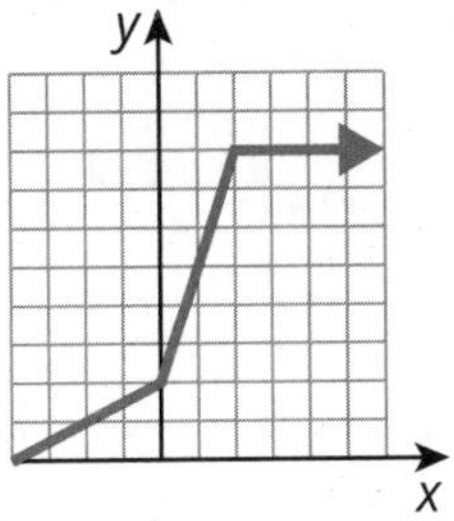	
Jelly Bean Challenge		Graph C 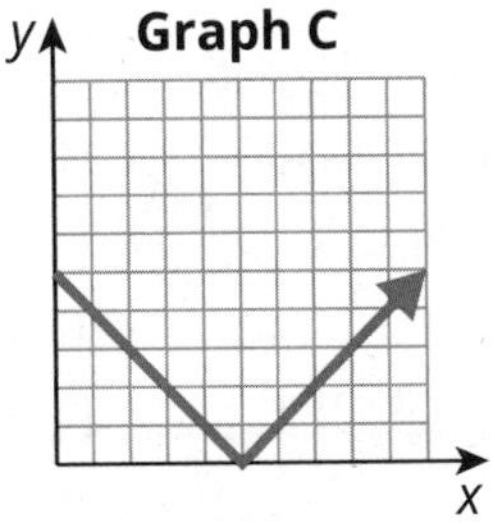	

Building Graphs from Characteristics

In this activity, you will write equations and sketch a graph based on given characteristics.

HABITS OF MIND

- Model with mathematics.
- Use appropriate tools strategically.

Use the given characteristics to create an equation and sketch a graph. Use the equations given in the box as a guide. When creating your equation, use a, b, and c values that are any real numbers between −3 and 3. Do not use any functions that were used previously in this topic.

1 Create an equation and sketch a graph with these characteristics.

- a function
- continuous
- exponential
- decreasing

FUNCTION

Linear Function

$f(x) = ax + b$

Exponential Function

$f(x) = a \cdot b^x + c$

Quadratic Function

$f(x) = ax^2 + bx + c$

Linear Absolute Value Function

$f(x) = a|x + b| + c$

Equation: ____________________

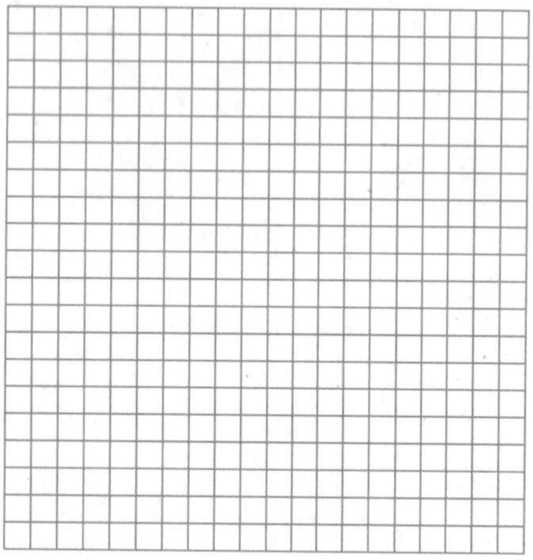

THINK ABOUT...

Don't forget about the function family graphic organizers you created if you need some help.

2 Create an equation and sketch a graph with these characteristics.

- has a minimum
- is discrete
- is a linear absolute value function

Equation: ____________________

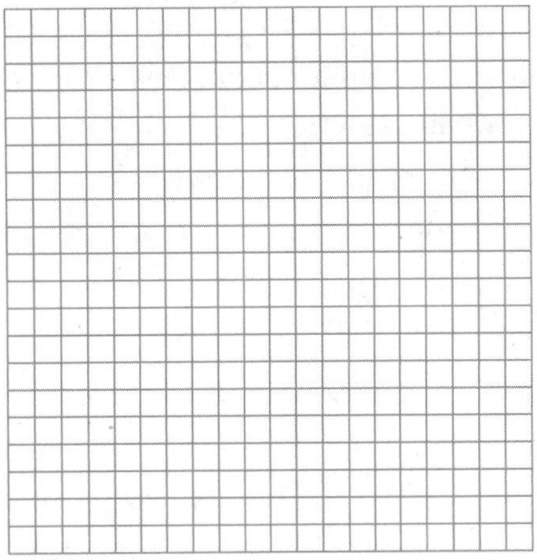

3 Create an equation and sketch a graph with these characteristics.

- linear
- discrete
- increasing
- a function

Equation: ____________________

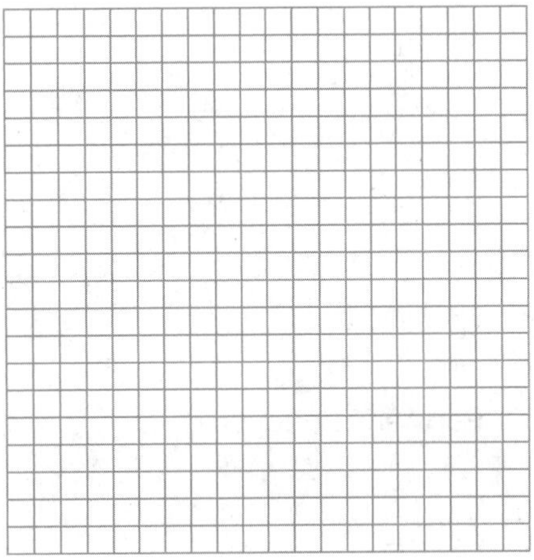

4 How could you modify the directions or the list of characteristics for any graph in Questions 1 through 3 to describe a unique graph?

Trying to Be Unique

> Create your own function. Describe certain characteristics of the function and see whether your partner can sketch it. Then sketch your partner's function based on characteristics provided.

1 Your Function

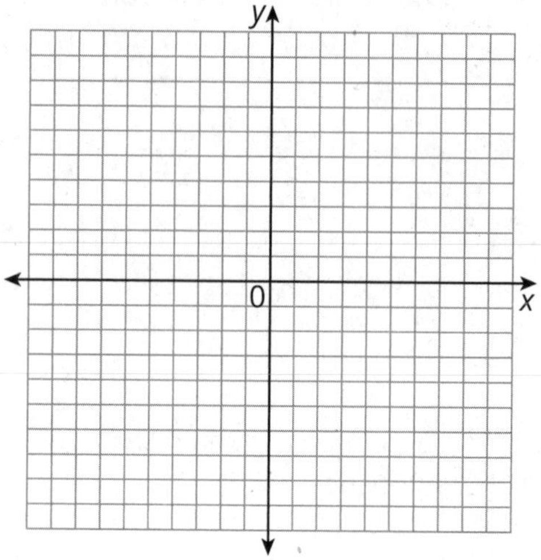

2 Your Partner's Function

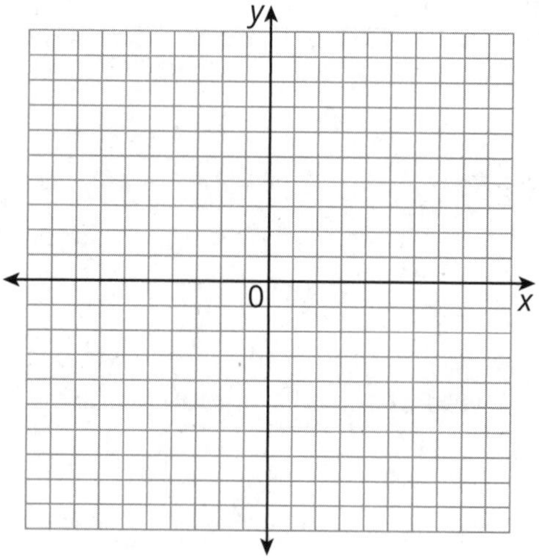

> Use a separate piece of paper for your Journal entry.

JOURNAL

Identify the function family or families that are described by the given characteristic(s). Choose from linear, linear absolute value, exponential, and quadratic functions.

REMEMBER

Function families have key characteristics that are common among all functions in the family. Knowing these key characteristics is useful when sketching a graph of the function.

1. The graph of this function family is decreasing over the entire domain.
2. The graph of this function family has an increasing interval and a decreasing interval and forms a U-shape.
3. The graph of this function family does not have an absolute maximum or absolute minimum and is a smooth curve.
4. The graph of this function family contains straight lines and does not have an absolute maximum or absolute minimum.

PRACTICE

> For each scenario and its graph, identify the appropriate function family. Then, based on the problem situation, identify whether the data values represented in the graph are discrete or continuous. Finally, identify the graphical behavior of the function that models the scenario based on the characteristics of its function family.

1. A manufacturing company finds that the daily cost associated with making tennis balls is high if they don't make enough balls and then becomes high again if they make too many balls. The function graphed models the daily costs of making *x* tennis balls.

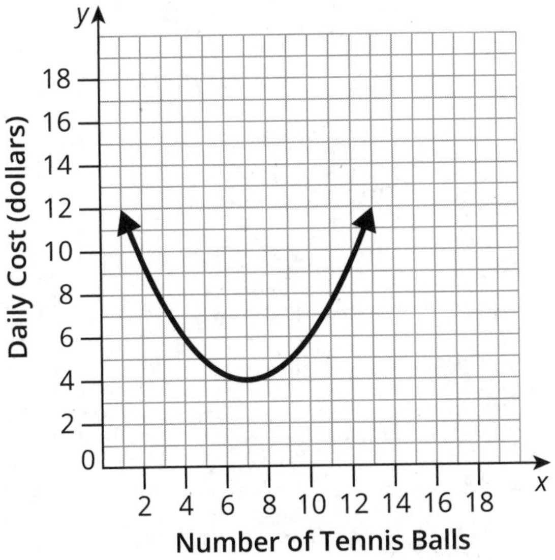

2 Greg is training for a mountain bike race. He leaves his car at the beginning of a trail and proceeds to bike 8 miles away and then comes back the same way to his car. If he bikes at a constant rate, the function graphed models the distance he is away from his car after x minutes.

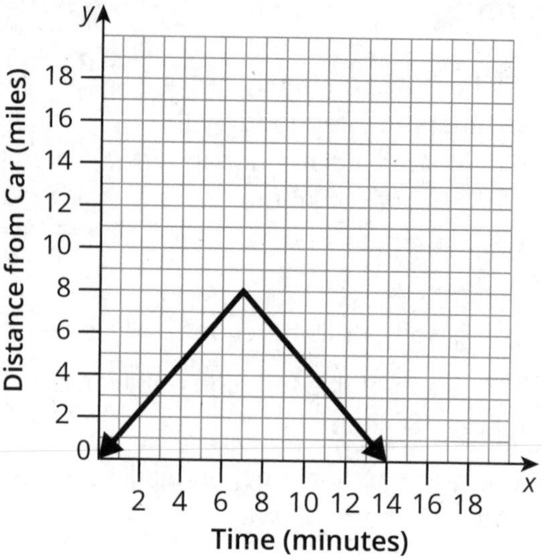

3 A local television company determines that the revenue it gets from running ads doubles each year. The function graphed models the revenue from advertising after x years.

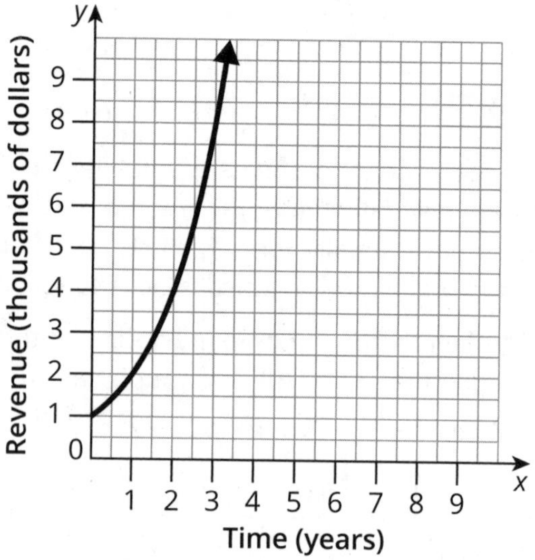

4 The Community Club is handing out glow sticks to all the children who attend the summer party. They start with 200 glow sticks and each child receives 3 glow sticks. The function graphed models the number of glow sticks they have left after x children have entered.

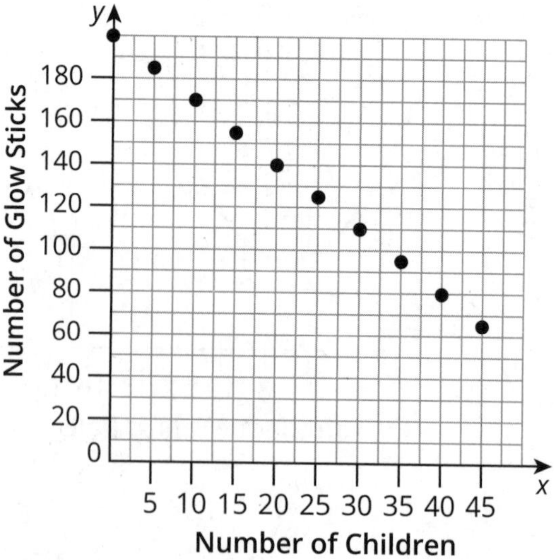

STRETCH Optional

> Write an equation and sketch a graph that has a minimum in Quadrant IV, is continuous, and is a linear absolute value function.

MIXED PRACTICE

> This Mixed Practice worksheet includes two sections: Spaced Review and End-of-Topic Review. **Use a separate piece of paper to show your work.**

Spaced Review

> Practice concepts from previous topics.

1 Solve each equation.

(a) $-2x + 8 = -3x + 14$

(b) $8y + 13 = 29$

2 Evaluate each expression.

(a) $x^2 - 3y + 12$ for $x = -2$ and $y = 5$

(b) $6z + 5(-2z - 7)$ for $z = -1$

3 Determine whether each relation represents a function. Explain your reasoning.

(a)

x	y
1	9
5	11
5	13
8	15

(b)

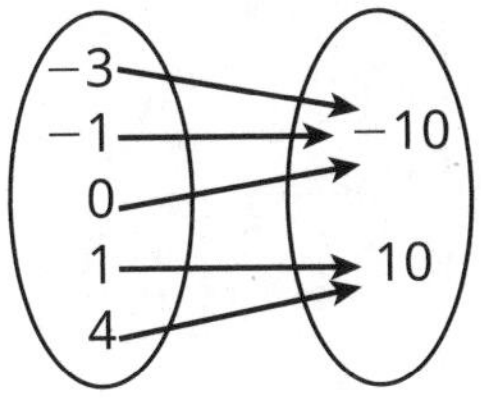

4 Write the ordered pair for each point plotted on the coordinate plane.

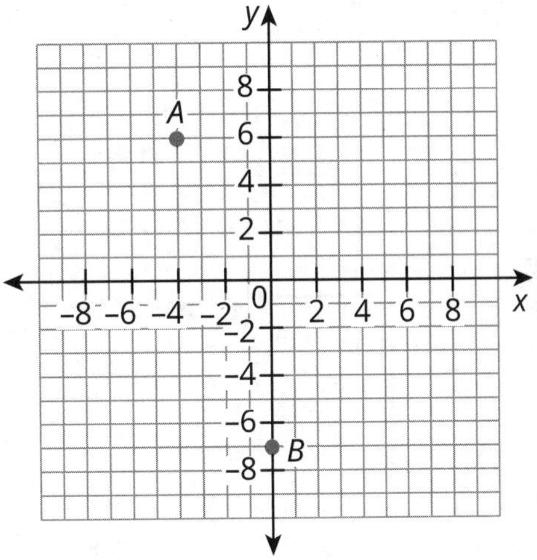

End-of-Topic Review

AVAILABLE ONLINE

1. A **Topic Summary** reviews the main concepts for the topic.
2. A video of the **Worked Example** is provided.

> Practice concepts you learned in **Quantities and Relationships.**

5 Identify the axis of symmetry each graph has, if any, and identify the number of quadrants it passes through

(a)

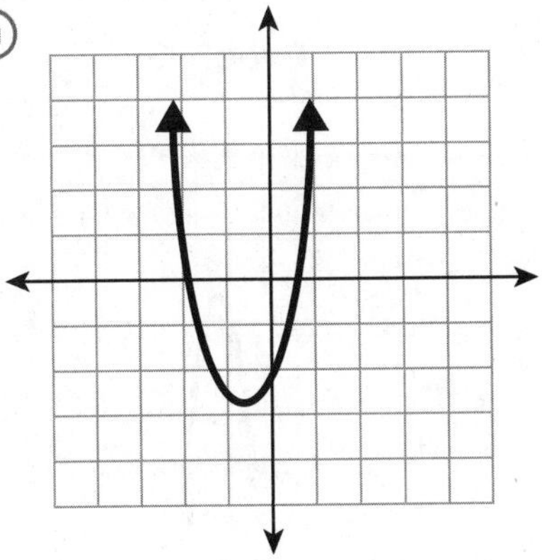

(b)

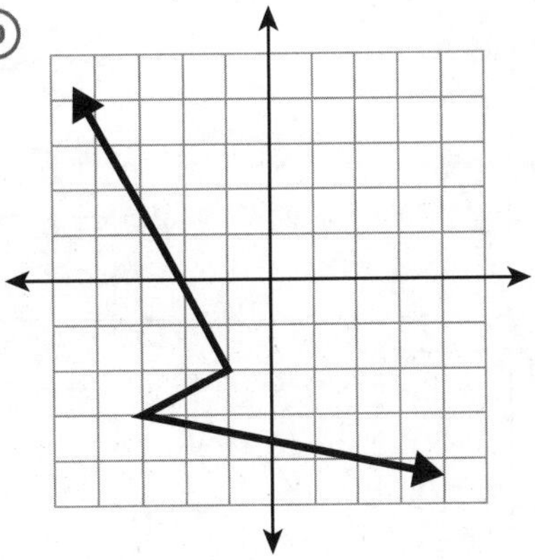

6 Determine whether each graph represents an increasing function, a decreasing function, a constant function, or a combination of increasing and decreasing functions.

ⓐ

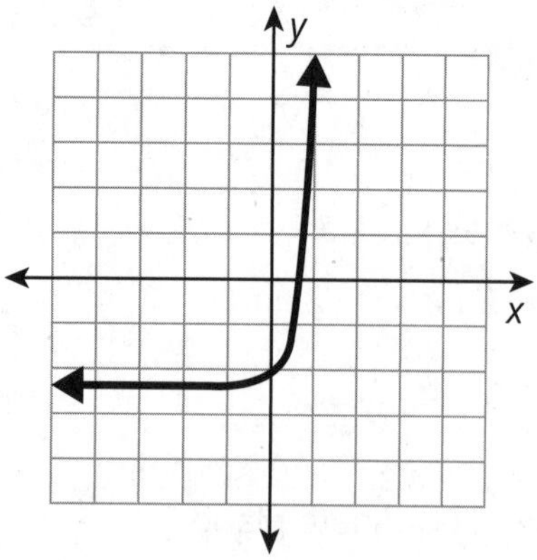

ⓑ

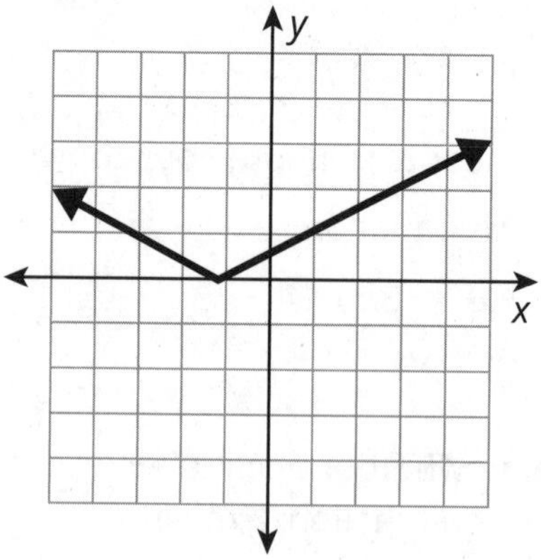

7 Identify the function family for each graph.

ⓐ

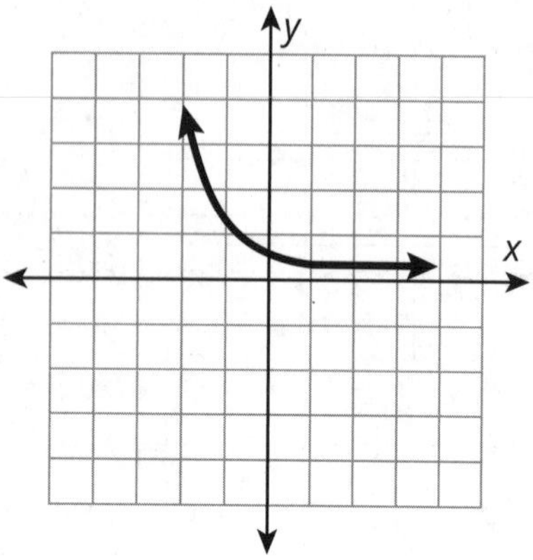

ⓑ

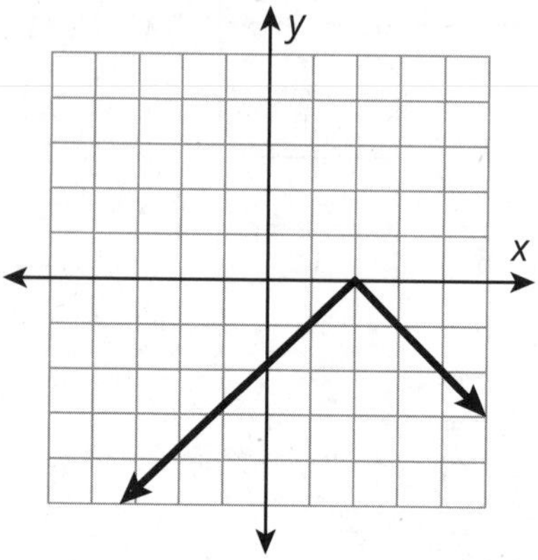

8 Determine the independent and dependent quantities in each scenario. Include units when possible.

ⓐ A lamp manufacturing company produces 750 lamps per shift.

ⓑ A grocery store sells pears by the pound. A customer purchases 3 pounds for $5.07.

9 Determine the function family for each equation.

ⓐ $g(x) = -15|x - 2| + 430$

ⓑ $h(x) = 3 \cdot (-5)^x - 17$

10 Choose the graph that represents a quadratic function.

Graph A

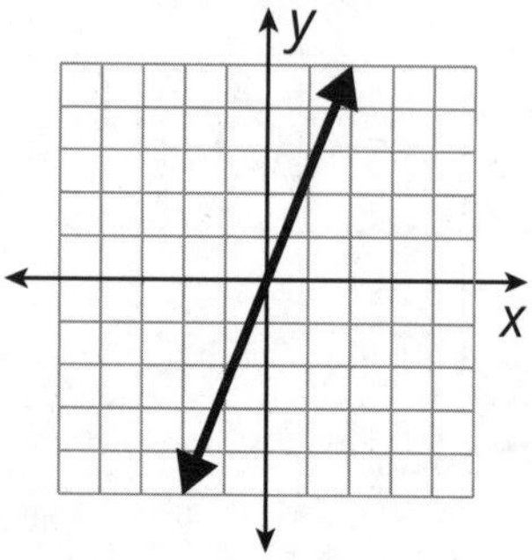

Graph B

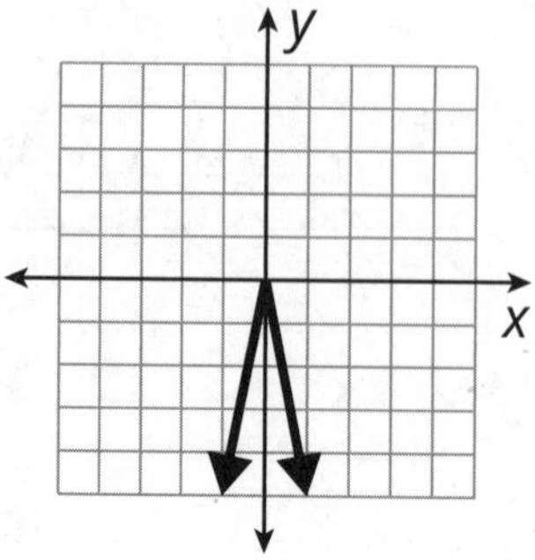

Graph C

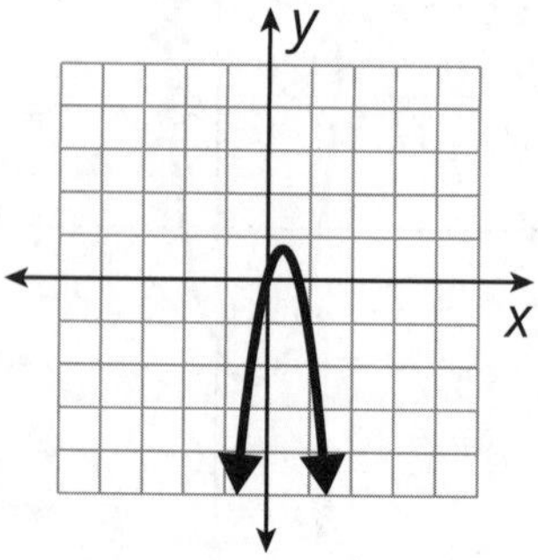

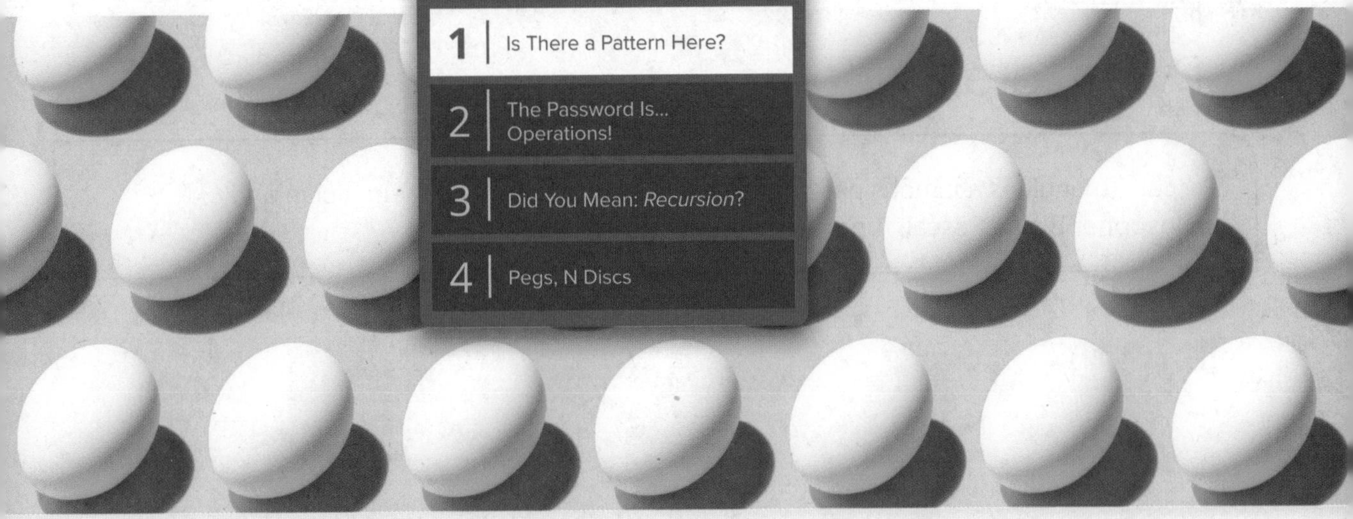

LESSON 1

Is There a Pattern Here?

Recognizing Patterns and Sequences

KEY TERMS

sequence

term of a sequence

infinite sequence

finite sequence

Learning Goals

- Recognize and describe patterns.
- Represent patterns as sequences.
- Predict the next term in a sequence.
- Represent a sequence as a table of values.

REVIEW (1–2 minutes)

> Each set shows the distance in miles a car traveled at the end of each hour for 4 hours. Determine whether each set shows a constant rate of change. If the rate is constant, write the rate.

1. {55, 110, 165, 220}

2. {11, 22, 33, 44}

3. {30, 35, 45, 60}

4. {0, 0, 0, 0}

Since early elementary school, you have been recognizing and writing patterns involving shapes, colors, letters, and numbers.

How do patterns relate to sequences and how can you represent them in tables?

A Pyramid of Patterns

Pascal's Triangle is a famous pattern named after the French mathematician and philosopher Blaise Pascal. A portion of the pattern is shown.

1
1 1
1 2 1
1 3 3 1
1 4 6 4 1
1 5 10 10 5 1
1 6 15 20 15 6 1

1. List at least 3 patterns that you notice.

2. Describe the pattern for the number of terms in each row.

3. Describe the pattern within each row.

4. Describe the pattern that results from determining the sum of each row.

5. Determine the next two rows in Pascal's Triangle. **Explain your reasoning.**

Patterns to Sequences to Tables

A **sequence** is a pattern involving an ordered arrangement of numbers, geometric figures, letters, or other objects. A **term of a sequence** is an individual number, figure, or letter in the sequence.

HABITS OF MIND
- Model with mathematics.
- Use appropriate tools strategically.

> Seven examples of sequences are given in this activity. For each sequence, describe the pattern, draw or describe the next terms, and represent each sequence numerically.

1 Positive Thinking

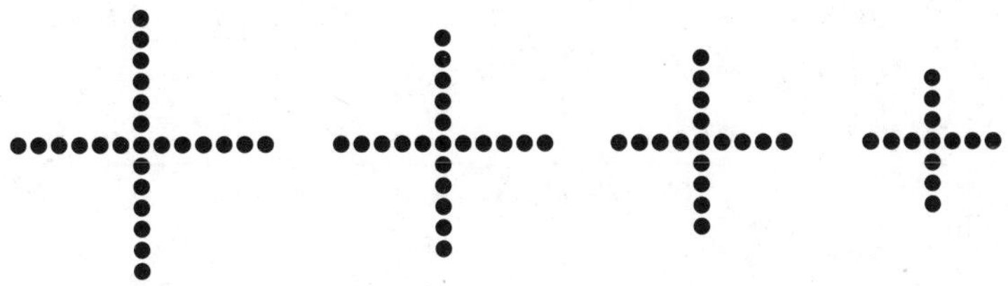

a) Analyze the number of dots. **Describe the pattern.**

b) Draw the next three figures of the pattern.

c) Represent the number of dots in each of the seven figures as a numeric sequence.

d) Represent the number of dots in each of the first seven figures as a function using a table of values.

Term Number	Term Value
1	
2	
3	
4	
5	
6	
7	

THINK ABOUT...
You can represent all numeric sequences as functions. The independent variable is the term number beginning with 1, and the dependent variable is the term of the sequence.

TOPIC 2

2 Family Tree

Jessica is investigating her family tree by researching each generation, or set, of parents. She learns all she can about the first four generations, which include her two parents, her grandparents, her great-grandparents, and her great-great-grandparents.

(a) Think about the number of parents. **Describe the pattern**.

(b) Determine the number of parents in the fifth and sixth generations.

(c) Represent the number of parents in each of the 6 generations as a numeric sequence. Then represent the sequence using a table of values.

Term Number	Term Value

3 A Collection of Squares

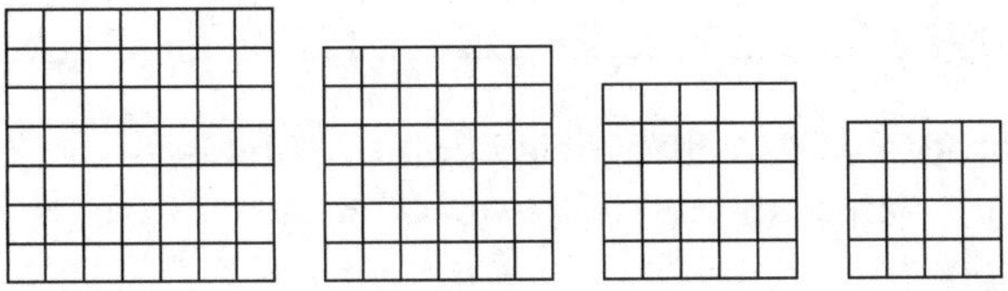

(a) Analyze the number of small squares in each figure. **Describe the pattern.**

(b) Draw the next three figures of the pattern.

(c) Represent the number of small squares in each of the first seven figures as a numeric sequence. Then represent the sequence using a table of values.

Term Number	Term Value

4 Donna's Daisies

Donna is decorating the top border of her bedroom walls with a daisy pattern. She is applying decals, with each column having a specific number of daisies.

(a) Think about the number of daisies in each column. **Describe the pattern.**

(b) Draw the number of daisies in each of the next three columns.

(c) Represent the number of daisies in each of the first 8 columns as a numeric sequence. Then represent the sequence using a table of values.

Term Number	Term Value

5 Gamer Guru

Mica unlocks some special mini-games where he earns points for each one he completes. After completing 1 mini-game, he has 550 points. After completing 2 mini-games, he has 600 points, and after completing 3 mini-games, he has 650 points.

(a) Think about the total number of points Mica gains from mini-games. **Describe the pattern.**

(b) Determine Mica's total points after he plays the next two mini-games.

(c) Represent Mica's total points after completing each of the first 5 mini-games as a numeric sequence. Be sure to include the number of points he started with. Then represent the sequence using a table of values.

Term Number	Term Value

6 Polygon Party

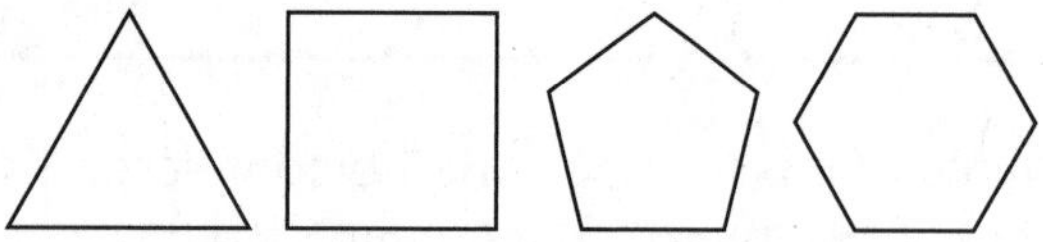

(a) Analyze the number of sides in each polygon. **Describe the pattern.**

(b) Draw the next two figures of the pattern.

(c) Represent the number of sides of each of the first 6 polygons as a numeric sequence. Then represent the sequence using a table of values.

Term Number	Term Value

7 Pizza Contest

After a pizza-making contest, Jacob plans to cut his whole pizza so that he can pass the slices out to share. After that, he cuts each of those slices in half. Then he cuts each of those slices in half, and so on.

(a) Think about the size of each slice in relation to the whole pizza. **Describe the pattern.**

(b) Determine the size of each slice compared to the whole pizza after the next two cuts.

(c) Represent the size of each slice compared to the whole pizza after each of the first 5 cuts as a numeric sequence. Include the whole pizza before any cuts. Then represent the sequence using a table of values.

Term Number	Term Value

Looking at Sequences More Closely

HABITS OF MIND
- Look for and make use of structure.
- Look for and express regularity in repeated reasoning.

Many different patterns can generate a sequence of numbers. For example, you may have noticed that you could generate some of the sequences in the previous activity by performing the same operation using a constant number. In other sequences, you may have noticed a different pattern.

You calculate the next term in a sequence by determining the sequence's pattern and then using that pattern on the last known term of the sequence.

1 Complete the table to describe each sequence from the previous activity.

Problem	Sequence	Increases (I) or Decreases (D)	Description
Positive Thinking	25, 21, 17, 13, 9, 5, 1	D	Begin at 25. Subtract 4 from each term.
Family Tree			
A Collection of Squares			
Donna's Daisies			
Gamer Guru			
Polygon Party			
Pizza Contest			

2 Which sequences are similar? **Explain your reasoning.**

3 What do all sequences have in common?

4 What is the domain of a sequence? What is the range?

5 Consider a sequence in which the first term is 64, and you calculate each term after that by dividing the previous term by 4. Margaret says that this sequence ends at 1. Jasmine disagrees and says that the sequence continues forever. Who is correct? If Margaret is correct, explain why. If Jasmine is correct, predict the next two terms of the sequence.

6 Which sequences in the table end? Which continue forever? **Explain your reasoning.**

When a sequence continues forever, it is an **infinite sequence**. When a sequence terminates, it is a **finite sequence**.

TAKE NOTE...

An ellipsis is three periods, which means "and so on." You can represent an infinite sequence using an ellipsis. For example, 2, 4, 6, ...

Searching for a Sequence

In this lesson, you have seen that many different patterns can generate a sequence of numbers.

1. Explain why all sequences represent functions.

2. Create a sequence to fit the given criteria. Describe your sequence using figures, words, or numbers. Provide the first four terms of the sequence. **Explain how you know that it is a sequence.**

   a. Create a sequence that begins with a positive integer, is decreasing by multiplication, and is finite.

   b. Create a sequence that begins with a negative rational number, is increasing by addition, and is infinite.

LESSON 1 ASSIGNMENT

Use a separate piece of paper for your Journal entry.

JOURNAL

Explain why all sequences represent functions.

REMEMBER

A sequence is a pattern involving an ordered arrangement of numbers, geometric figures, letters, or other objects. It is a function whose domain is the set of natural numbers.

PRACTICE

Consider the three sequences given. For each sequence, describe the pattern. Then, represent the sequence as a numeric sequence and as a table of values.

1. Matchstick Mayhem

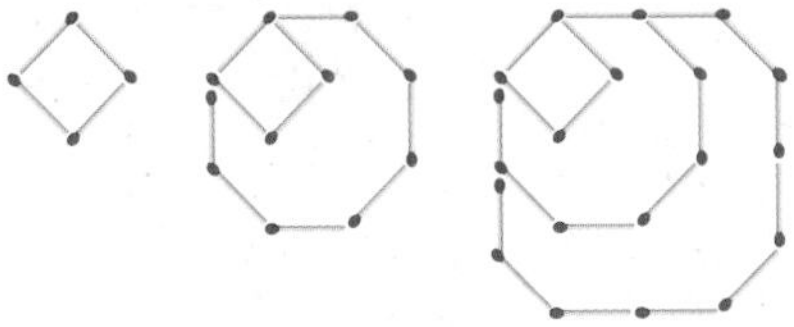

Term Number	1	2	3	4	5	6
Term Value						

2. Hancox Homes

Hancox Homes is a popular construction company that builds affordable housing. When the company first started, they sold 1 home the first month, 3 homes the second month, 9 homes the third month, and 27 homes the fourth month.

Term Number	1	2	3	4	5	6
Term Value						

Go to LiveHint.com for help on the PRACTICE questions.

3 Violet's Videos

Violet is a yoga instructor who regularly posts new exercise videos on a website for her clients. One week after launching the website, she had posted a total of 6 videos. At the end of week 2, she had a total of 10 videos. At the end of week 3, she had a total of 14 videos. At the end of week 4, she had a total of 18 videos.

Term Number	1	2	3	4	5	6
Term Value						

STRETCH Optional

Robin is opening a restaurant and tells her staff they must go above and beyond to please their customers, especially on opening day. She reasons that when one customer is pleased with the restaurant, that person is likely to tell 4 people about it. Then each of those people is likely to tell 4 people about it, and so on.

1. Describe the pattern for the number of customers Robin's Restaurant will reach with each telling.
2. Determine how many customers Robin reaches after the 5th, 6th, and 7th tellings.
3. Represent the number of customers reached with each telling as a numeric sequence. Then represent the sequence using a table of values.
4. Identify the appropriate function family for the function. Then describe whether the function is continuous or discrete.

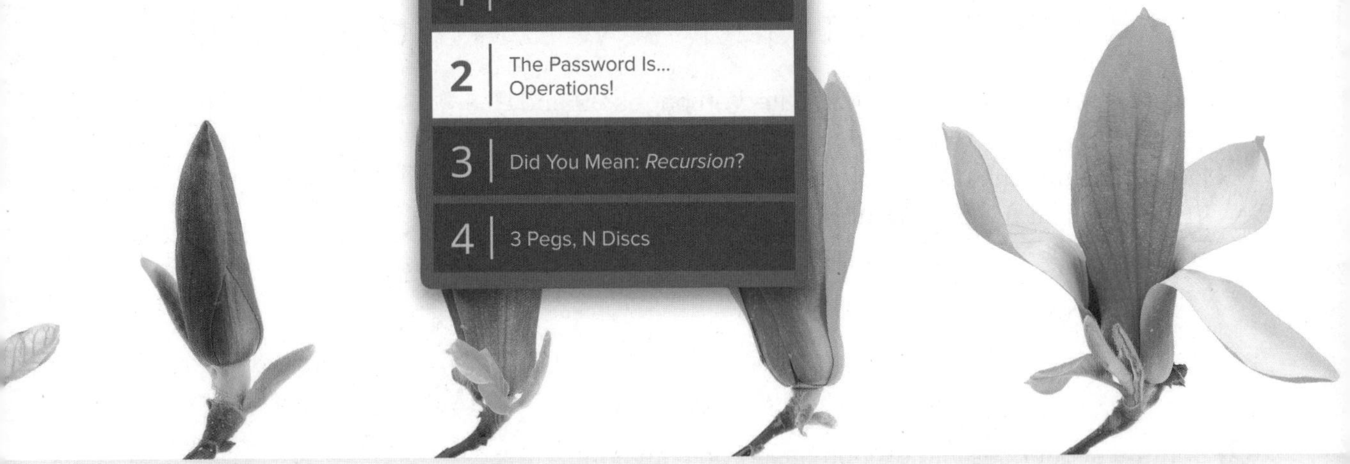

LESSON 2

The Password Is...Operations!

Arithmetic and Geometric Sequences

KEY TERMS

- **arithmetic sequence**
- **common difference**
- **geometric sequence**
- **common ratio**

Learning Goals

- Determine the next term in a sequence.
- Recognize arithmetic sequences and geometric sequences.
- Determine the common difference or common ratio for a sequence.
- Graph arithmetic and geometric sequences.
- Recognize graphical behavior of sequences.
- Sort sequences that are represented graphically.

REVIEW (1–2 minutes)

> Evaluate the expression $2x + 15$ given each value of x.

1. $x = -8$
2. $x = \frac{2}{3}$
3. $x = 3\frac{1}{2}$

You have represented patterns as sequences of numbers—a relationship between term numbers and term values.

How can you organize sequences based on common characteristics?

What Comes Next, and How Do You Know?

> Cut out Sequences A through M located on pages 89 and 91.

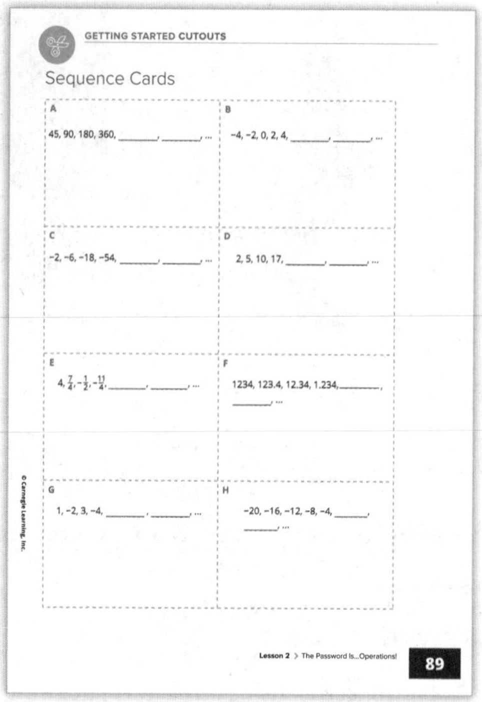

GETTING STARTED CUTOUTS

Sequence Cards

A
45, 90, 180, 360, ____, ____, …

B
−4, −2, 0, 2, 4, ____, ____, …

C
−2, −6, −18, −54, ____, ____, …

D
2, 5, 10, 17, ____, ____, …

E
$4, \frac{7}{4}, -\frac{1}{2}, -\frac{11}{4}$, ____, ____, …

F
1234, 123.4, 12.34, 1.234, ____, ____, …

G
1, −2, 3, −4, ____, ____, …

H
−20, −16, −12, −8, −4, ____, ____, …

© Carnegie Learning, Inc.

Lesson 2 > The Password Is...Operations! 89

1 Determine the unknown terms of each sequence. **Then describe the pattern under each sequence.**

2 Sort the sequences into groups based on common characteristics. In the space provided, record the following information for each of your groups.

- List the letters of the sequences in each group
- **Provide a rationale for the groups you formed.**

3 Which mathematical operation(s) did you perform to determine the next terms of each sequence?

Defining Arithmetic and Geometric Sequences

HABITS OF MIND
- Look for and make use of structure.
- Look for and express regularity in repeated reasoning.

You just described patterns for various sequences. For some of the sequences, you described the pattern as adding a constant to each term to determine the next term. This pattern creates an *arithmetic sequence*.

An **arithmetic sequence** is a sequence of numbers in which the difference between any two consecutive terms is a constant. This constant is the **common difference**, typically represented by the variable *d*.

- The common difference of a sequence is positive when you add the same positive number to each term to produce the next term.
- The common difference of a sequence is negative when you add the same negative number to each term to produce the next term.

REMEMBER...
When you add a negative number, it is the same as subtracting a positive number.

WORKED EXAMPLE

Consider the sequence shown.

11, 9, 7, 5, ...

The pattern is to add the same negative number, −2, to each term to determine the next term.

Sequence: 11, (add −2) 9, (add −2) 7, (add −2) 5, ...

This sequence is arithmetic and the **common difference *d* is −2.**

1. Suppose a sequence has the same starting number as the sequence in the worked example, but its common difference is 4.

   a. How would the pattern change?

   b. Explain whether or not the new sequence is arithmetic. If so, write the first 5 terms of the new sequence.

2 Analyze the sequences you cut out in the Getting Started.

(a) List the sequences that are arithmetic.

(b) Write the common difference of each arithmetic sequence you identified on its Sequence Card.

In another subset of sequences, you described the pattern as multiplying each term by a constant to determine the next term. This pattern creates a *geometric sequence*. A **geometric sequence** is a sequence of numbers in which the ratio between any two consecutive terms is a constant. This constant is the **common ratio**, represented by the variable *r*.

WORKED EXAMPLE

Consider the sequence shown.

1, 2, 4, 8, ...

The pattern is to multiply each term by the same number, 2, to determine the next term.

multiply by 2   multiply by 2   multiply by 2

Sequence: 1, 2, 4, 8, ...

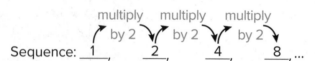

This sequence is geometric and the common ratio *r* is 2.

3 Suppose a sequence has the same starting number as the sequence in the worked example, but its common ratio is 3.

(a) How would the pattern change?

(b) Explain whether or not the new sequence is still geometric. If so, write the first 5 terms of the new sequence.

4 Suppose a sequence has the same starting number as the sequence in the worked example, but its common ratio is $\frac{1}{3}$.

(a) How would the pattern change?

(b) Explain whether or not the new sequence is still geometric. If so, write the first 6 terms of the new sequence.

5 Suppose a sequence has the same starting number as the sequence in the worked example, but its common ratio is −2.

(a) How would the pattern change?

(b) Explain whether or not the new sequence is still geometric. If so, write the first 6 terms of the new sequence.

6 Consider the sequence.
270, 90, 30, 10, ...

Devon says that he can determine each term of this sequence by multiplying each term by $\frac{1}{3}$, so the common ratio is $\frac{1}{3}$. Chase says that he can determine each term of this sequence by dividing each term by 3, so the common ratio is 3. Who is correct? **Explain your reasoning.**

7 Consider the sequences you cut out in the Getting Started. List the geometric sequences. Then write the common ratio on each Sequence Card.

The remaining sequences have patterns that are neither arithmetic nor geometric.

8 List these sequences. **Explain why these sequences are neither arithmetic nor geometric.**

9 Consider the first two terms of the sequence 3, 6, ...

Dante
This is how I wrote the sequence for the given terms.
3, 6, 9, 12, ...

Kira
This is the sequence I wrote.
3, 6, 12, 24, ...

Who is correct? **Explain your reasoning.**

10 Using the terms given in Question 9, write a sequence that is neither arithmetic nor geometric. Then, have your partner tell you what the pattern is in your sequence.

11 How many terms did your partner need before they recognized the pattern?

12 Consider the sequence 2, 2, 2, 2, 2, ... Identify the sequence. **Then describe the pattern**.

Throughout this topic, you will learn more about arithmetic and geometric sequences. Begin to complete the graphic organizers located on pages 97–106.

13 Identify and glue each arithmetic sequence and each geometric sequence to a separate graphic organizer according to its type. Discard all other sequences.

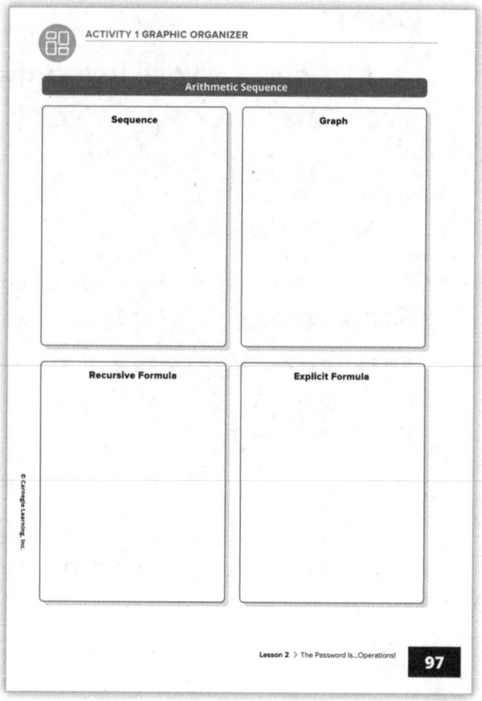
ACTIVITY 1 GRAPHIC ORGANIZER

Arithmetic Sequence

Sequence

Graph

Recursive Formula

Explicit Formula

© Carnegie Learning, Inc.

Lesson 2 > The Password Is...Operations! 97

Matching Graphs and Sequences

As you have already discovered when studying functions, graphs can help you see trends of a sequence—and at times can help you predict the next term in a sequence.

HABITS OF MIND
- Model with mathematics.
- Use appropriate tools strategically.

1. Cut out the graphs located on pages 93 and 95 that represent the arithmetic and geometric sequences from the previous activity. Match each graph to its appropriate sequence and glue it into the *Graph* section of its graphic organizer.

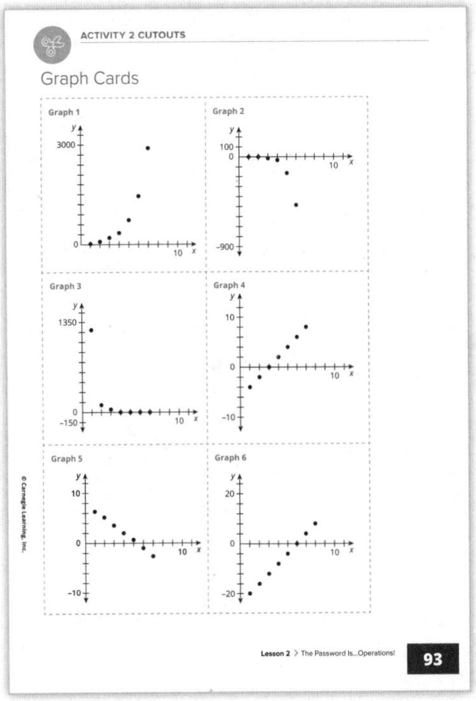

2. What strategies did you use to match the graphs to their corresponding sequences?

3. How can you use the graphs to verify that all sequences are functions?

Name That Sequence!

> Write the first five terms of each sequence described and identify the sequence as arithmetic or geometric.

1. The first term of the sequence is 8 and the common difference is 12.

2. The first term of the sequence is −9 and the common ratio is −2.

3. The first term of the sequence is 0 and the common difference is −6.

4. The first term of the sequence is −3 and the common ratio is $-\frac{1}{4}$.

Sequence Cards

A 45, 90, 180, 360, ________, ________, ...	**B** −4, −2, 0, 2, 4, ________, ________, ...
C −2, −6, −18, −54, ________, ________, ...	**D** 2, 5, 10, 17, ________, ________, ...
E $4, \frac{7}{4}, -\frac{1}{2}, -\frac{11}{4},$ ________, ________, ...	**F** 1234, 123.4, 12.34, 1.234, ________, ________, ...
G 1, −2, 3, −4, ________, ________, ...	**H** −20, −16, −12, −8, −4, ________, ________, ...

Why is this page blank?

So you can cut out the sequence cards on the other side.

I

$-5, -\frac{5}{2}, -\frac{5}{4}, -\frac{5}{8}$, ________, ________, ...

J

6.5, 5, 3.5, 2, ________, ________, ...

K

86, 85, 83, 80, 76, ________, ________, ...

L

$-16, 4, -1, \frac{1}{4}$, ________, ________, ...

M

−4, 12, −36, 108, ________, ________, ...

Why is this page blank?

So you can cut out the sequence cards on the other side.

Graph Cards

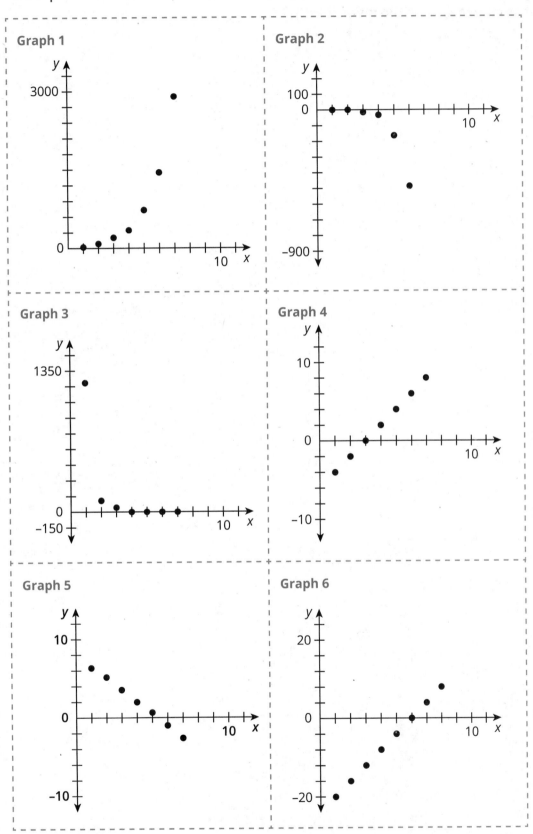

Graph 1

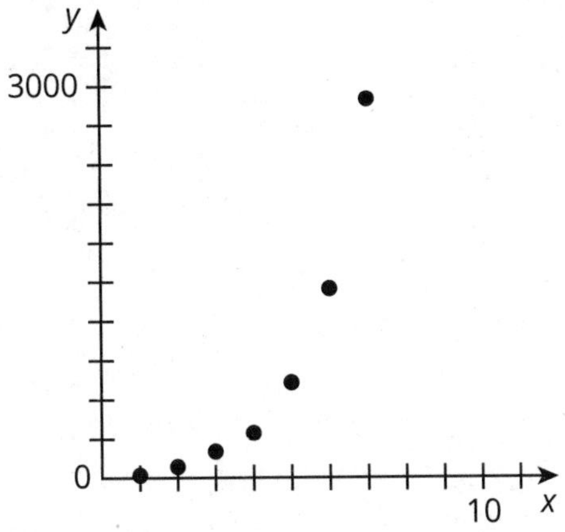

Graph 2

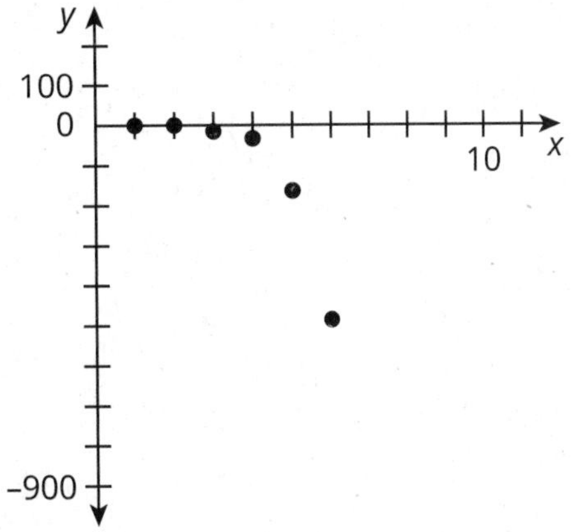

Graph 3

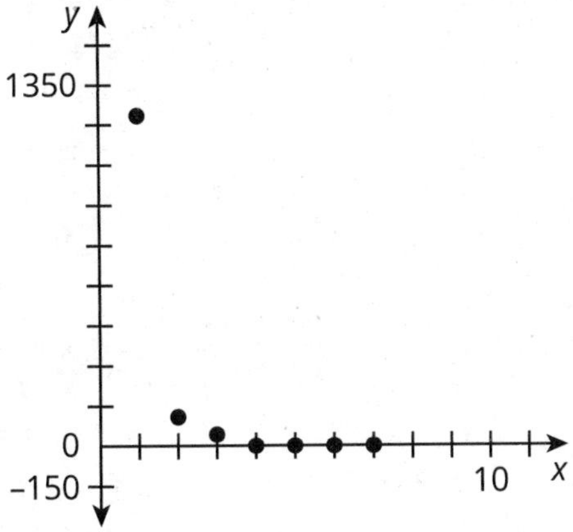

Graph 4

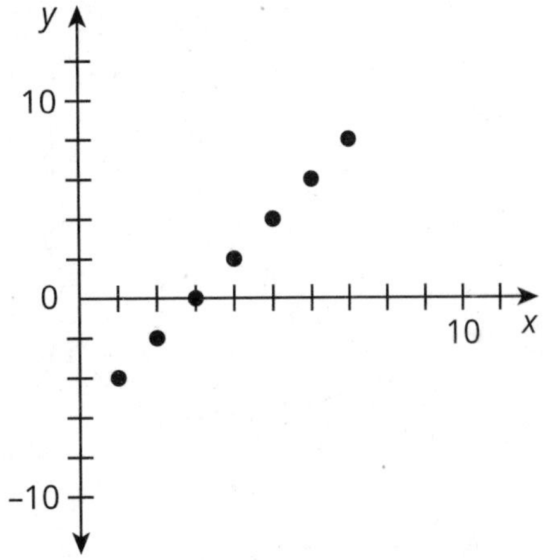

Graph 5

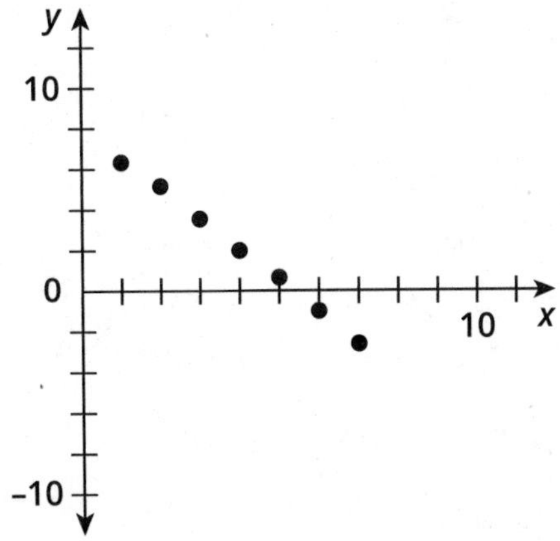

Graph 6

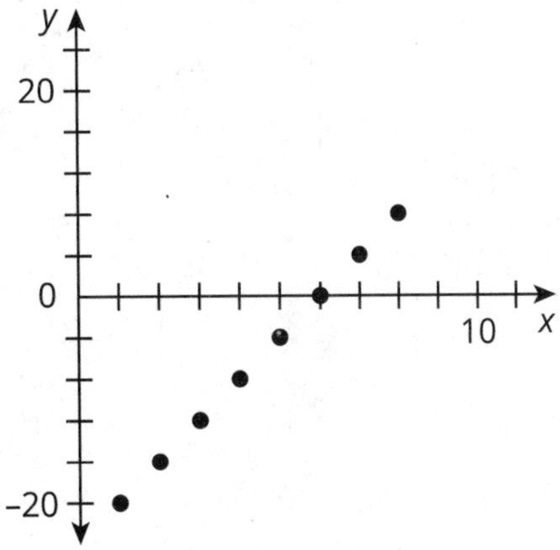

Why is this page blank?

So you can cut out the graphs on the other side.

Graph 7

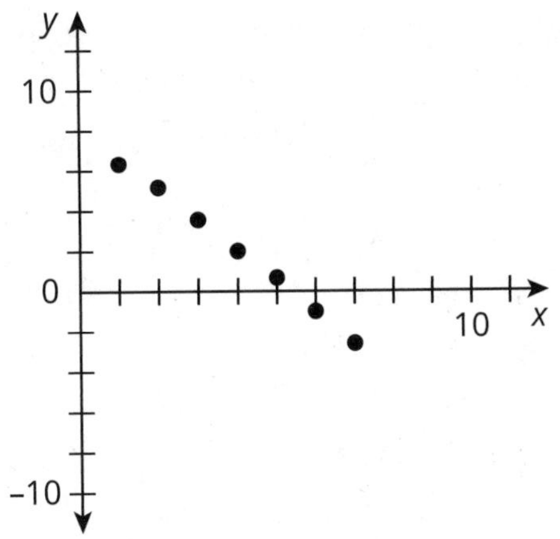

Graph 8

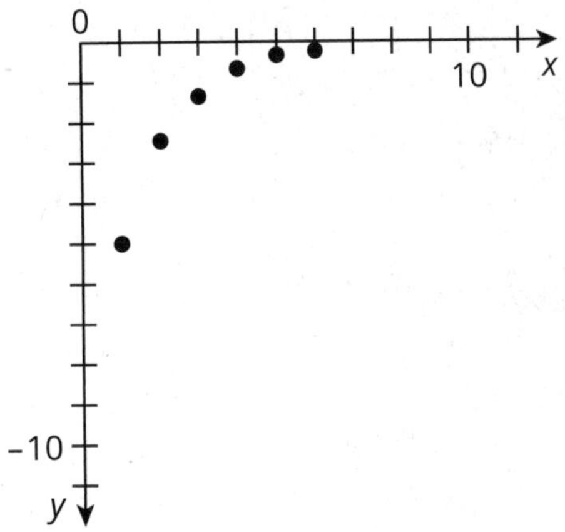

Graph 9

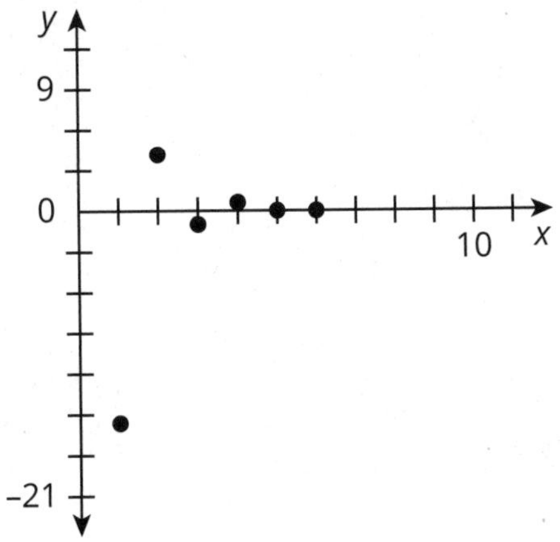

Graph 10

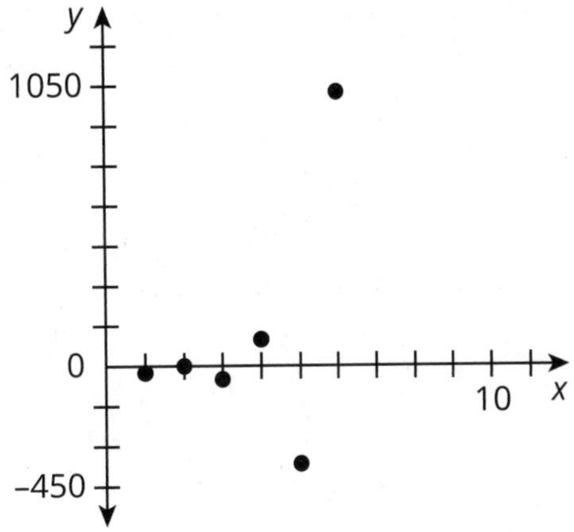

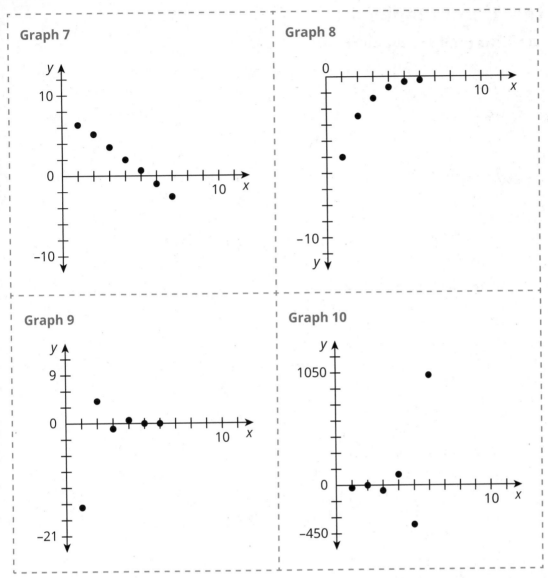

Why is this page blank?

So you can cut out the graphs on the other side.

Arithmetic Sequence

Sequence	Graph

Recursive Formula	Explicit Formula

Arithmetic Sequence

Sequence	Graph

Recursive Formula	Explicit Formula

Arithmetic Sequence

Sequence	Graph

Recursive Formula	Explicit Formula

Arithmetic Sequence

Sequence	Graph

Recursive Formula	Explicit Formula

Geometric Sequence

Sequence	Graph

Recursive Formula	Explicit Formula

Geometric Sequence

Sequence

Graph

Recursive Formula

Explicit Formula

Geometric Sequence

Sequence	Graph

Recursive Formula	Explicit Formula

Geometric Sequence

Sequence	Graph

Recursive Formula	Explicit Formula

Geometric Sequence

Sequence	Graph

Recursive Formula	Explicit Formula

Geometric Sequence

Sequence	Graph

Recursive Formula	Explicit Formula

LESSON 2 ASSIGNMENT

> Use a separate piece of paper for your Journal entry.

JOURNAL

Describe how you can determine whether a sequence is arithmetic, geometric, or neither in your own words.

REMEMBER

An arithmetic sequence is a sequence of numbers in which the difference between any two consecutive terms is a constant.

A geometric sequence is a sequence of numbers in which the ratio between any two consecutive terms is a constant.

PRACTICE

> Consider the first 2 terms of the sequence 28, 14, ...

1. Determine whether the sequence is arithmetic or geometric. Explain your reasoning.

2. Suppose the sequence 28, 14, ... is arithmetic.

   a. Determine the common difference.

   b. List the next 3 terms in the sequence. Explain your reasoning.

Go to LiveHint.com for help on the PRACTICE questions.

3 Suppose the sequence 28, 14, ... is geometric.

(a) Determine the common ratio.

(b) List the next 3 terms in the sequence. Explain your reasoning.

4 Using the first two terms, 28 and 14, write the next 3 terms of a sequence that is neither arithmetic nor geometric. Explain your pattern.

STRETCH Optional

> Consider the first 2 terms of the sequence −6, 18, ...

1 Determine the next 5 terms in the sequence if the sequence is arithmetic. Then write a function to represent the arithmetic sequence.

2 Determine the next 5 terms in the sequence if the sequence is geometric. Then write a function to represent the geometric sequence.

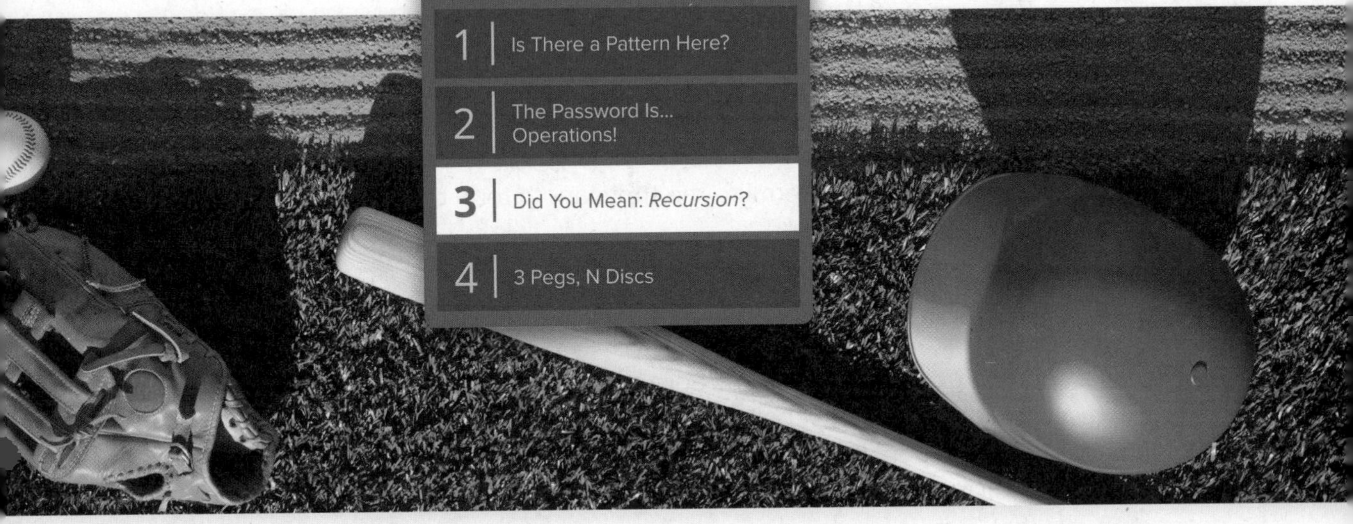

LESSON 3

Did You Mean: *Recursion*?

Determining Recursive and Explicit Expressions from Contexts

KEY TERMS

recursive formula

explicit formula

Learning Goals

- Write recursive formulas for arithmetic and geometric sequences from contexts.
- Write explicit expressions for arithmetic and geometric sequences from contexts.
- Use formulas to determine unknown terms of a sequence.

REVIEW (1–2 minutes)

> Write a linear equation for each, given the slope of the line and a point through which the line passes.

1. Slope: 1
   Point: (1, 5)

2. Slope: −2
   Point: (0, 0)

3. Slope: $\frac{1}{2}$
   Point: (2, 3)

You have learned that arithmetic and geometric sequences always describe functions.

How can you write equations to represent these functions?

Can I Get a Formula?

While a common ratio or a common difference can help you determine the next term in a sequence, how can they help you determine the thousandth term of a sequence? The ten-thousandth term of a sequence?

> Consider the sequence represented in this situation.

Rico owns a sporting goods store. He has agreed to donate \$125 to the Owl Valley High School baseball team for their equipment fund. In addition, he will donate \$18 for every home run the Owls hit during the season. The sequence shown represents the possible dollar amounts that Rico could donate for the season.

125, 143, 161, 179, ...

THINK ABOUT...

Notice that the 1st term in this sequence is the amount Rico donates if the team hits 0 home runs.

1. Identify the sequence type. **Describe how you know.**

2. Determine the common difference or common ratio for the sequence.

3. Complete the table.

Number of Home Runs	Term Number (n)	Donation Amount (dollars)
0	1	
1		
2		
3		
4		
5		
6		
7		
8		
9		

4. Explain how you can calculate the tenth term based on the ninth term.

Writing Formulas for Arithmetic Sequences

HABITS OF MIND

- Look for and make use of structure.
- Look for and express regularity in repeated reasoning.

A **recursive formula** expresses each new term of a sequence based on the preceding term in the sequence. The recursive formula to determine the *n*th term of an arithmetic sequence is:

$$a_n = a_{n-1} + d$$

*n*th term → a_n; a_{n-1}: previous term; d: common difference

WORKED EXAMPLE

Consider the sequence −2, −9, −16, −23, ...

You can use the recursive formula to determine the 5th term.

$$a_n = a_{n-1} + d$$
$$a_5 = a_{5-1} + (-7)$$

The expression a_5 represents the 5th term. The previous term is −23, and the common difference is −7.

$$a_5 = a_4 + (-7)$$
$$a_5 = -23 + (-7)$$
$$a_5 = -30$$

The 5th term of the sequence is −30.

THINK ABOUT...

You only need to know the previous term and the common difference to use the recursive formula.

> Consider the sequence from the Getting Started showing Rico's contribution to the Owls' baseball team in terms of the number of home runs hit.

1. Use a recursive formula to determine the 11th term in the sequence. **Explain what this value means in terms of this problem situation.**

2. Is there a way to calculate the 20th term without first calculating the 19th term? **If so, describe the strategy.**

You can determine the 93rd term of the sequence by calculating each term before it, and then adding 18 to the 92nd term, but this will probably take a while! A more efficient way to calculate any term of a sequence is to use an *explicit formula*.

An **explicit formula** of a sequence is a formula to calculate the nth term of a sequence using the term's position in the sequence. The explicit formula to determine the nth term of an arithmetic sequence is:

nth term — common difference

$$a_n = a_1 + d(n-1)$$

1st term — previous term number

WORKED EXAMPLE

You can use the explicit formula to determine the 93rd term in this problem situation.

$$a_n = a_1 + d(n - 1)$$
$$a_{93} = 125 + 18(93 - 1)$$

The expression a_{93} represents the 93rd term. The first term is 125, and the common difference is 18.

$$a_{93} = 125 + 18(92)$$
$$a_{93} = 125 + 1656$$
$$a_{93} = 1781$$

The 93rd term of the sequence is 1781.

This means Rico will contribute a total of $1781 if the Owls hit 92 home runs.

REMEMBER...

The 1st term in this sequence is the amount Rico donates if the team hits 0 home runs. So, the 93rd term represents the amount Rico donates if the team hits 92 home runs.

3 Use the explicit formula to determine the amount of money Rico will contribute for each number of home runs hit.

(a) 35 home runs

(b) 48 home runs

(c) 86 home runs

(d) 214 home runs

Rico decides to increase his initial contribution and amount donated per home run hit. He decides to contribute $500 and will donate $75 for every home run the Owls hit.

4 Write the first 5 terms of the sequence representing the new contribution Rico will donate to the Owls.

5 Determine Rico's contribution for each number of home runs hit.

(a) 39 home runs

(b) 50 home runs

MATHia CONNECTION

- Writing Recursive Formulas
- Writing Recursive Formulas to Model Sequence Situations
- Writing Explicit Formulas
- Writing Explicit Formulas to Model Sequence Situations

Writing Formulas for Geometric Sequences

You can also write recursive and explicit formulas for geometric sequences.

HABITS OF MIND

- Look for and make use of structure.
- Look for and express regularity in repeated reasoning.

Animals, plants, fungi, slime, molds, and other living creatures are composed of eukaryotic cells. During growth, generally there is a cell called a "mother cell" that divides itself into two "daughter cells." Each of those daughter cells then divides into two more daughter cells, and so on.

1 The sequence shown represents the growth of eukaryotic cells.

1, 2, 4, 8, 16, ...

(a) Describe why this sequence is geometric and identify the common ratio.

TAKE NOTE...

Notice that the 1st term in this sequence is the total number of cells after 0 divisions (that is, the mother cell).

(b) Complete the table of values. Use the number of cell divisions to identify the term number and the total number of cells after each division.

Number of Cell Divisions	Term Number (n)	Total Number of Cells
0	1	
1		
2		
3		
4		
5		
6		
7		
8		
9		

(c) Explain how you can calculate the tenth term based on the ninth term.

The recursive formula to determine the *n*th term of a geometric sequence is:

$$\underbrace{g_n}_{n\text{th term}} = \underbrace{g_{n-1}}_{\text{previous term}} \cdot \underbrace{r}_{\text{common ratio}}$$

WORKED EXAMPLE

Consider the sequence shown.

4, 12, 36, 108, ...

You can use the recursive formula to determine the 5th term.

$$g_n = g_{n-1} \cdot r$$
$$g_5 = g_{5-1} \cdot (3)$$

The expression g_5 represents the 5th term. The previous term is 108, and the common ratio is 3.

$$g_5 = g_4 \cdot (3)$$
$$g_5 = 108 \cdot (3)$$
$$g_5 = 324$$

The 5th term of the sequence is 324.

TOPIC 2

> Consider the sequence of cell divisions and the total number of resulting cells.

2. Write a recursive formula for the sequence and use the formula to determine the 11th term in the sequence. **Explain what your result means in terms of this problem situation.**

The explicit formula to determine the *n*th term of a geometric sequence is:

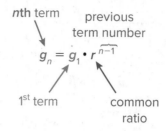

*n*th term — previous term number

$$g_n = g_1 \cdot r^{\overbrace{n-1}}$$

1st term — common ratio

WORKED EXAMPLE

You can use the explicit formula to determine the 20th term in this problem situation.

$$g_n = g_1 \cdot r^{n-1}$$
$$g_{20} = 1 \cdot 2^{20-1}$$

The expression g_5 represents the 20th term. The first term is 1, and the common ratio is 2.

$$g_{20} = 1 \cdot 2^{19}$$
$$g_{20} = 1 \cdot 524{,}288$$
$$g_{20} = 524{,}288$$

The 20th term of the sequence is 524,288.

This means that after 19 cell divisions, there are a total of 524,288 cells.

REMEMBER...

The 1st term in this sequence is the total number of cells after 0 divisions. So, the 20th term represents the total number of cells after 19 divisions.

3 Use the explicit formula to determine the total number of cells for each number of divisions.

(a) 11 divisions

(b) 14 divisions

(c) 18 divisions

(d) 22 divisions

Suppose that a scientist has 5 eukaryotic cells in a petri dish. She wonders how the growth pattern would change if each mother cell divided into 3 daughter cells.

4 Write the first 5 terms of the sequence for the scientist's hypothesis.

5 Determine the total number of cells in the petri dish for each number of divisions.

(a) 13 divisions

(b) 16 divisions

Pros and Cons

In the previous lesson you identified sequences as either arithmetic or geometric and then matched a corresponding graph.

1. Go back to the graphic organizers from the previous lesson. Write the recursive and explicit formulas for each sequence.

2. Explain the advantages and disadvantages of using a recursive formula.

3. Explain the advantages and disadvantages of using an explicit formula.

LESSON 3 ASSIGNMENT

> Use a separate piece of paper for your Journal entry.

JOURNAL

Explain the difference between a recursive formula and an explicit formula in your own words.

REMEMBER

The explicit formula for an arithmetic sequence is $a_n = a_1 + d(n - 1)$, where n is the term number, a_1 is the first term in the sequence, a_n is the nth term in the sequence, and d is the common difference.

The explicit formula for a geometric sequence is $g_n = g_1 \cdot r^{(n-1)}$ where n is the term number, g_1 is the first term in the sequence, g_n is the nth term in the sequence, and r is the common ratio.

PRACTICE

1. Greta must volunteer 225 hours for a community service project. She plans to volunteer for 6 hours each week. The sequence shown represents the number of volunteer hours she has left after three weeks have passed.

   225, 219, 213, 207, ...

   (a) Describe this sequence.

   (b) Use a formula to determine how many volunteer hours Greta has left to fulfill her requirement after 33 weeks have passed. Show your work.

   (c) Which formula should you use to determine how many volunteer hours Greta has left to fulfill her requirement after 40 weeks have passed? Explain your reasoning.

Go to LiveHint.com for help on the PRACTICE questions.

(d) Calculate the number of volunteer hours Greta has left to fulfill her requirement after 40 weeks have passed. Explain what your answer means in terms of the problem situation.

2 The half-life of a substance is defined as the period of time it takes for the amount of the substance to decay by half. The sequence shows the amount of a substance that will remain after a certain number of half-lives have elapsed.

$1, \frac{1}{2}, \frac{1}{4}, \frac{1}{8}, \ldots$

(a) Describe this sequence.

(b) Calculate how much of the substance will remain after 21 half-lives have elapsed. Show your work. Does your answer make sense in this problem context? Why or why not?

STRETCH Optional

> Consider the first two terms of this sequence $\frac{1}{16}, -\frac{3}{16}, \ldots$

1 Determine the 63rd term when this is an arithmetic sequence. Write your answer as a reduced improper fraction.

2 Determine the 63rd term when this is a geometric sequence. Write your answer in scientific notation.

LESSON 4

3 Pegs, N Discs

Modeling Using Sequences

KEY TERM

mathematical modeling

Learning Goals

- Model situations using recursive and explicit formulas.
- Translate between recursive and explicit expressions of a mathematical model.
- Explore the process of mathematical modeling.

REVIEW (1–2 minutes)

> Write an explicit formula for the geometric sequence represented in the table.

x	*y*
1	2
2	4
3	8
4	16

You have written recursive and explicit formulas for arithmetic and geometric sequences.

What strategies can you use to think and reason with recursive and explicit formulas to solve problems?

Notice and Wonder

In this lesson, you will explore the process of *mathematical modeling*.

Let's play a game to gather information.

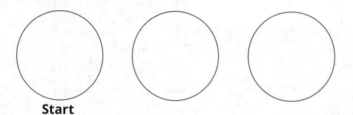

TAKE NOTE...

Mathematical modeling is explaining patterns in the real world based on mathematical ideas.

The object of the game is to move an entire stack of discs or coins from the start circle to any of the other circles.

The rules of the game are simple:

- You can only move one disc at a time.
- You cannot put a larger disc on top of a smaller disc.

Let's first play with 3 discs.

To begin, place a quarter, nickel, and dime on top of each other in that order in a stack in the Start circle. Or, use the cutout discs located on page 129 stacked from largest to smallest inside the Start circle.

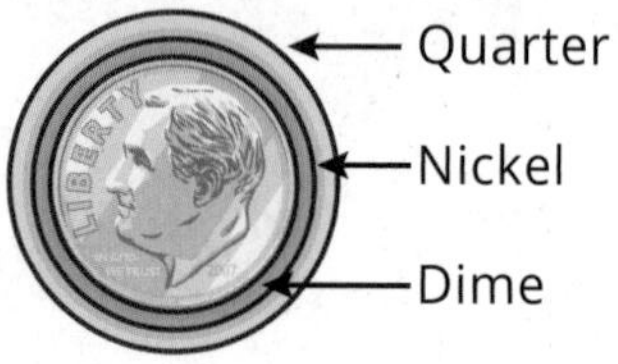

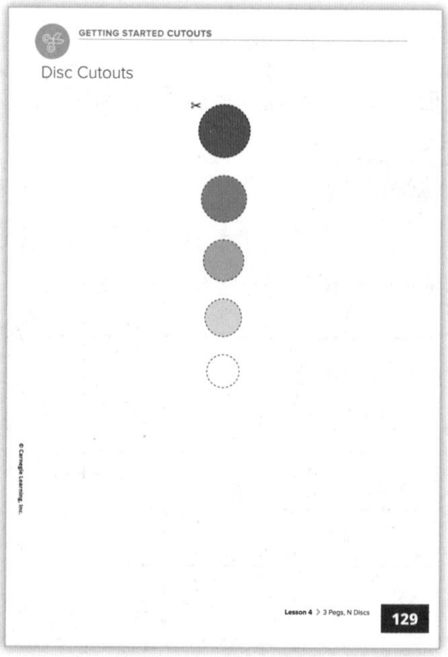

> Play this game with a partner.

The Modeling Process

Now that you have played the game, let's begin the modeling process to analyze the game mathematically.

The first step in modeling a situation mathematically is to gather information, notice patterns, and formulate mathematical questions about what you notice.

HABITS OF MIND
- Reason abstractly and quantitatively.
- Construct viable arguments and critique the reasoning of others.

1. Play the game again and record your results in the table.

Number of Discs	Minimum Number of Moves
1	
2	
3	

THINK ABOUT...
Is there a relationship between the number of discs and the number of moves it takes to complete the game?

2. What pattern do you notice in your results?

ASK YOURSELF...
How do you know you did it in the least number of moves?

The second step in the modeling process is to organize your information and represent it using mathematical notation.

> Consider the question: Is there a relationship between the number of discs and the minimum number of moves?

3. Use mathematical notation to represent the pattern you have identified in your results. **Explain your reasoning.**

The third step of the modeling process is to extend the patterns you created, complete operations, make predictions, and analyze the mathematical results. You can use different representations, like tables and graphs, to help you analyze results.

4 Use your results to extend the pattern in the table from Question 1.

Number of Discs	Minimum Number of Moves
1	1
2	3
3	7
4	
5	

5 Write a recursive formula to represent the pattern shown in your table. **What predictions does this formula make for the minimum number of moves required for 4 and 5 discs?**

6 Write an explicit formula to represent the pattern shown in your table. **What predictions does this formula make for the minimum number of moves required for 4 and 5 discs?**

ASK YOURSELF...
Can you write an exponential equation as the explicit formula?

7 Construct a graph to represent your explicit formula. **Describe the characteristics of the graph in terms of the situation.**

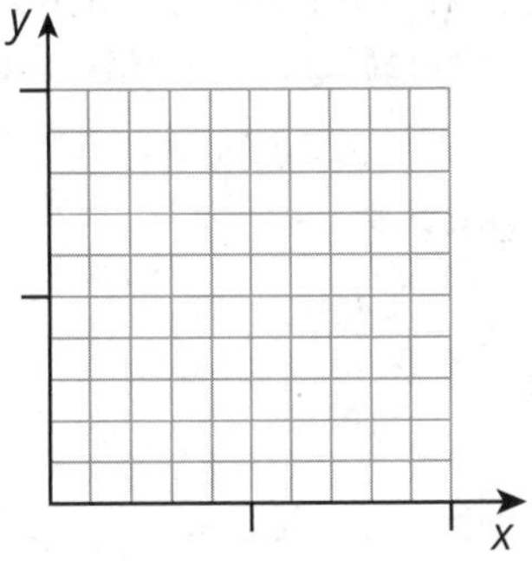

The final step in the modeling process is to interpret your results and test your mathematical predictions in the real world. If your predictions are incorrect, you can revisit your mathematical work and make adjustments—or start all over!

8 Play the game again to test that your prediction for 4 discs and 5 discs is accurate. **Record your observations.**

9 Write a conclusion statement to answer the question: What is the relationship between the number of discs and the minimum number of moves it takes to complete the game?

ASK YOURSELF...
What is the level of accuracy appropriate for this situation?

Model Your Thoughts

In this lesson, you used a modeling process to figure out whether the number of moves in the disc game relates to the number of discs. The diagram located on page 127 summarizes the basic steps of the mathematical modeling process.

1. Summarize what is involved in each phase of this modeling process.

STEP 1 Notice and Wonder

STEP 2 Organize and Mathematize

STEP 3 Predict and Analyze

STEP 4 Test and Interpret

2. Suppose you could make 1 move every second. How long would it take to complete a game with 25 discs? **Show your work.**

The Modeling Process

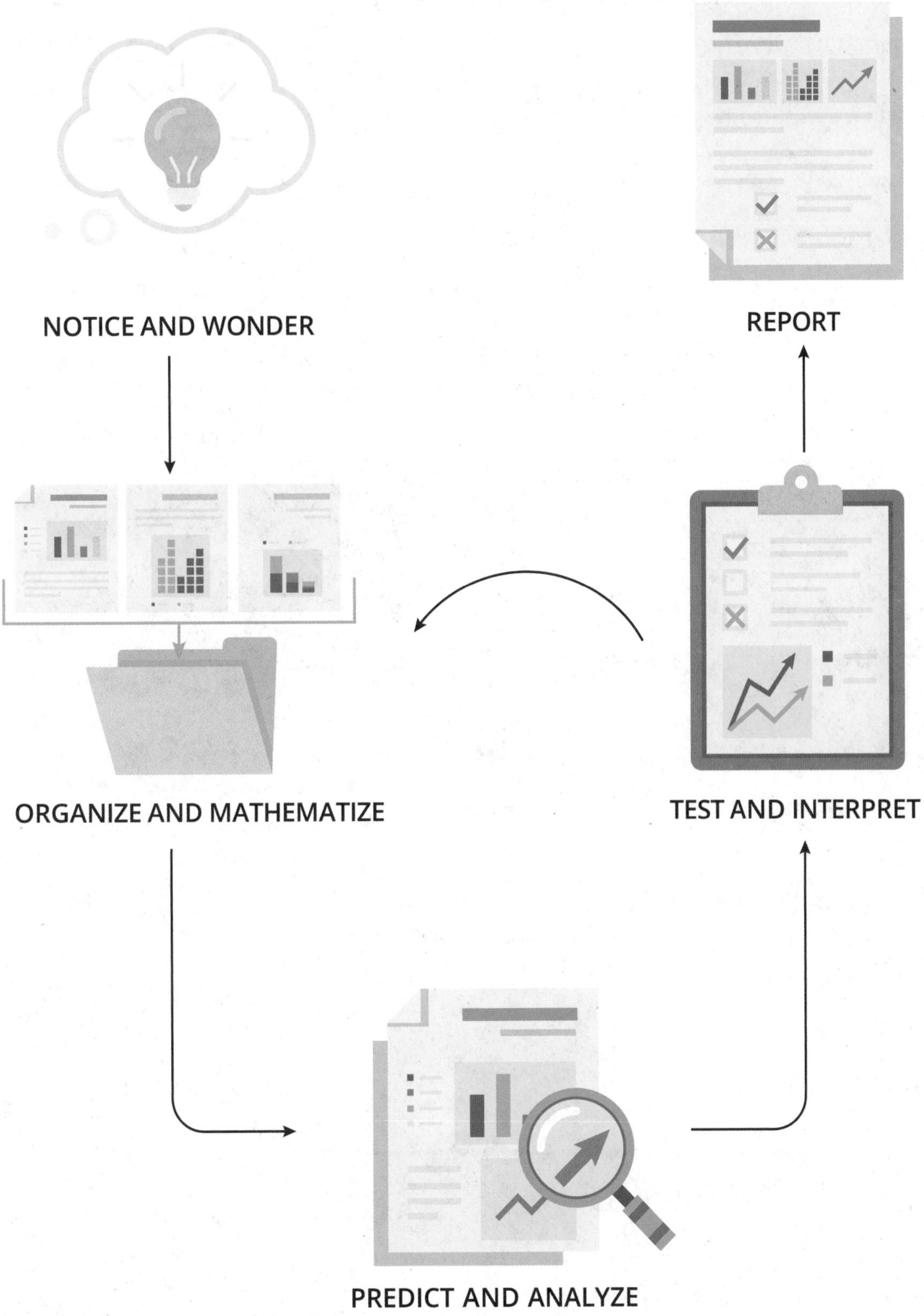

Why is this page blank?

So you can tear out the Modeling Process on the other side.

Disc Cutouts

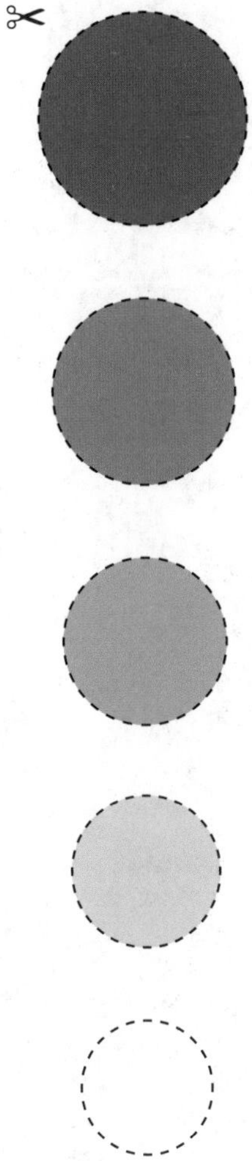

Why is this page blank?

So you can cut out the discs on the other side.

LESSON 4 ASSIGNMENT

> Use a separate piece of paper for your Journal entry.

JOURNAL

Explain why you might need to repeat steps in the Modeling Process.

REMEMBER

The 4 steps of the mathematical modeling process are:

STEP 1 Notice and Wonder

STEP 2 Organize and Mathematize

STEP 3 Predict and Analyze

STEP 4 Test and Interpret

PRACTICE

1. Triplets seem to run in the Tribiani family. Great-grandma Tribiani had triplets, each of her triplets had triplets, and each of those triplets had triplets.

STEP 1 Notice and Wonder

(a) What do you notice about the situation?

(b) Circle the mathematical question you can ask about this situation.

- Can you represent triplets by a function?
- How many children did Great-grandma Tribiani's siblings have?
- Is there a relationship between the generation and the number of triplets in that generation?

STEP 2 Organize and Mathematize

(c) Represent the number of triplets in each generation as a numeric sequence with 4 terms. Then describe the sequence.

(d) Create a table of values using the first 4 terms of the sequence.

Generation	Number of Triplets

Go to LiveHint.com for help on the PRACTICE questions.

STEP 3 Predict and Analyze

(e) Write an explicit formula to represent this sequence.

(f) Create a graph for the explicit formula you built.
Describe the characteristics of the graph in terms of the situation.

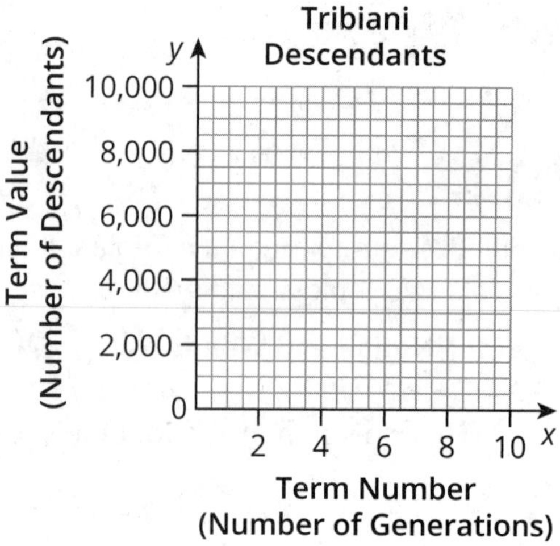

(g) Predict the number of descendants in the Tribiani family in 20 generations.
Show your work.

STEP 4 Test and Interpret

(h) Determine whether a discrete or continuous graph makes more sense in this scenario. Explain your reasoning.

(i) Describe the shape of your graph and explain what this means.

STRETCH Optional

Aaron just paid \$7.40 for a new pair of sunglasses. He did some research and found that the prices have changed over 20 years, but not by much. Ten years ago, the average price for a generic pair of sunglasses was \$6.80, and 20 years ago, it was \$6.20.

1. Describe a possible arithmetic relationship between the decade and the price in that decade. Represent the relationship with a table, an explicit formula, and a graph. Describe the characteristics of each.
2. Describe a possible geometric relationship between the decade and the price in that decade. Represent the relationship with a table, an explicit formula, and a graph. Describe the characteristics of each.
3. Predict the price of a pair of sunglasses in 5 decades using both sequences.
4. Which type of sequence better represents the situation? Explain your reason.

MIXED PRACTICE

> This Mixed Practice worksheet includes two sections: Spaced Review and End-of-Topic Review. **Use a separate piece of paper to show your work.**

Spaced Review

> Practice concepts from previous topics.

1 Determine whether each data set represents a function.

(a) {(−5, 8), (−6, 2), (−2, −6), (−1, 8), (4, 6)}

(b)

x	2	6	4	2	8
y	9	8	7	4	2

2 Enter each function into your graphing calculator to determine the shape of its graph. Then determine the function family, whether the function is increasing or decreasing, whether the function has an absolute maximum or minimum and the shape of the graph.

(a) $h(x) = 5x^2 - 2.8x + 40$

(b) $g(x) = 30x - 55$

3 Solve each equation.

(a) $4(2x + 1) - 3(x - 2) = 10 + 5x$

(b) $10(x - 2) + 15 = 8x + 7$

(c) $2(x + 3) + 2 = 2(x + 4)$

(d) $3(2x + 2) = 6(x + 6)$

4 Determine whether each table represents a proportional relationship.

(a)

x	***y***
−1	−24
2	48
4	90
8	192

(b)

x	***y***
2	13.5
5	33.75
10	67.5
15	101.25

5 School event committee members are designing banners for a school dance. They are experimenting by drawing different-sized rectangles. In each rectangle, the width is $\frac{1}{4}$ the length. Complete the table for rectangles with the given lengths.

Length (inches)	4	8	12	16	20
Width (inches)					
Area (square inches)					

(a) Write the ordered pairs from the table, using area as the dependent variable and length as the independent variable.

(b) Is the relationship between the length and the area linear? Explain your reasoning.

End-of-Topic Review

AVAILABLE ONLINE

1. A **Topic Summary** reviews the main concepts for the topic.
2. A video of the **Worked Example** is provided.

> Practice concepts you learned in **Sequences.**

6 Determine whether each given sequence is arithmetic or geometric. Then write the next 3 terms of the sequence.

(a) 3, −12, 48, −192,...

(b) 2.45, 3.86, 5.27, 6.68,...

7 Determine the 58th term of the sequence 540, 495, 450,...

8 Determine the 13th term of the sequence 0.4, −1.2, 3.6,...

9 Juan updates his blog regularly with trivia questions for readers to answer. The month he started this, there were 8 trivia questions on his blog. The next month, there were 19 trivia questions on his blog. The month after that, there were 30 trivia questions on his blog.

(a) Think about the number of trivia questions on Juan's blog each month. Describe the pattern.

(b) Determine how many trivia questions will be on Juan's blog during months 4, 5, and 6.

(c) Represent the number of trivia questions on Juan's blog for the first 6 months as a numeric sequence. Then represent the sequence using a table of values.

10 A maintenance worker in a factory notices that a water tank is leaking. She records the amount of water in the tank each day in a table.

Day	Volume of Water (L)
1	16,000
2	12,000
3	9,000
4	6,750

(a) Write a recursive formula to represent the pattern shown in the table. What predictions does this formula make for the amount of water in the tank on the 5th day?

(b) Write an explicit formula to represent the pattern shown in the table. What predictions does this formula make for the amount of water in the tank on the 10th day?

11 Harrison draws a rectangle, and then in each successive figure he splits the rectangles into two rectangles as shown.

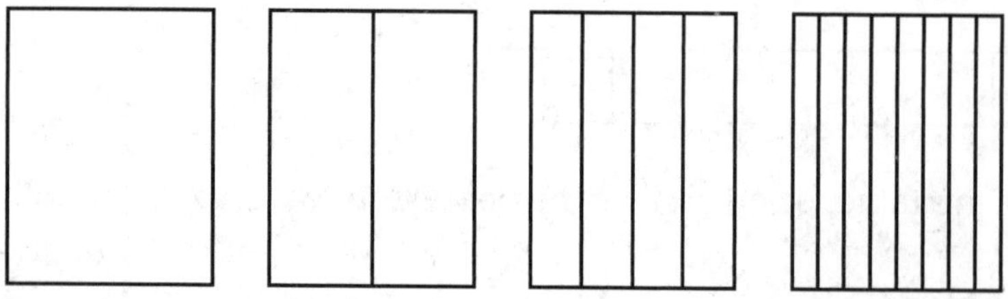

(a) Analyze the number of rectangles in each figure. Describe the pattern.

(b) Write the number of rectangles in each of the first six figures as a numeric sequence.

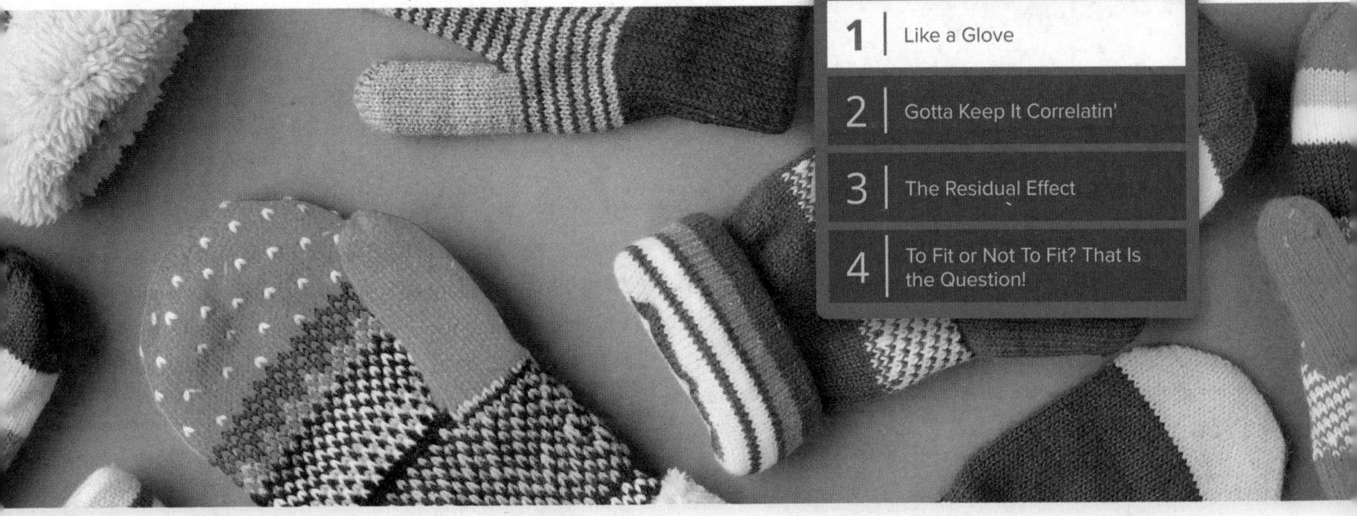

LESSON 1

Like a Glove

Least Squares Regressions

KEY TERMS

- Least Squares Method
- centroid
- regression line
- interpolation
- extrapolation

Learning Goals

- Create a graph of data points with and without technology.
- Determine an equation for a line of best fit by visual approximation of a hand-drawn line.
- Determine a linear regression equation using technology.
- Make predictions about data using a linear regression equation.
- Explain the calculations involved in the Least Squares Method.
- Choose a level of accuracy appropriate when reporting quantities.

REVIEW (1–2 minutes)

> Use the slope formula to write an equation for each.

1. A line that passes through the point (2, 5) with a slope of 5

2. A line that passes through the points (5, 2) and (3, 8)

You have searched for patterns in graphs and sequences of numbers.

How can you use what you know to identify patterns in sets of data?

Frozen Yogurt...When It's Freezing?

Mr. Templeton's Future Business Leaders Club (FBLC) helps a frozen yogurt shop analyze how the weather affects business. The owner wonders whether a relationship exists between the temperature and the number of customers who buy yogurt during the 2 hours immediately after school. The FBLC collected this data.

Temperature (°F)	Number of Customers
45	97
25	55
60	85
15	37
100	100

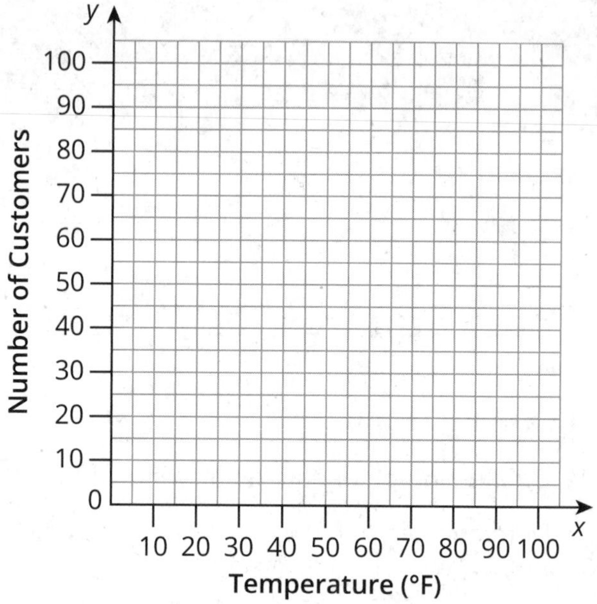

1. Construct a scatter plot of the collected data.

   a) Plot the first data point. Is there a pattern? Use a piece of spaghetti to approximate a line that models the data.

   b) Add the second data point to the graph. Is there a pattern? Adjust the piece of spaghetti to approximate a line that models the data with the additional point.

   c) Add the third data point to the graph. Approximate the line by using the spaghetti. **Describe the pattern that you see.**

   d) Continue this process until you plot all five data points.

2. Use your linear model to describe the relationship between the temperature outside and the number of customers at the frozen yogurt shop.

A Line of Best Fit

HABITS OF MIND
- Model with mathematics.
- Use appropriate tools strategically.

In the previous activity, you adjusted the line representing the data as you added each point. You have approximated the line that best represents the data.

1. Use the full data set and the line that you approximated to write an equation that you think best represents the data.

2. Based on your equation, predict the number of customers to visit the frozen yogurt shop in the two hours after school for each given temperature.

   (a) 85°F (b) 115°F (c) 10°F

3. Compare your predictions with your classmates'. Did your predictions differ from the other groups? **Explain why or why not.**

You have noticed that estimating a line of best fit can give different predictions. Fortunately, with technology, you can create prediction equations and scatter plots from tables of data. You just need to build a data table that has an independent variable and a dependent variable.

4. Identify the independent and dependent variables. **What is the significance of those designations?**

5. Use the data table and graphing technology to generate a line of best fit. What is the slope and y-intercept of the line and what do they represent?

6 Use the new line of best fit to predict the number of customers at the frozen yogurt shop immediately after school for each given temperature.

ⓐ 85°F

ⓑ 115°F

ⓒ 10°F

7 How do your predictions compare to the predictions from the other groups?

The equation that your calculator uses to give you the line of best fit is the **Least Squares Method**. This is a method that creates a line of best fit for a scatter plot that has two basic requirements:

- The line must contain the centroid of the data set. The **centroid** is a point whose *x*-value is the mean of all the *x*-values of the points on the scatter plot, and its *y*-value is the mean of all the *y*-values of the points on the scatter plot.
- Even though infinitely many lines can pass through the centroid, the **regression line** has the smallest possible vertical distances from each given data point to the regression line. The sum of the squares of those distances is at a minimum with this line.

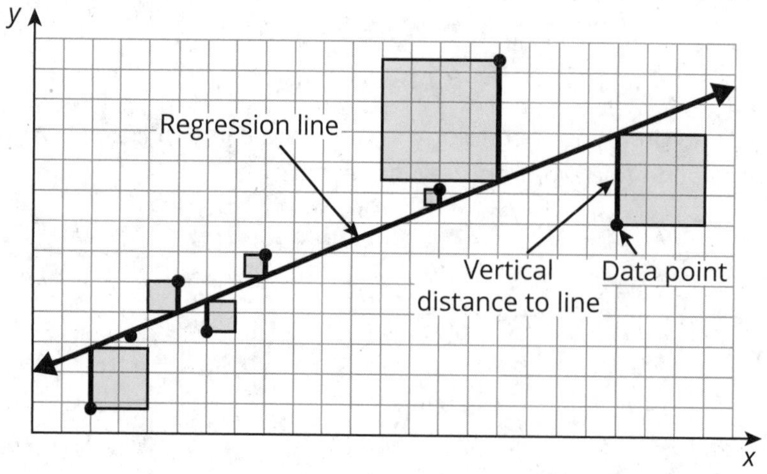

8 Consider the graph of the sample regression line.

(a) What do the vertical lines in bold represent?

(b) What do the shaded squares represent? How do they relate to the Least Squares Method?

9 Alysse and Bonito each draw a regression line to model a set of data. They both record the vertical distances between each point and the regression line.

Alysse
Vertical Distances: 2, 2, 2, 2, 2

Bonito
Vertical Distances: 1, 1, 1, 1, 6

Both students believe they drew the least square regression line. Who's correct? **Justify your choice.**

10 How does your decision in Question 9 inform you about the placement of a line of best fit using the Least Squares Method?

Making Predictions

When you represent data using a regression line, you can then use the linear function to make predictions about future data.

HABITS OF MIND

- Model with mathematics.
- Use appropriate tools strategically.

The table shown lists the average global temperature in 5-year spans from 1957 to 2016.

Years	Span	Average Temperature (°F)
1957–1961	1	57.250
1962–1966	2	57.121
1967–1971	3	57.196
1972–1976	4	57.189
1977–1981	5	57.495
1982–1986	6	57.445
1987–1991	7	57.780
1992–1996	8	57.700
1997–2001	9	58.053
2002–2006	10	58.262
2007–2011	11	58.244
2012–2016	12	58.448

1. What is the range of the data set?

2. Identify the independent and dependent quantities and their units of measure.

3. Do the data represent a function? Does it appear that there is a specific function that could model this data set? **If so, describe the function. If not, state why not.**

4. Use technology to graph a scatter plot demonstrating the relationship between time spans and temperature. **What association do you notice?**

5. Between which consecutive spans was there a decrease in average global temperature?

6 Use your graphing technology to determine the regression equation for the average global temperature data. Then sketch the data points and the line of best fit that you see.

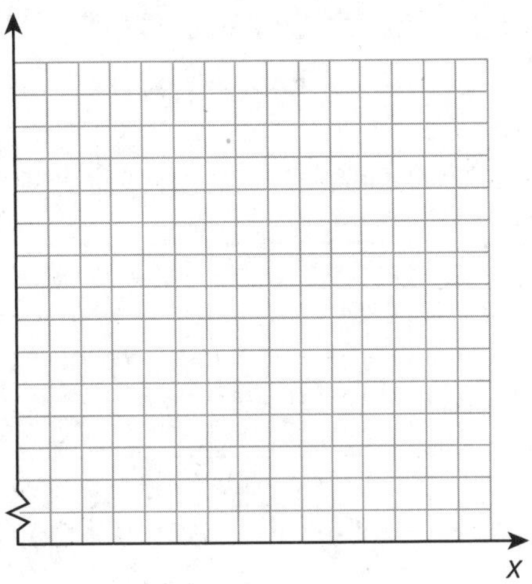

7 What is the relationship between the equation for the line of best fit and any association you notice in the graph? Do you think that this line fits the data well?

8 For each expression from your linear regression equation about global temperatures, write an appropriate unit of measure and describe the contextual meaning. Then, choose a term from the word bank to describe the mathematical meaning of each part.

WORD BANK

- **input value**
- **output value**
- **rate of change**
- ***y*-intercept**

		What It Means	
Expression	**Unit**	**Contextual Meaning**	**Mathematical Meaning**
$f(x)$			
0.1259			
x			
56.863			

9 Use your linear regression equation to predict the average global temperature for the years 2032–2036.

Making Predictions Within and Outside a Data Set

HABITS OF MIND
• Attend to precision.

There are different kinds of predictions you can make with linear regressions.

The music industry is continually changing how it delivers music to its listeners. The table shows the percent of total U.S. music sales revenues from streaming.

Year	2010	2011	2012	2013	2014	2015
Percent of Total U.S. Music Sales Revenue From Streaming	7	9	15	21	27	34

1. Use graphing technology to determine the linear regression equation for the data.

ASK YOURSELF...
What is an appropriate level of accuracy needed throughout this situation?

2. Interpret the equation of the line in terms of this problem situation.

When there is a linear association between the independent and dependent variables of a data set, you can use a linear regression to make predictions within the data set. Using a linear regression to make predictions within the data set is **interpolation**.

3. Use your equation to predict the percent of streaming revenues in 2013. Compare the predicted value percent in 2013 with the actual value.

4. Compute the predicted value percent for 2011 and compare it with the actual value.

5 Do you think a prediction made using interpolation will always be close to the actual value? **Explain your reasoning.**

Using a linear regression to make predictions for values of *x* outside of the data set is **extrapolation**.

6 Use the equation to predict the percent of streaming revenues for each year.

(a) 2040

(b) 2004

7 Are these predictions reasonable? **Explain your reasoning.**

Tell Me Ev-ery-thing

You have used technology to determine linear regression equations. You have then used those linear regression equations to predict unknown values inside and outside a data set.

1. Why is the linear regression line generated using technology more accurate than the line of best fit you can write using two points?

2. Why are predictions made by extrapolation more likely to be less accurate than predictions made by interpolation?

LESSON 1 ASSIGNMENT

> Use a separate piece of paper for your Journal entry.

JOURNAL

Describe the Least Squares Method in your own words.

REMEMBER

You can model patterns in data with lines of best fit. The Least Squares Method is one way to create a linear regression equation, and it is the method that graphing applications tend to use.

PRACTICE

1 One of the jobs of the National Center for Education Statistics is to gather information about public high schools and their dropout rates. This includes anyone who leaves school without a high school diploma or an equivalent credential. The table shows the average percent of high school dropouts from the year 2005 through the year 2017.

Year	High School Dropout Rate (percent)
2005	3.8
2006	3.8
2007	3.5
2008	3.5
2009	3.4
2010	3.0
2011	3.4
2012	3.4
2013	4.7
2014	5.2
2015	4.9
2016	4.8
2017	4.7

(a) Create a scatter plot of the high school dropout data. What information can you gather about the dropout rates from the scatter plot?

(b) Use the data table and graphing technology to generate a line of best fit.

(c) Interpret the slope and y-intercept of the linear regression equation. What do these values represent in terms of the problem situation?

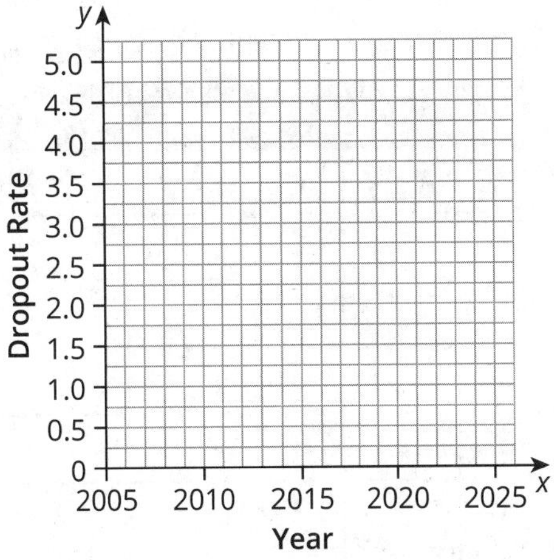

Go to LiveHint.com for help on the PRACTICE questions.

ⓓ Determine the dropout rate for the year 2010. Is this the same as the dropout rate recorded in the table? If not, explain the difference.

STRETCH Optional

> Consider the two sets of data shown in the graphs.

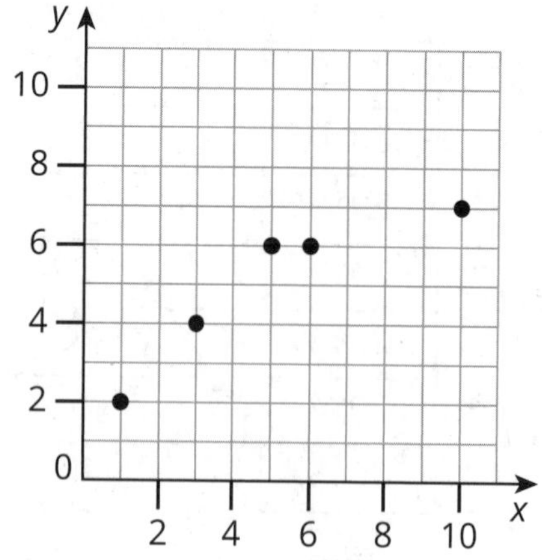

Graph A

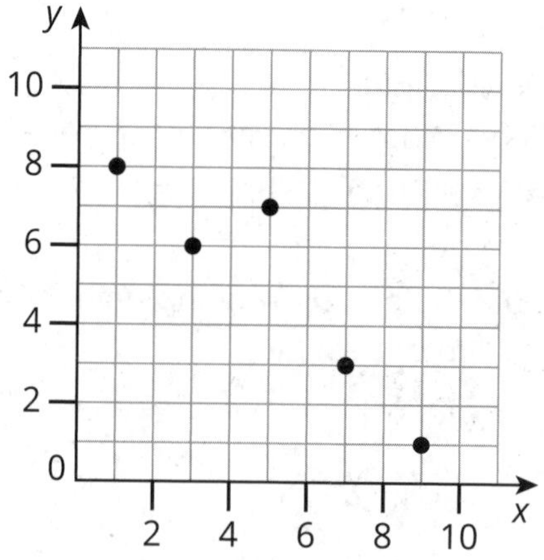

Graph B

1. Calculate the mean of the x-values, x, and the mean of the y-values, y, for each graph.
2. Complete the tables for each graph.

Graph A				
x	$x - \bar{x}$	y	$y - \bar{y}$	$(x - \bar{x})(y - \bar{y})$
1	−4	2	−3	12
3		4		
5		6		
6		6		
10		7		
				SUM =

Graph B				
x	$x - \bar{x}$	y	$y - \bar{y}$	$(x - \bar{x})(y - \bar{y})$
1	−4	8	3	−12
3		6		
5		7		
6		3		
9		1		
				SUM =

3. Compare the two sums in the last column of each table. Determine whether there seems to be a connection between the sums and the graphs of the data set.

LESSON 2

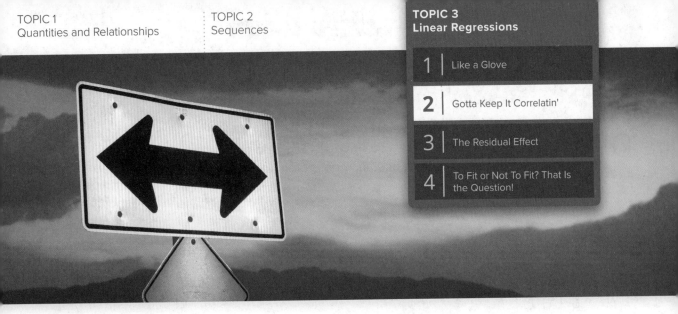

Gotta Keep It Correlatin'

Correlation

Learning Goals

- Determine the correlation coefficient using technology.
- Interpret the correlation coefficient for a set of data.
- Understand the difference between r and r^2.
- Understand the difference between correlation and causation.
- Understand necessary and sufficient conditions.
- Choose a level of accuracy appropriate when reporting quantities.

KEY TERMS

correlation

correlation coefficient

coefficient of determination

causation

common response

confounding variable

REVIEW (1–2 minutes)

> List the slope values of the lines in order from least to greatest.

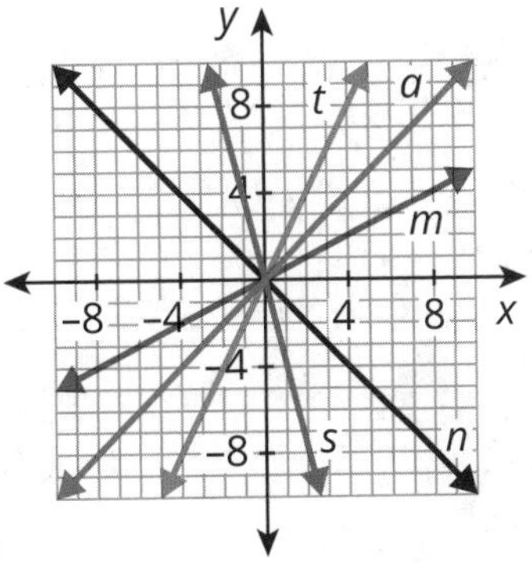

You have learned how to write a line of best fit relating two variables using the Least Squares Method.

Is there a way to measure the strength of the linear relationship between the variables?

Associate, Formulate, Correlate!

> Consider each relationship shown.

1 Describe any associations between the independent and dependent variables, and then draw a line of best fit, if possible.

REMEMBER...
Data comparing two variables can show a positive association, negative association, or no association.

(a)

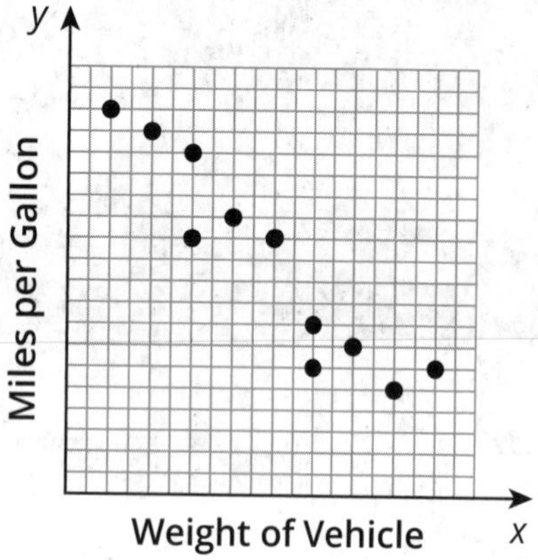

(b)

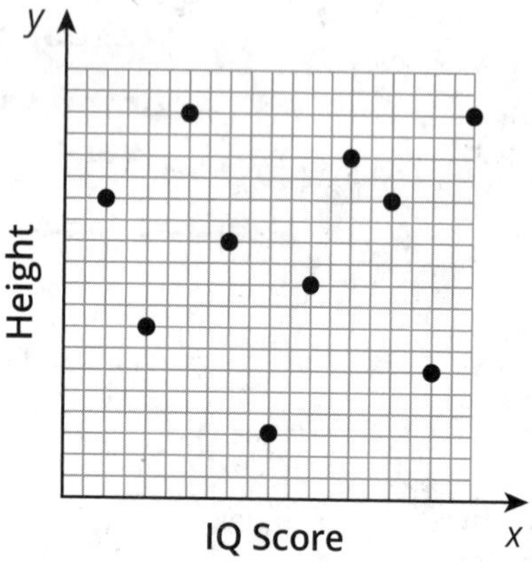

(c)

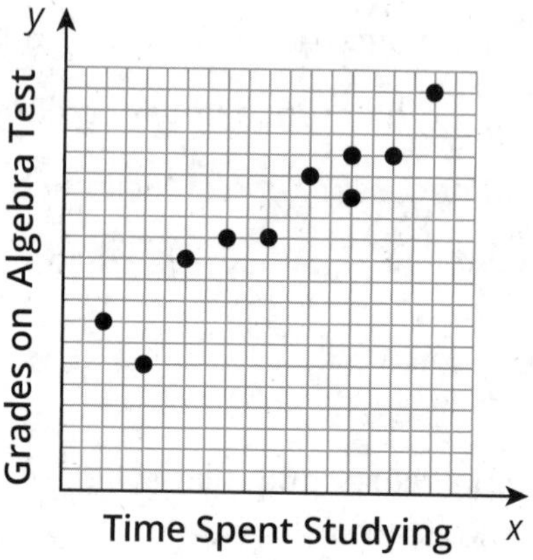

The Correlation Coefficient

HABITS OF MIND
- Attend to precision.

Correlation is a measure of how well a regression fits a set of data. The **correlation coefficient** is a numeric summary of bivariate data that measures the strength of the relationship between two variables. You use the variable *r* to represent the correlation coefficient.

- The *r*-value value falls between −1 and 0 when the data show a negative association or between 0 and 1 when the data show a positive association.
- The closer the correlation coefficient is to 1 or −1, the stronger the relationship is between the two variables.
- The closer the *r*-value gets to 0, the less of a linear relationship there is in the data.

1 Determine whether the points in each scatter plot have a positive correlation, a negative correlation, or no correlation. Circle the *r*-value you think is most appropriate. **Explain your reasoning.**

a) 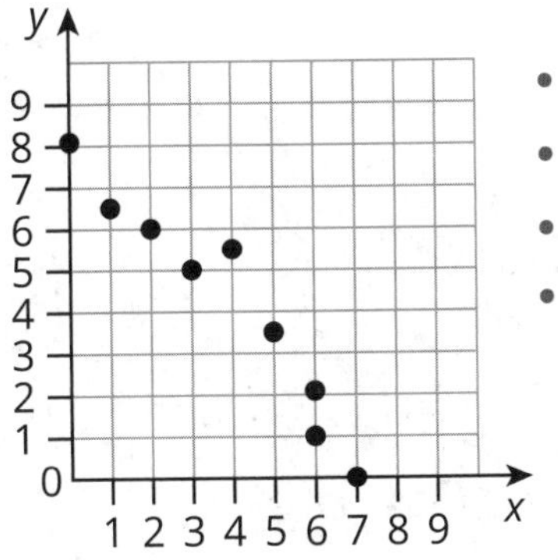

- $r = 0.9$
- $r = -0.9$
- $r = 0.09$
- $r = -0.09$

b) 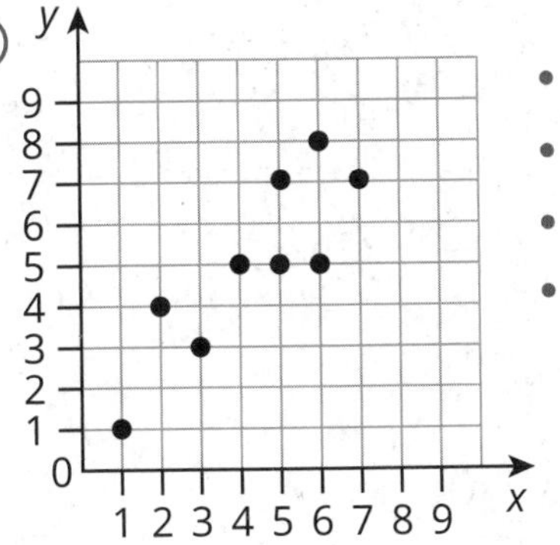

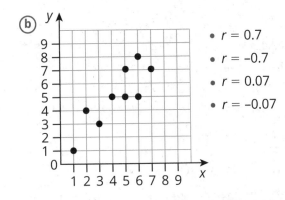

- $r = 0.7$
- $r = -0.7$
- $r = 0.07$
- $r = -0.07$

c) 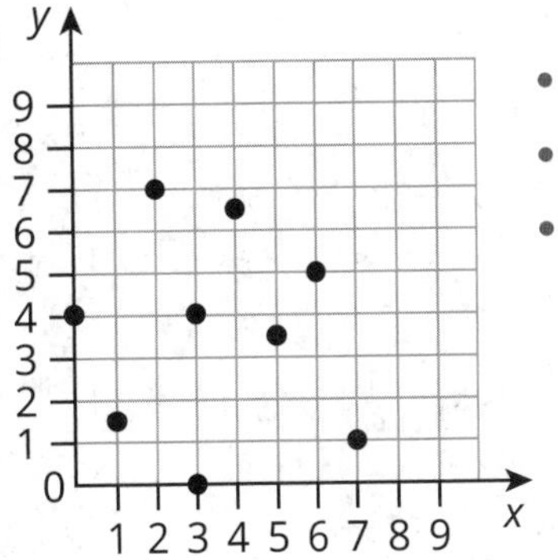

- $r = 1$
- $r = 0.5$
- $r = 0.01$

You can calculate the correlation coefficient of a data set using the formula:

$$r = \frac{\sum_{i=1}^{n}(x_i - \overline{x})(y_i - \overline{y})}{\sqrt{\sum_{i=1}^{n}(x_i - \overline{x})^2}\sqrt{\sum_{i=1}^{n}(y_i - \overline{y})^2}}$$

Fortunately, your graphing calculator can do this arithmetic. Previously you used a graphing calculator to determine the linear regression using the Least Squares Method. Along with calculating the equation for the line, the calculator also calculated the value *r*, the correlation coefficient.

> Let's use technology to compute the value of the correlation coefficient.

2 Consider the data set (23, 23), (1, 2), and (3, 4).

(a) Use technology to compute the correlation coefficient.

(b) Interpret the correlation coefficient of the data set.

Is It Linear?

It is important to decide that a set of data models a linear relationship before using a linear regression equation to analyze the data.

> **HABITS OF MIND**
> - Model with mathematics.
> - Use appropriate tools strategically.

A group of friends completed a survey about their monthly income and how much they pay for rent each month. The table shows the results.

Monthly Net Income (dollars)	Monthly Rent (dollars)
1400	450
1550	505
2000	545
2600	715
3000	930
3400	1000

ASK YOURSELF...
What do you notice as you read through the data?

1. Identify the independent and dependent quantities in this problem situation.

2. Construct a scatter plot of the data using technology.

   a. Sketch and label the scatter plot.

   b. Do you think a linear regression equation would best describe this situation? **Explain your reasoning.**

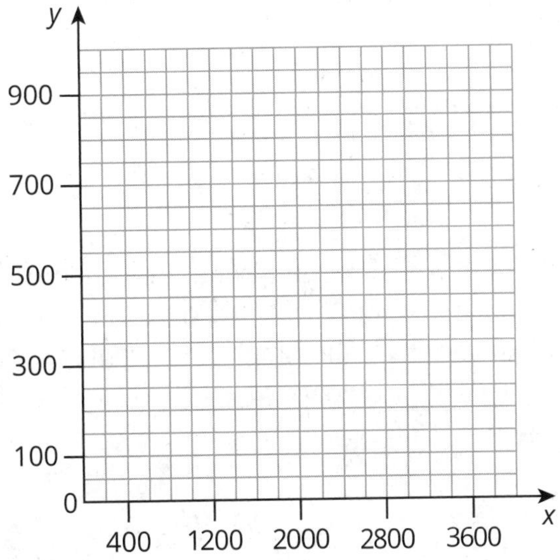

3 Use technology to determine whether a line of best fit is appropriate for these data.

(a) Determine and interpret the linear regression equation.

ASK YOURSELF...
What is the appropriate level of accuracy needed for this linear regression equation?

(b) Compute the correlation coefficient.

4 Would a line of best fit be appropriate for this data set? **Explain your reasoning.**

The correlation coefficient, r, indicates the type (positive or negative) and strength of the relationship that may exist for a given set of data points. The **coefficient of determination, r^2**, measures how well the graph of the regression fits the data. It represents the percentage of variation of the observed values of the data points from their predicted values.

Using the Correlation Coefficient to Assess a Line of Best Fit

HABITS OF MIND

- Reason abstractly and quantitatively.
- Construct viable arguments and critique the reasoning of others.

Let's use the calculation of the correlation coefficient to tell whether a line of best fit models a set of data well or poorly.

The amount of antibiotic remaining in your body over time varies from one drug to the next. The table shows the amount of Antibiotic X that stays in your body for two days.

Time (hours)	Amount of Antibiotic X in Body (mg)
0	60
6	36
12	22
18	13
24	7.8
30	4.7
36	2.8
42	1.7
48	1

1. Determine and interpret a linear regression equation for this data set.

2. Compute and interpret both the correlation coefficient and coefficient of determination of this data set.

3. Does it seem appropriate to use a line of best fit? **If not, explain your reasoning.**

4. Sketch a scatter plot of the data.

5. Look at the graph of the data. Do you still agree with your answer to Question 3? **Explain your reasoning.**

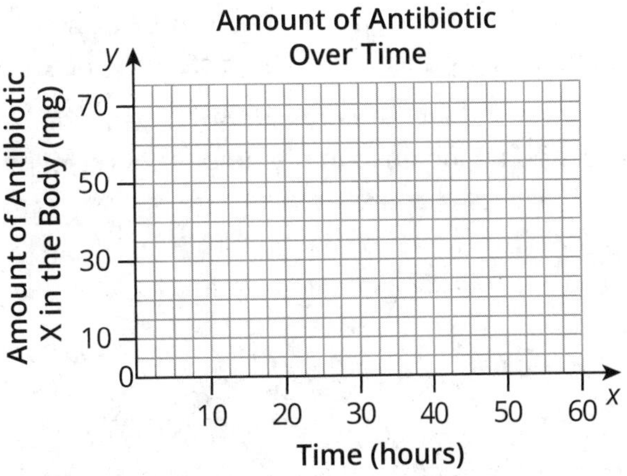

Correlation vs. Causation

HABITS OF MIND
- Reason abstractly and quantitatively.
- Construct viable arguments and critique the reasoning of others.

Does correlation mean causation? What do you think causation means? That is a question that statisticians are always trying to determine.

> Read the three true statements that Alonzo and Richard's teacher gives them. She asks them to decide what conclusions they can draw from the data. Do you agree with them? **If so, why? If not, why not?**

1. The number of smartphones sold in the United States has increased every year since 2005. The number of flat-screen televisions sold in the United States has also increased during the same time.

   Alonzo and Richard concluded that owning a cell phone causes a person to buy a flat-screen television.

2. Since 2004, the average salary of an NFL football player has increased every year. The average weight of an NFL player has also increased yearly since 2004.

   After much discussion, Alonzo and Richard concluded that higher salaries cause the players to gain weight.

3. Worldwide, the number of automobiles sold annually has steadily increased since 1920. Gasoline production has also steadily increased since 1920.

   Alonzo and Richard concluded that the increase in the number of automobiles sold caused an increase in the amount of gasoline produced.

Proving causation is challenging. The scenarios Alonzo and Richard analyzed demonstrate that even though there is a correlation between two quantities, this does not mean that one quantity caused the other. This is one of the most misunderstood and misapplied uses of statistics.

Causation is when one event affects the outcome of a second event. A correlation is a necessary condition for causation, but a correlation is not a sufficient condition for causation. While determining a correlation is straightforward, using statistics to establish causation is very difficult.

4 Many medical studies have tried to prove that smoking causes lung cancer.

(a) Is smoking a necessary condition for lung cancer? **Why or why not?**

(b) Is smoking a sufficient condition for lung cancer? **Why or why not?**

(c) Is there a correlation between people who smoke and people who get lung cancer? **Explain your reasoning.**

(d) Is it true that smoking causes lung cancer? **If so, how was it proven?**

5 People often say that teenage drivers cause automobile accidents.

(a) Is being a teenage driver a necessary condition to have an automobile accident? **Why or why not?**

(b) Is being a teenage driver a sufficient condition to have an automobile accident? **Why or why not?**

(c) Is there a correlation between teenage drivers and automobile accidents? **Explain your reasoning.**

(d) Is it true that teenage drivers cause automobile accidents? **Explain your reasoning.**

Does school absenteeism cause poor performance in school? A correlation between the independent variable of days absent to the dependent variable of grades makes sense. However, this alone does not prove causation.

6 To prove that the number of days that a student is absent causes the student to get poor grades, we would need to conduct more controlled experiments.

(a) List several ways that you could design experiments to attempt to prove this assertion.

(b) Will any of these experiments prove the assertion? **Explain your reasoning.**

There are two relationships that are often mistaken for causation.

- A **common response** is a factor that influences both the independent and dependent variables.
- A **confounding variable** is an unknown or unobserved factor that influences the dependent variable.

7 Consider each relationship. List two or more common responses or confounding variables that could also cause this result.

(a) In North Carolina, the number of shark attacks increases when the temperature increases. Therefore, a temperature increase appears to cause sharks to attack.

(b) A company claims that their pill caused people to lower their cholesterol when following the accompanying exercise program.

Correlations R Us

> Consider the given data sets.

Set A

x	*y*
0	24
2	19
5	12
10	6
20	0

Set B

x	*y*
8	13
10	4
14	15
15	14
19	73

1. Determine the linear regression for each set.

2. Compare the correlation coefficient and the coefficient of determination of each data set. **Describe which regression equation is the better fit and why.**

LESSON 2 ASSIGNMENT

> Use a separate piece of paper for your Journal entry.

JOURNAL

Describe the difference between correlation and causation in your own words.

REMEMBER

You can model a data set by using a linear function called a regression equation. You can also calculate a numeric summary called the correlation coefficient to determine the strength and direction of the relationship between the two variables.

PRACTICE

1 The table shows the percent of the United States population who did not receive needed dental care services due to cost.

Year	1999	2000	2001	2002	2003	2004	2005	2006	2007	2008	2009
Percent	7.9	8.1	8.7	8.6	9.2	10.7	10.7	10.8	10.5	12.6	13.3

(a) Do you think a linear regression equation would best describe this situation? Why or why not?

(b) Determine the linear regression equation for these data. Interpret the equation in terms of this problem situation.

(c) Compute and interpret the correlation coefficient of this data set. Does it seem appropriate to use a line of best fit? Explain your reasoning.

2 A teacher claims that students who study will receive good grades.

(a) Do you think that studying is a necessary condition for a student to receive good grades?

(b) Do you think that studying is a sufficient condition for a student to receive good grades?

Go to LiveHint.com for help on the PRACTICE questions.

(c) Do you think that there is a correlation between students who study and students who receive good grades?

(d) Do you think that it is true that studying will cause a student to receive good grades?

(e) List two or more confounding variables that could have an effect on this claim.

3 For each situation, decide whether the correlation implies causation. List reasons why or why not.

(a) The number of violent video games sold in the U.S. correlates strongly to crime rates in real life.

(b) The number of newspapers sold in a city correlates strongly to the number of runs scored by the city's professional baseball team.

(c) The number of mouse traps found in a person's house correlates strongly to the number of mice found in their house.

STRETCH Optional

> Consider the points: (1, 2), (2, 3), (3, 2), (4, 5), (5, 2.5), (6, 6), (7, 3), (8, 7). The line of best fit for the graph of the points is $y = 0.5x + 1.4$.

1 Determine the predicted values of y for each value of x using the line of best fit, and the values of the differences between the observed y-values from the points and the predicted values of y from the line of best fit.

2 Determine whether there is a pattern in the differences between the observed and predicted y-values. Explain what this might indicate about using the line of best fit to make predictions.

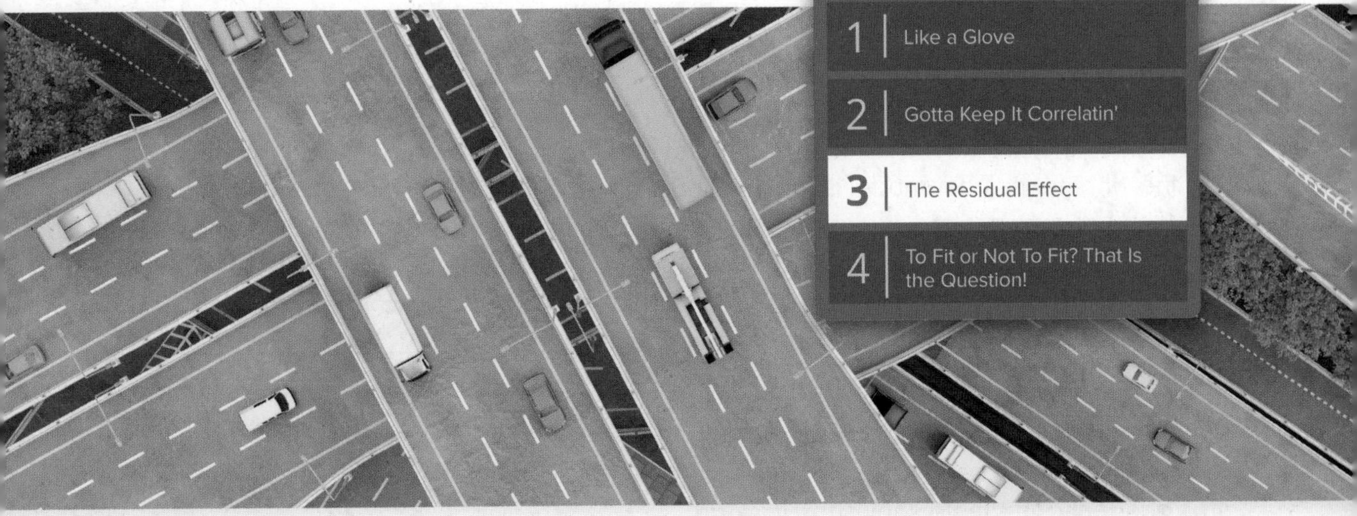

LESSON 3

The Residual Effect

Creating Residual Plots

KEY TERMS

residual

residual plot

Learning Goals

- Create residual plots.
- Analyze the shapes of residual plots.

REVIEW (1–2 minutes)

> Determine the distance between each pair of points.

1 A (10, 12) and B (10, 17)

2 A (10, 12) and C (10, 7)

3 Is point A closer to point B or point C?

4 Can you represent the distance between two points by a negative value? **Explain your reasoning.**

You have used the correlation coefficient, r, to indicate the strength of the linear relationship for a given set of data points.

How can you determine whether another function type would better fit the data?

Hit the Brakes!

You have used the shape of data in a scatter plot and the correlation coefficient to help you determine whether a linear model is an appropriate model for a data set. For some data sets, these measures may not provide enough information to determine whether a linear model is most appropriate.

To be a safe driver, there are a lot of things to consider. For example, you have to leave enough distance between your car and the car in front of you in case you need to stop suddenly. The table shows the braking distance for a particular car when traveling at different speeds.

Speed (mph)	Braking Distance (feet)
30	48
40	80
50	120
60	180
70	240
80	320

1. Construct a scatter plot of the data. Then calculate the line of best fit.

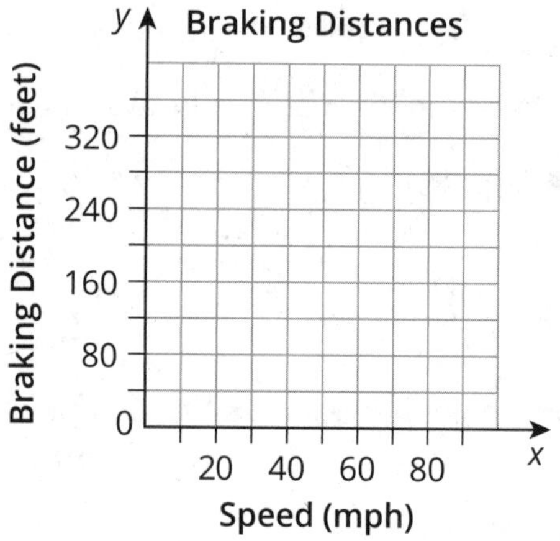

2. Determine and interpret the correlation coefficient.

3. Write a function to represent the braking distance, $d(s)$, given the speed of a car, s. Interpret the function in terms of this problem situation.

ASK YOURSELF...
Do you think a linear model is appropriate?

MATHia CONNECTION
- Analyzing Residuals of Lines of Best Fit

The Residual Effect

HABITS OF MIND
- Reason abstractly and quantitatively.
- Construct viable arguments and critique the reasoning of others.

In addition to the shape of the scatter plot and the correlation coefficient, one additional method to determine whether a linear model is appropriate for the data is to analyze the *residuals*. A **residual** is the vertical distance between an observed data value and its predicted value using the regression equation.

1 Complete the table to determine the residuals for the braking distance data.

Speed (mph)	Observed Braking Distance (feet)	Predicted Braking Distance (feet)	Residual Value Observed Value – Predicted Value
30	48		
40	80		
50	120		
60	180		
70	240		
80	320		

Now, let's analyze the relationship between the observed braking distances and the predicted braking distances using graphs.

2 Examine the scatter plot and the line of best fit.

(a) Show the residual values on the scatter plot by connecting each observed value to its predicted value using a vertical line segment.

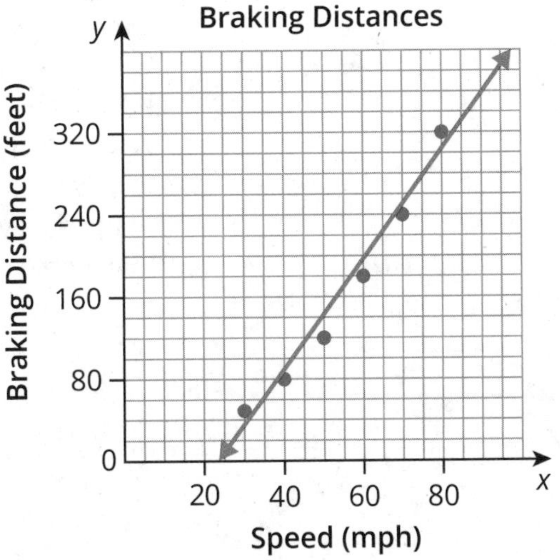

REMEMBER...
The vertical distance from each observed data point to the line is the residual for that *x*-value.

ⓑ When does a residual have a positive value?

ⓒ When does a residual have a negative value?

You can now use the residual data to create a *residual plot*. A **residual plot** is a scatter plot of the independent variable on the x-axis and the residuals on the y-axis.

3 Construct a residual plot of the speed and braking distance data.

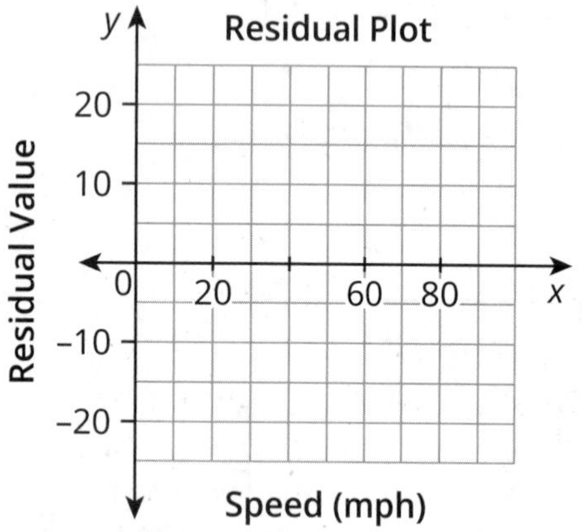

TAKE NOTE...
The residual plot displays the residual values you calculated in the table.

4 Interpret each residual in the context of the problem situation.

- At 30 mph, the braking distance is ______________.
- At 40 mph, the braking distance is ______________.
- At 50 mph, the braking distance is ______________.
- At 60 mph, the braking distance is ______________.
- At 70 mph, the braking distance is ______________.
- At 80 mph, the braking distance is ______________.

THINK ABOUT...
A residual plot cannot tell you whether a linear model is appropriate. It can only tell you that there may be a model other than linear that is more appropriate.

5 What pattern, if any, do you notice in the residuals?

You can use the shape of the residual plot to determine whether there may be a more appropriate model other than a linear model for a data set.

When a residual plot results in no identifiable pattern or a flat pattern, then the data may be linearly related. When there is a pattern in the residual plot, the data may not be linearly related. Even when the data are not linearly related, the data may still have some other type of nonlinear relationship.

Residual Plots Indicating a Possible Linear Relationship

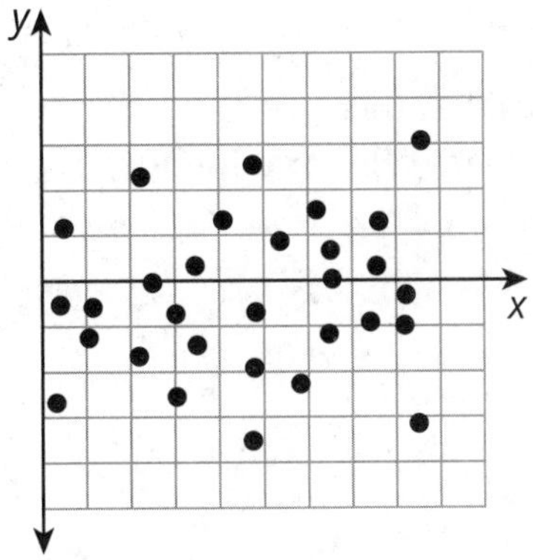

There is no pattern in the residual plot.
The data may have a linear relationship.

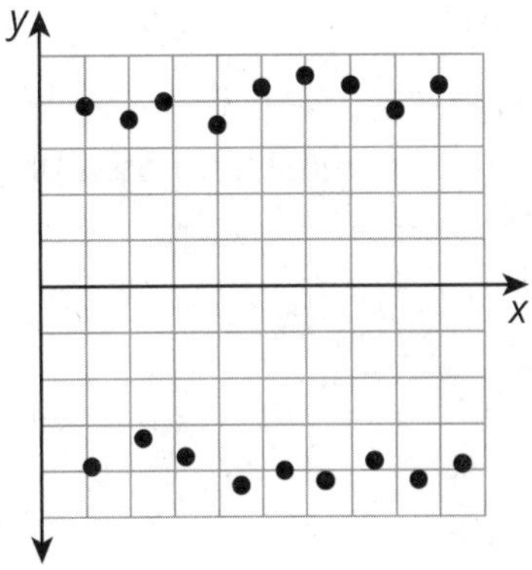

There is a flat pattern in the residual plot.
The data may have a linear relationship.

Residual Plots Indicating a Nonlinear Relationship

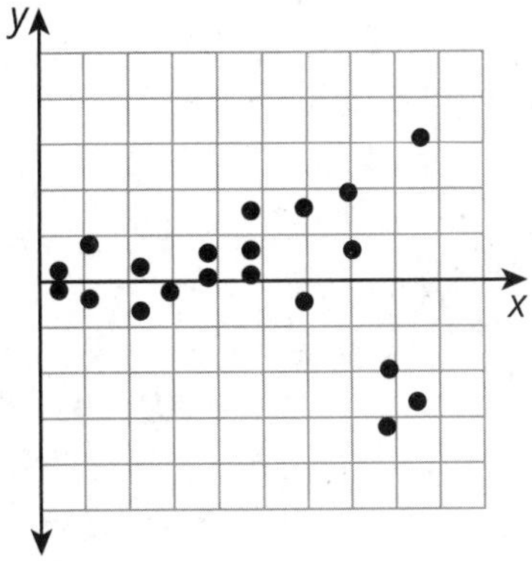

There is a pattern in the residual plot.
As the *x*-value increases, the residuals become more spread out. The data may not have a linear relationship.

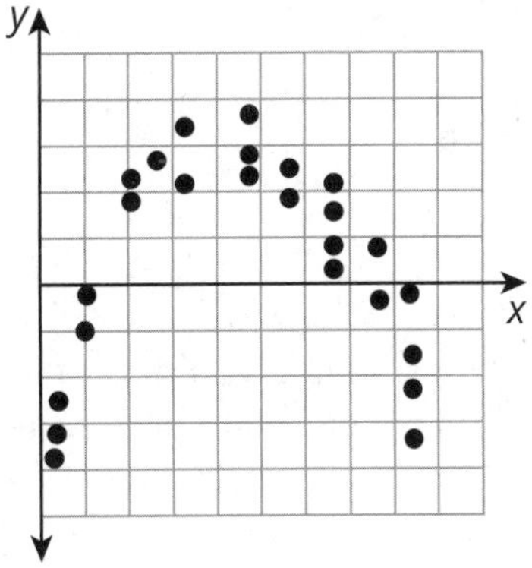

There is a pattern in the residual plot.
The residuals form a curved pattern. The data may not have a linear relationship.

6 Interpret the residual plot for the braking distance data.

7 Anita thinks the residual plot looks like it forms a curve. She says that this means the data must be more quadratic than linear. Is Anita correct? **Why or why not?**

8 Is the regression line you determined in the Getting Started a good fit for this data set? **Explain your reasoning.**

THINK ABOUT...
Keep in mind that this represents only a portion of the entire data set.

Attendance Matters

Let's analyze the residuals of another set of data.

HABITS OF MIND
- Reason abstractly and quantitatively.
- Construct viable arguments and critique the reasoning of others.

Over the last semester, Mr. Finch kept track of the number of student absences. Now that the semester is over, he wants to see whether there is a linear relationship between the number of absences and a student's grade for the semester. The table shows the data he collected.

Student	Number of Absences	Grade (percent)
James	0	95
Tiona	5	73
Mikala	3	84
Paul	1	92
Danasia	2	92
Erik	3	80
Rachael	10	65
Cheyanne	0	90
Chen	6	70
Javier	1	88

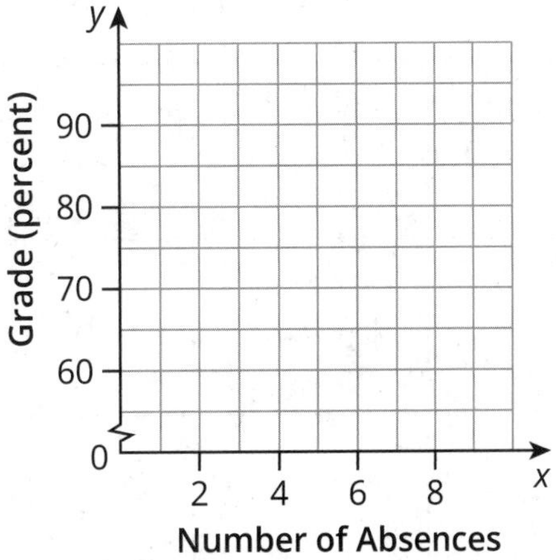

1. Construct a scatter plot of the data.

2. Describe the association shown in the scatter plot.

3. Determine the equation of the least-squares regression line. Interpret the equation for this problem situation.

4. Compute and interpret the correlation coefficient.

5 Determine the residuals for the data. Interpret each residual.

Student	Number of Absences	Algebra Grade (percent)	Predicted Value	Residual	Interpretation
James	0	95	92.6	2.4	2.4% greater than predicted
Tiona	5	73			
Mikala	3	84			
Paul	1	92			
Danasia	2	92			
Erik	3	80			
Rachael	10	65			
Cheyanne	0	90			
Chen	6	70			
Javier	1	88			

6 Construct and interpret a residual plot of the data.

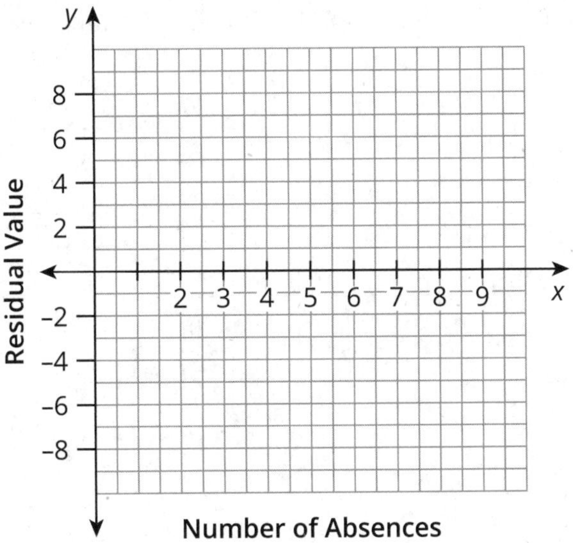

REMEMBER…
When determining the fit of a curve, you need to look at the pattern of the scatter plot, correlation coefficient, and residuals.

The Shape Beyond the Shape!

1. Explain what you can conclude from each residual plot about whether a linear model is appropriate.

(a)

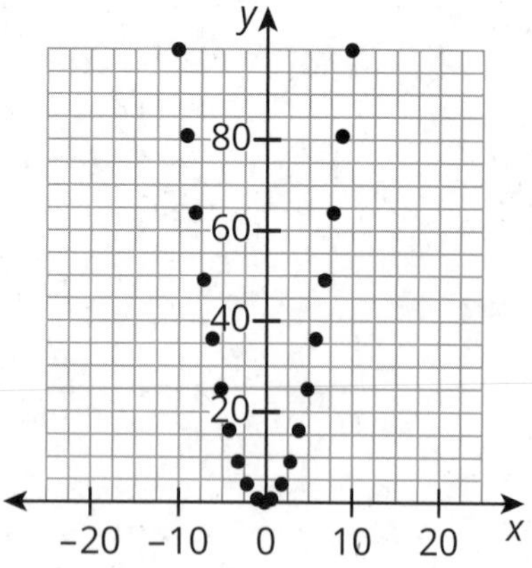

(b)

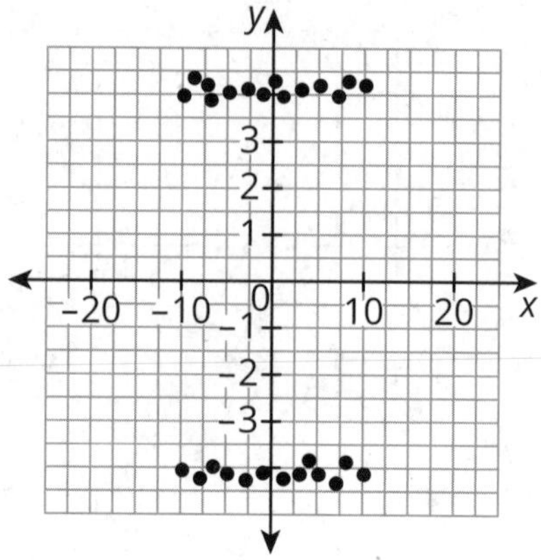

(c)

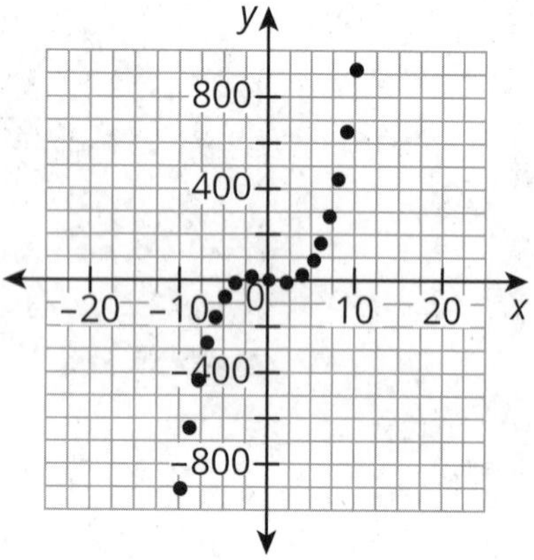

(d)

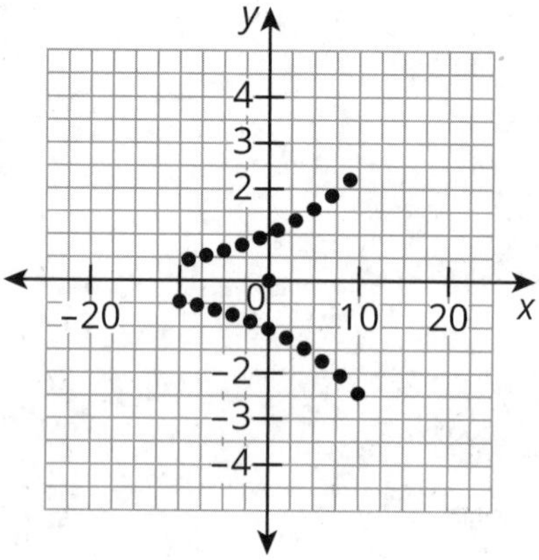

2. How would you describe the difference between the line of best fit and the most appropriate model?

LESSON 3 ASSIGNMENT

> Use a separate piece of paper for your Journal entry.

JOURNAL

> Write a definition for each term.

1 residual

2 residual plot

REMEMBER

A residual plot of a linear regression equation is an important tool when determining its appropriateness. The pattern in the residual data indicates whether or not there may be a linear relationship.

PRACTICE

1 A manager of a telemarketing firm is trying to increase his employees' productivity. The table shown indicates the number of months the employees have been working and the number of calls they successfully complete with customers per day.

Employee	Number of Months of Employment	Observed Number of Successful Calls
A	10	19
B	11	22
C	14	23
D	15	25
E	17	27
F	18	28
G	21	31
H	22	32
I	25	33
J	29	33

(a) Construct a scatter plot of the data.

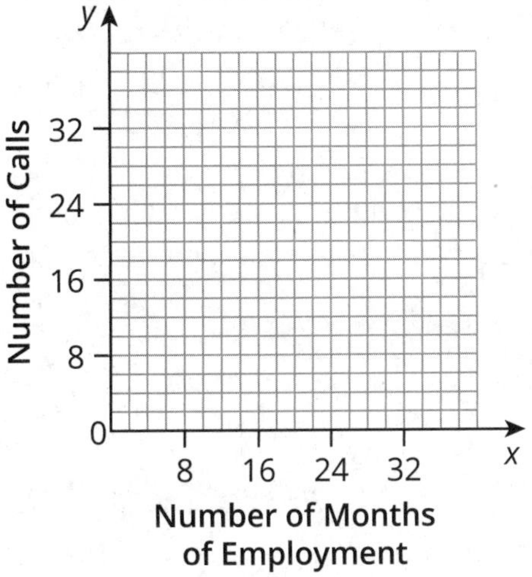

(b) Based on the shape of the scatter plot, is a linear regression appropriate? What type of correlation appears to be present?

(c) Write a function $c(m)$ to represent the line of best fit. Then interpret the function in terms of the problem situation.

(d) Compute and interpret the correlation coefficient.

(e) Calculate the residuals for the data and create a residual plot of the data.

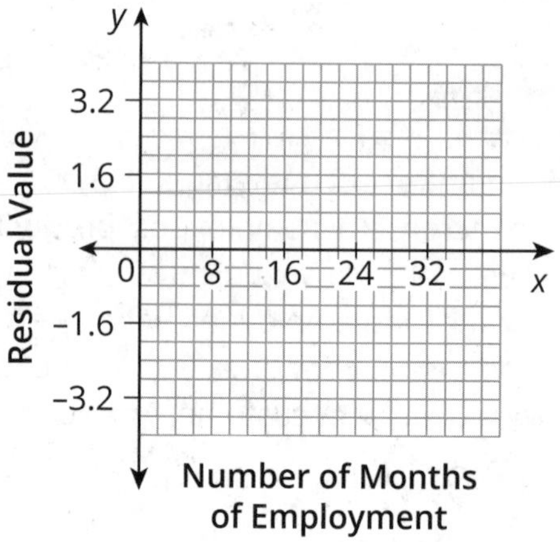

(f) Based on the residual plot, is a linear model appropriate for the data? Explain your reasoning.

(g) Should the manager use a linear regression equation to predict how many successful calls an employee will make if they have worked for 36 months? Explain your reasoning.

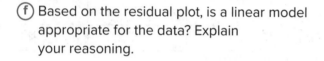

STRETCH Optional

> Consider the table of values.

1. Generate a line of best fit using the data in the table.
2. Determine the residuals for the data.
3. Plot the residuals (dependent variable) versus the x-values (independent variable) on one graph and the residuals (dependent variable) versus the predicted y-values (independent variable) on another graph.
4. Compare the shape of the two graphs from Question 3.

Point	x	y
A	3	1
B	4	3
C	7	5
D	10	9
E	11	9
F	14	12
G	17	14

LESSON 4

To Fit or Not To Fit? That Is the Question!

Using Residual Plots

Learning Goals

- Use scatter plots and correlation coefficients to determine whether a linear regression is a good fit for data.
- Use residual plots to help determine whether a linear regression is the best fit for data.
- Choose a level of accuracy appropriate when reporting quantities.

REVIEW (1–2 minutes)

> Which correlation coefficient shows the strongest linear relationship between two quantities? **Explain your reasoning.**

- $r = 0.55$
- $r = -0.91$
- $r = 0.816$
- $r = -0.03$

You have learned about correlation coefficients and residual plots.

How can you use these measures to determine whether a linear model is a good fit for a data set?

What Aren't You Telling Me?

1 For each data set determine the linear regression equation and the value of r.

Set 1		Set 2		Set 3		Set 4	
x	y	x	y	x	y	x	y
10	8.04	10	9.14	10	7.46	8	6.58
8	6.95	8	8.14	8	6.77	8	5.76
13	7.58	13	8.74	13	12.74	8	7.71
9	8.81	9	8.77	9	7.11	8	8.84
11	8.33	11	9.26	11	7.81	8	8.47
14	9.96	14	8.10	14	8.84	8	7.04
6	7.24	6	6.13	6	6.08	8	5.25
4	4.26	4	3.10	4	5.39	19	12.50
12	10.84	12	9.13	12	8.15	8	5.56
7	4.82	7	7.26	7	6.42	8	7.91
5	5.68	5	4.74	5	5.73	8	6.89

2 Calculate the average of the x values in each data set. Then calculate the average of the y values in each data set.

DID YOU KNOW?

Francis J. Anscombe talked about the dangers of relying on the analytic side of statistics without looking at the graphical side to help draw conclusions.

3 What does all this data tell you about the similarities between the four data sets? What does the data tell you about the differences between the four data sets? **Explain your reasoning.**

4 Construct a scatter plot for each of the data sets. What does each scatter plot tell you about the data sets?

Data Set 1

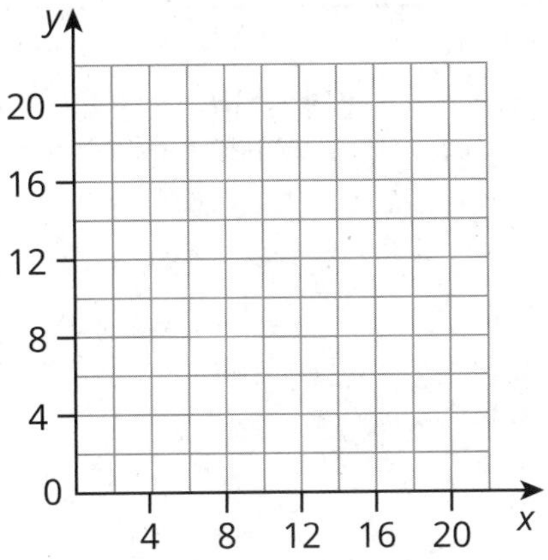

Data Set 2

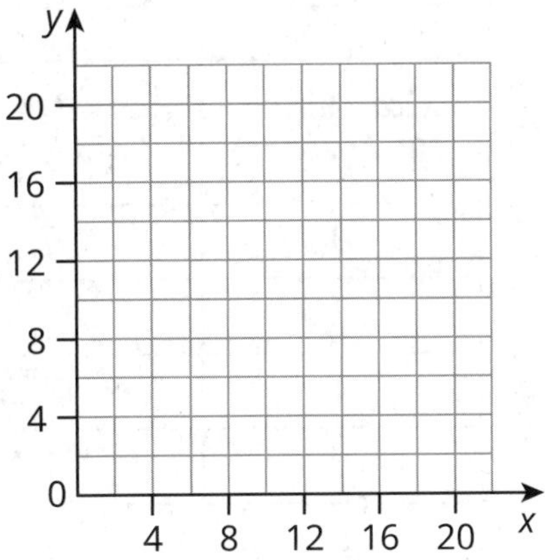

Data Set 3

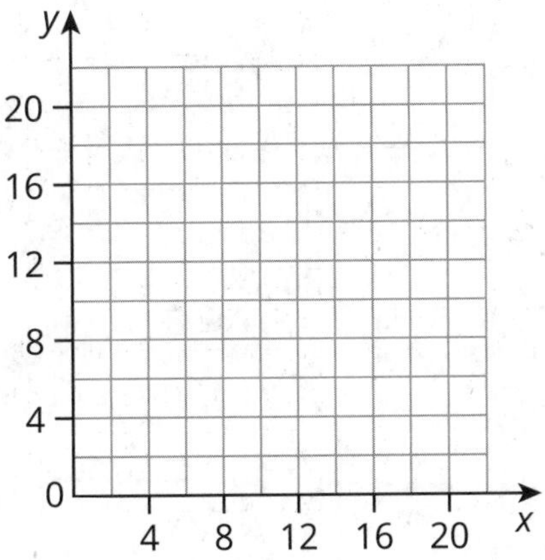

Data Set 4

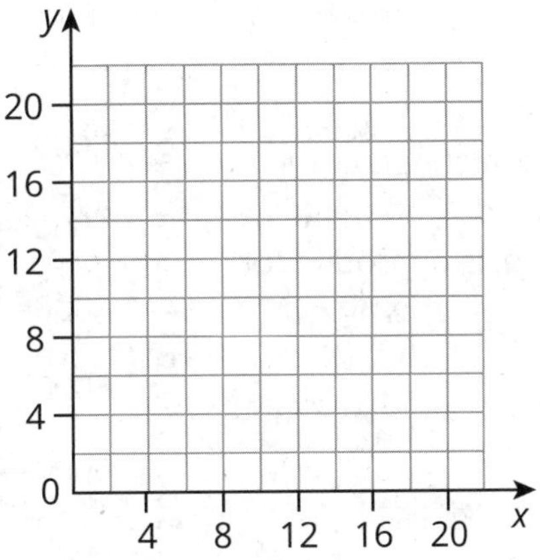

Determining the Best Model

Let's use the tools for analyzing a data set to determine whether a linear regression is the best model.

HABITS OF MIND
- Model with mathematics.
- Use appropriate tools strategically.

The table shows the number of books sold in bookstores in the United States since 2000. Danae wants to know whether she can model the relationship between the time in years since 2007 and the number of books sold with a linear function.

Time Since 2007 (years)	Bookstore Books Sold (millions)
0	17,170
2	15,800
4	13,720
6	11,490
8	11,010
10	10,110
12	10,000

THINK ABOUT...
What does this table tell you?

1. Construct a scatter plot of the data on the coordinate plane shown.

2. Based on the shape of the scatter plot, do you think a linear model is a good fit for the data? **Why or why not?**

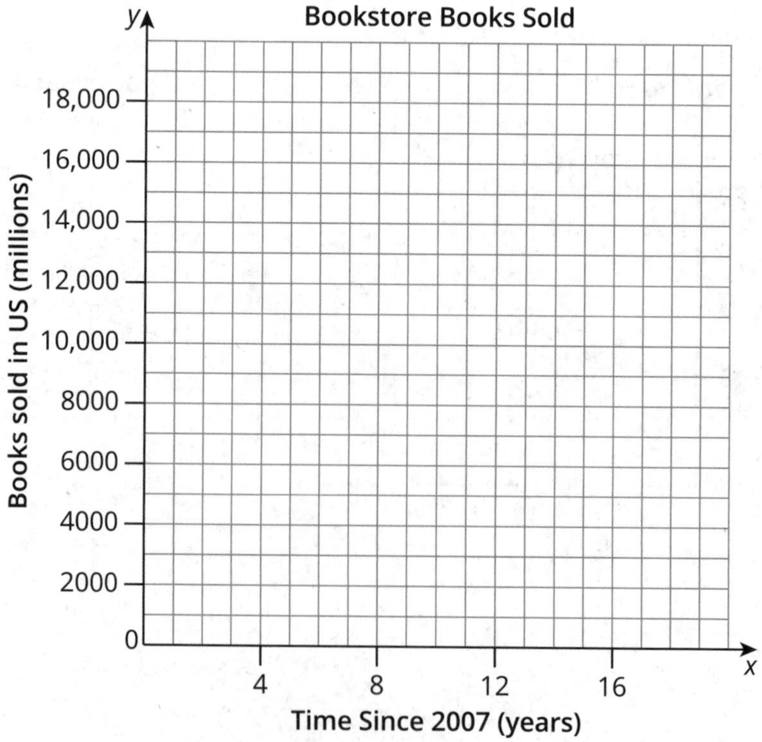

3. Calculate the line of best fit for the data. Write a function to represent the number of books sold, $b(t)$, given the time since 2007, t. Interpret the line of best fit in terms of this problem situation. Then, graph the line of best fit on the same coordinate plane as the scatter plot.

ASK YOURSELF...
What is the appropriate level of accuracy needed for the linear regression equation?

4. Compute and interpret the correlation coefficient.

5. Based on the correlation coefficient, do you think a linear model is a good fit for the data? **Why or why not?**

6. Use the line of best fit to predict the number of bookstore book sales, in millions, each year.

   (a) 2008

   (b) 2020

   (c) 2030

7 Calculate and interpret the residuals for the data.

Time Since 2007 (years)	Bookstore Books Sold (millions)	Predicted Value	Residual	Interpretation
0	17,170			
2	15,800			
4	13,720			
6	11,490			
8	11,010			
10	10,110			
12	10,000			

THINK ABOUT...
Don't always trust what you see. A little more analysis is in order!

8 Create a residual plot of the data on the coordinate plane shown.

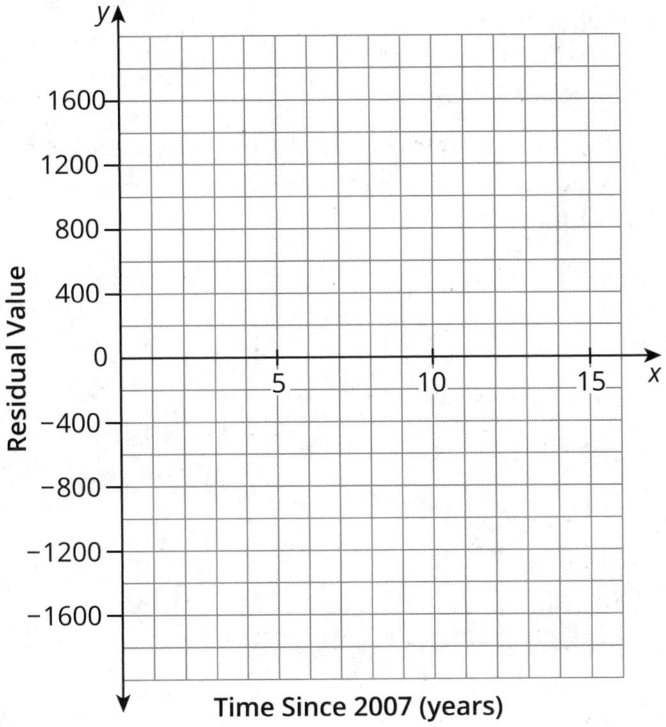

9 Based on the residual plot, do you think a linear model is a good fit for the data? **Why or why not?**

REMEMBER...
A residual plot can't tell you whether a linear model is appropriate. It can only tell you that there may be something better.

Nonlinear Regression

HABITS OF MIND
- Attend to precision.

You used the shape of the scatter plot, the correlation coefficient, and the residual plot to determine whether a linear model was a good fit for the data. Let's consider a different function family.

1. The scatter plot shows the relationship between the number of bookstore books sold and the time in years since 2007. Graph the function $q(t) = 46.7262t^2 - 1196.3t + 17{,}506$ using technology. Sketch the curve of $q(t)$ on the graph shown.

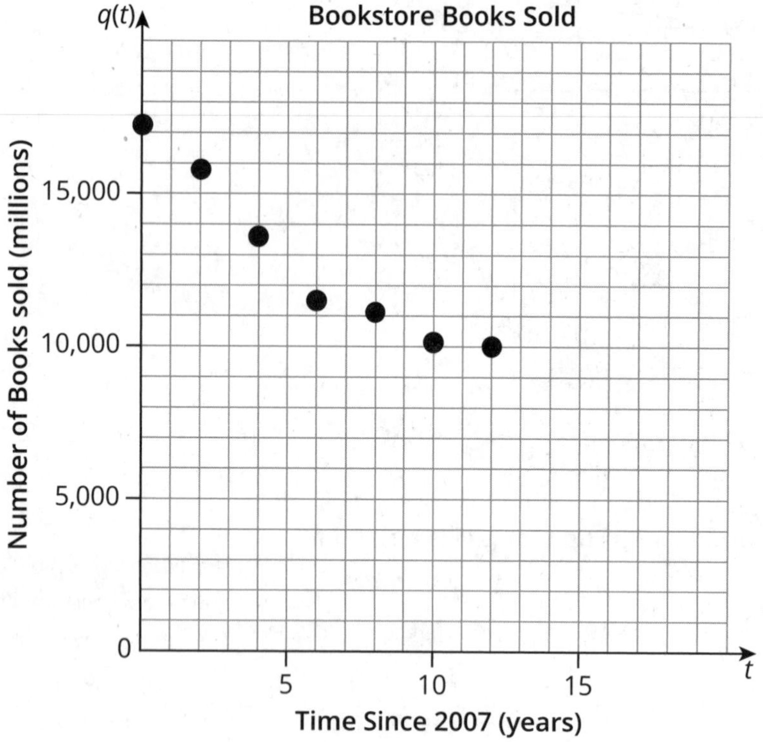

2. Do you think the function $q(t)$ is a better fit for the data than the line of best fit? **Explain your reasoning.**

3 Use the function $q(t)$ to predict the number of books sold in each year.

ⓐ 2012

ⓑ 2015

ⓒ 2030

4 Compare the predictions using the line of best fit $b(t)$ and the predictions using the function $q(t)$. **What do you notice?**

Does it Really Fit?

1. Explain how you can use each representation to determine whether a linear model is an appropriate fit for a data set.

   a. Shape of scatter plot

   b. Correlation coefficient

   c. Residual plot

2. Why is it important to use more than one measure to determine whether a linear model is a good fit for a data set?

3. Do you think determining the best fit for a data set is more important for interpolation or extrapolation? **Explain your reasoning.**

LESSON 4 ASSIGNMENT

> Use a separate piece of paper for your Journal entry.

JOURNAL

Describe the analytic and graphic representations you can use to determine whether a linear model is an appropriate fit for a data set.

REMEMBER

To assess the appropriate model for a set of data, you must consider the graph, the correlation coefficient (*r*), and the residual plot.

PRACTICE

1 The value of a new car starts to depreciate the minute a new owner drives it off the lot. The table shows the values of 15 used cars and their ages.

(a) Construct a scatter plot of the data.

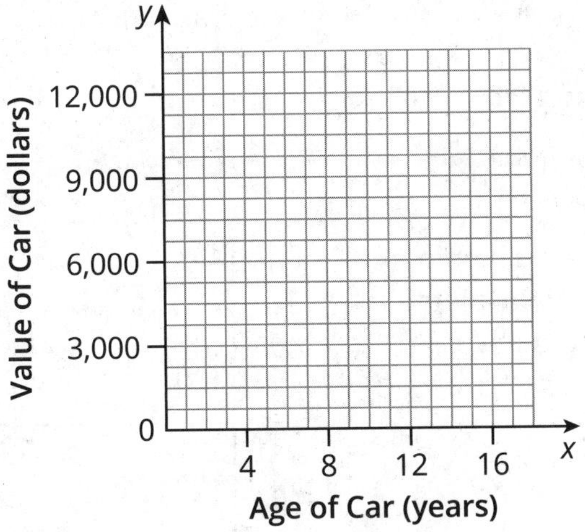

Age of Car (years)	Price (dollars)
1	11,500
2	10,500
3	9100
4	8000
5	7500
6	5100
9	3000
11	3000
11	2900
13	2500

(b) Write a function $P(x)$ to represent the line of best fit for the data. Graph and then interpret the line of best fit in terms of the problem situation.

(c) Does the line of best fit appear to be a good model for this data set? Explain your reasoning.

(d) Calculate the residuals for the data to the nearest whole number and create a residual plot of the data.

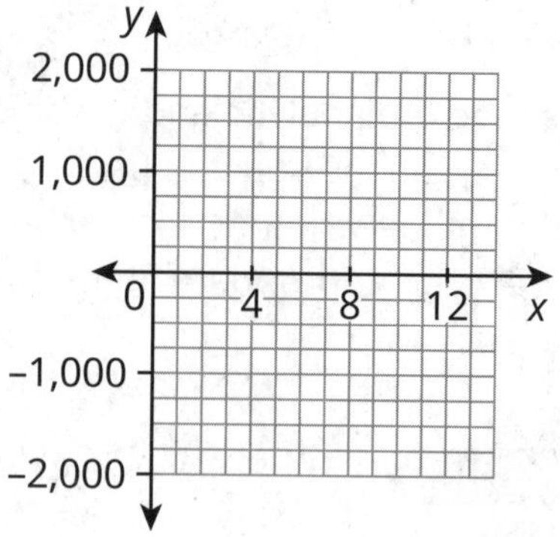

(e) Based on the residual plot, do you think a linear model is a good fit for the data? Why or why not?

(f) The quadratic function $f(x) = 63.2x^2 - 1666.6x + 13{,}455.8$ also represents this data set. Graph this function on the same graph as the scatter plot and line of best fit. Does it appear to fit the data better than the line of best fit?

(g) Calculate the residuals for the function $f(x)$ and create a residual plot of the data. What does the residual plot tell you about the quadratic model used for the data?

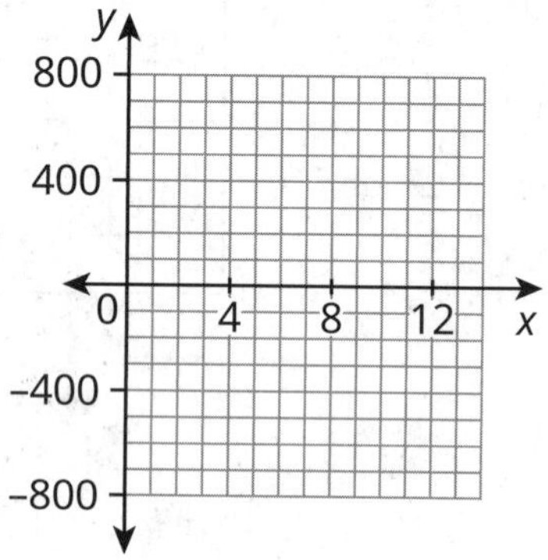

STRECH Optional

> The table shows the population of Lakewood over eight years.

1. Construct a scatter plot of the data.
2. Based on the shape of the scatter plot, determine if a linear model is a good fit for the data.
3. Determine the type of model that you would use if the population in 2017 is 27,500. Explain your reasoning.
4. Determine the model that you would use if the population in 2017 is 29,876.
5. Based on your answers to parts (c) and (d), discuss the influence of one point on determining a model of a data set.

Year	Population
2009	16,450
2010	17,220
2011	18,490
2012	19,222
2013	21,365
2014	22,161
2015	24,987
2016	27,001

MIXED PRACTICE

> This Mixed Practice worksheet includes two sections: Spaced Review and End-of-Topic Review. **Use a separate piece of paper to show your work.**

Spaced Review

> Practice concepts from previous topics.

1 Calculate the slope of the line represented by each table.

(a)

x	0	4	8	16
y	10	5	0	−10

(b)

x	3	6	15	21
y	6	8	14	18

2 Determine whether the slope of the line represented by each equation is positive, negative, zero, or undefined.

(a) $y = -x + 5$

(b) $x = 0$

3 Solve each equation.

(a) $-4x - 2 = 6x + 2$

(b) $\frac{1}{2}x - 5 = 8 + 2x$

4 Create a scatter plot for each set of points and draw a line of best fit for each scatter plot. Then, write the equation for each line.

(a) {(0, 18), (5, 16), (7, 10), (10, 8), (15, 3), (20, 0)}

(b) {(0, 10), (5, 5), (6, 4), (7, 3), (10, 0)}

5 Consider the geometric sequence 5, −15, 45, −135, ...
Determine the common ratio and write the next 3 terms of the sequence.

End-of-Topic Review

AVAILABLE ONLINE

1. A **Topic Summary** reviews the main concepts for the topic.
2. A video of the **Worked Example** is provided.

> Practice concepts you learned in **Linear Regressions**.

6 The table shows the highest maximum temperature for the month of October in Philadelphia, Pennsylvania, over ten years.

Year	2008	2009	2010	2011	2012	2013	2014	2015	2016	2017
Highest Maximum Temperature (°F)	64.9	53.1	61	54	63	68	61	57.9	64.9	66.9

(a) Identify the independent and dependent quantities and their units of measure.

(b) Use the data table and graphing technology to generate a line of best fit. What is the slope and y-intercept of the line and what do they represent?

7 Determine whether the points in each scatter plot have a positive association, a negative association, or no association. Explain your reasoning.

ⓐ

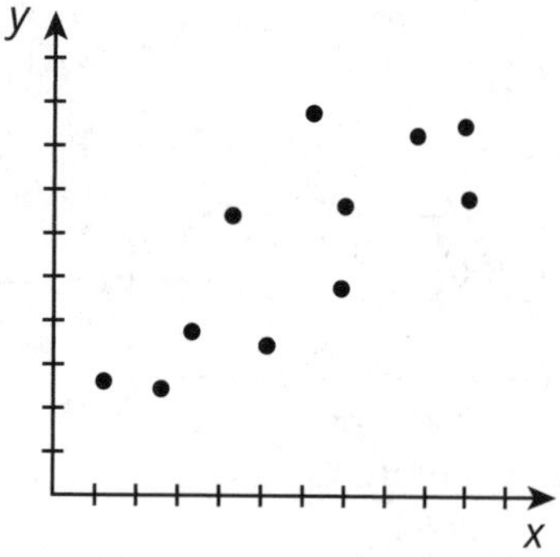

ⓑ

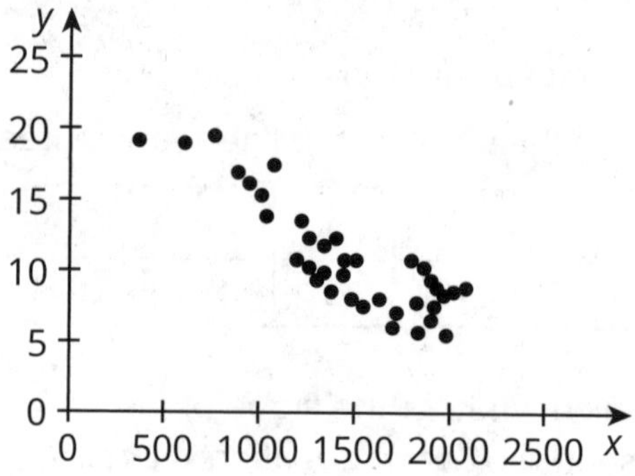

8 Students collected data on the earnings of teenagers aged 13 through 18 who work outside of school, and the number of hours they work in a week. The line of best of fit, $y = 8.25x + 35.7$, where x represents the number of hours worked, and y represents the earnings in dollars, was calculated for the data. One teenager in the study works 15 hours a week and earns $119.95. Determine the residual for the data point and explain the meaning in words.

9 Consider the residual plot.

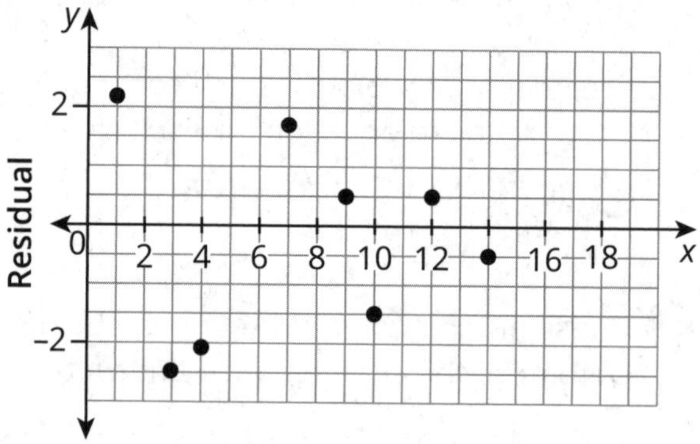

Determine whether the plot indicates that there is a possible linear relationship between the data. Explain your reasoning.

10 The linear regression equation for the given data is $y = -x + 19.7$. Complete the table for the linear regression equation, rounding your answers to the nearest tenth.

x	y	Predicted Value	Residual Value
2	17		
4	16		
6	15		
8	12		
10	9		
12	8		

Exploring Constant Change

Getting Ready for Module 2

Exploring Constant Change

You will connect your work with arithmetic sequences to linear functions. You will explore function transformations. You will continue your work with solving equations and solve literal equations. You will expand your understanding of systems to include systems in linear inequalities. You will investigate linear absolute value and piecewise functions.

The lessons in this module build on your prior experiences with inequalities, transformations, and identifying solutions on graphs.

Review these key terms and identifying solutions from graphs to get ready to explore constant change.

KEY TERMS

inequality

An inequality is a comparison of two values showing one value is greater than (>), greater than or equal to (≥), less than (<), or less than or equal to (≤) the second value.

$8 > 2$ $\qquad$ $a \le b$

$6.009 < 6.051$ $\qquad$ $2x + 4 \ge 16$

transformations

A transformation is an operation that maps, or moves, a figure according to a common action. Transformations include translations, reflections, and dilations.

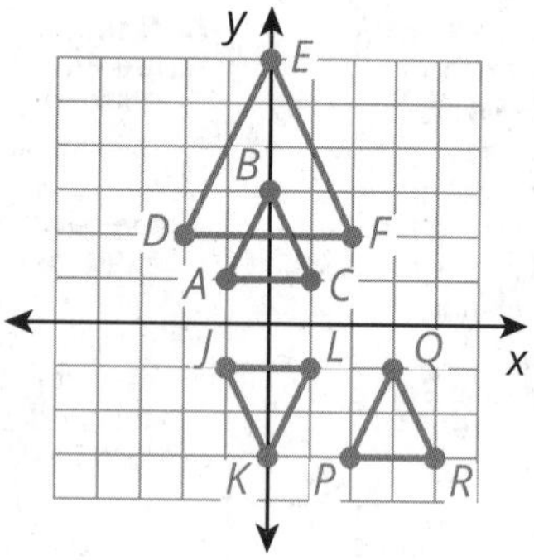

SKILLS YOU WILL NEED

Identifying Solutions From a Graph

Graphs represent the solutions to equations. Consider the graphs of $y = -\frac{1}{2}x - 1$, $y = 2x - 6$, and $y = 4$.

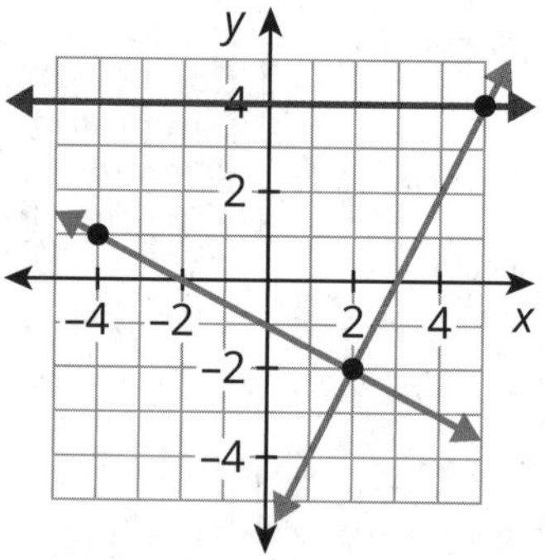

Any point on the graph of an equation is a solution to that equation. So (−4, 1) is a solution to $y = -\frac{1}{2}x - 1$.

The solution to $2x - 6 = 4$ is the x-value where $y = 2x - 6$ and $y = 4$ intersect. So the solution is $x = 5$.

Similarly, the solution to a system of linear equations is the point where the graphs intersect. So (2, −2) is the solution to the system formed by $y = -\frac{1}{2}x - 1$ and $y = 2x - 6$.

REVIEW

› Solve each equation.

1. $x - 7 = -24$
2. $-11x + 15 = 48$
3. $2(x + 9) = -10$
4. $5x - 7 = 8 - 3x$

MATHia

Brush up on your skills.
If you need more practice with these skills, ask your teacher for access to corresponding workspaces in MATHia.

See Appendix on page 457 for answers.

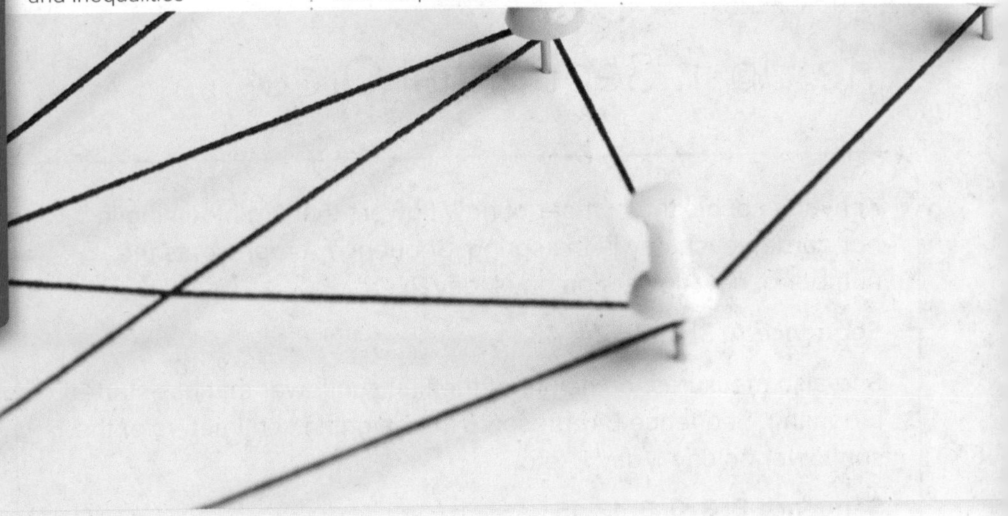

LESSON 1

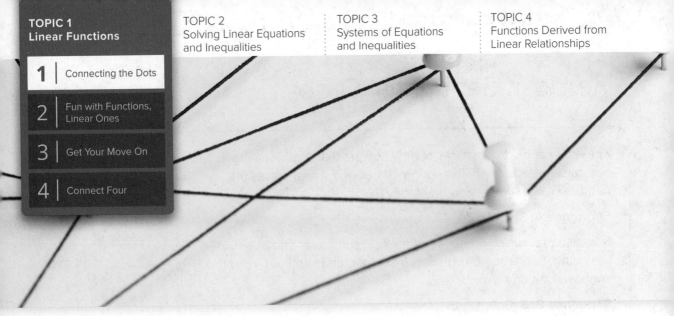

Connecting the Dots

Making Connections Between Arithmetic Sequences and Linear Functions

KEY TERMS

conjecture

average rate of change

first differences

Learning Goals

- Use algebraic properties to prove the explicit formula for an arithmetic sequence is equivalent to the equation of a linear function.
- Relate the defining characteristics of an arithmetic sequence, the first term and common difference, and the defining characteristics of a linear function, the y-intercept and slope.
- Connect the slope of a line to the average rate of change of a function.

REVIEW (1–2 minutes)

> Use what you know about arithmetic sequences to complete each task.

1. Write the first 5 terms of the sequence generated by $a_n = 10 - 3(n - 1)$.

2. Given the function $f(x) = -3x + 10$, calculate $f(1)$, $f(2)$, $f(3)$, $f(4)$, and $f(5)$.

You know that all sequences are functions.

Which type of function is an arithmetic sequence?

Line Up in Sequential Order

Kenyatta counts the number of new flowers that are blooming in her garden each day in the spring. Sequence A represents the number of new flowers on day 1, day 2, etc.

Sequence A: 3, 6, 12, 24, 48

She also measures the height of the first sunflower that has started blooming. Sequence B represents the height in centimeters of the sunflower on day 1, day 2, etc.

Sequence B: 3, 6, 9, 12, 15

ASK YOURSELF...

What is the difference between an arithmetic and geometric sequence?

1. For each sequence, determine whether it is arithmetic or geometric and write the explicit formula that generates the sequence. Then graph each on the coordinate plane using the given symbol.

   Sequence A: ▲

   Sequence B: ■

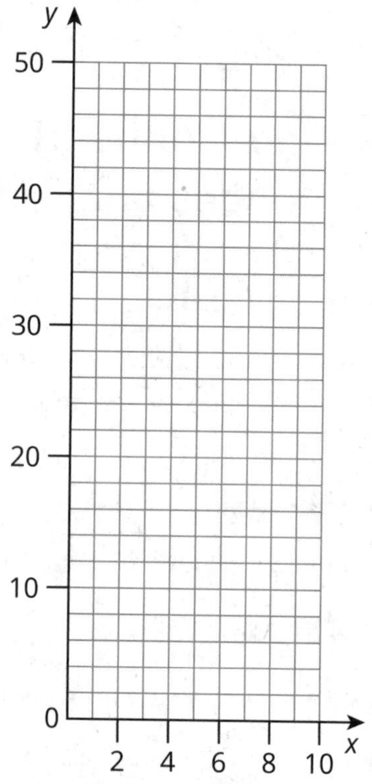

2. List at least three common characteristics of the graphs. **How do the two sequences compare?**

ACTIVITY 1

MATHia CONNECTION
- Writing Sequences as Linear Functions
- Understanding Linear Functions

Connecting Forms

> Consider the four explicit formulas, each representing a different arithmetic sequence.

HABITS OF MIND
- Look for and make use of structure.
- Look for and express regularity in repeated reasoning.

- $a_n = 2 - 4(n - 1)$
- $a_n = 2 + 4(n - 1)$
- $a_n = -4 + 2(n - 1)$
- $a_n = 4 + 2(n - 1)$

ASK YOURSELF...
How do you know by the form of the explicit formula that it represents an arithmetic sequence?

1 Match each explicit formula with its graph.
Describe the strategies you used.

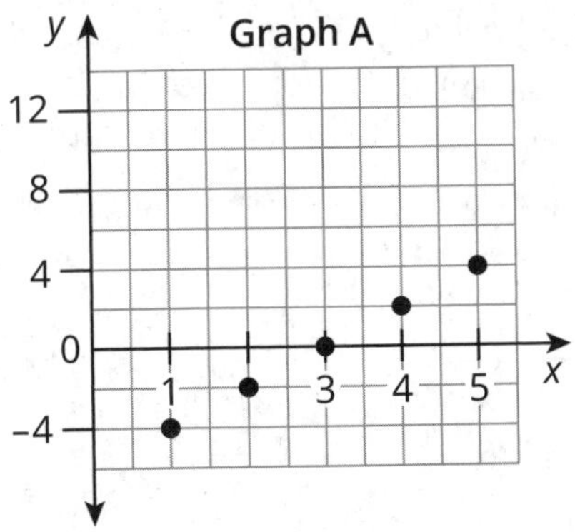

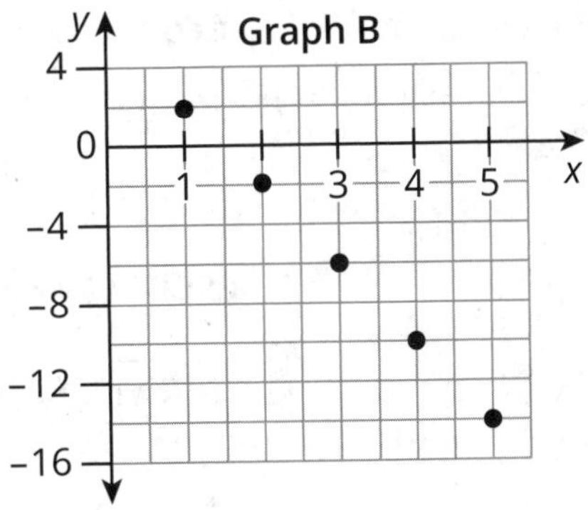

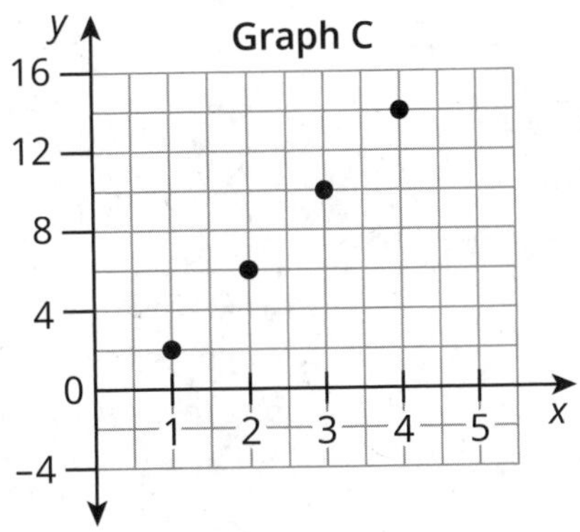

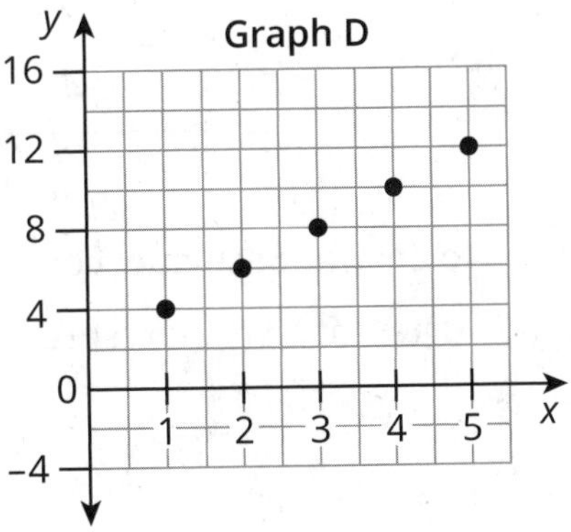

2 Consider the set of graphs, identify the function family represented. Based on these formulas and graphs, do you think that all arithmetic sequences belong to this function family? **Explain your conjecture.**

TAKE NOTE...
A **conjecture** is a mathematical statement that appears to be true, but has not been formally proven.

Let's take a closer look at the relationship between arithmetic sequences and the family of linear functions. You know a lot about each relationship. Consider Graph C and the corresponding explicit formula and table of values that represents Graph C.

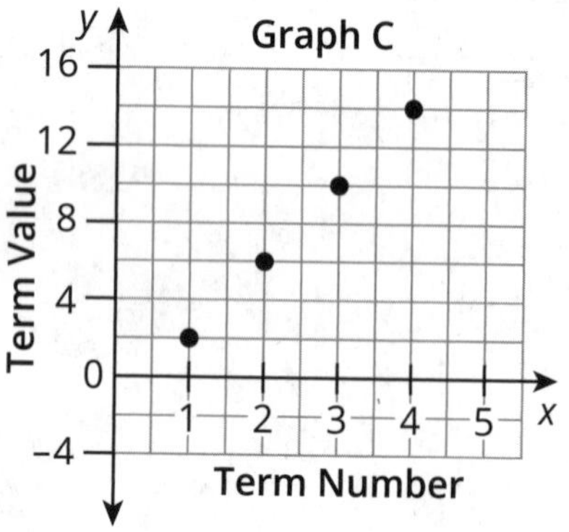

Explicit Formula: $a_n = 2 + 4(n - 1)$

Term Number n	Term Value a_n	
1	a_1	2
2	a_2	6
3	a_3	10
4	a_4	14

3 Use the representations to answer each question.

(a) Identify the common difference in each representation.

REMEMBER...
An arithmetic sequence is a sequence of numbers in which the differences between any two consecutive terms is constant. The explicit formula is of the form $a_n = a_1 + d(n - 1)$.

(b) Draw a line to model the linear relationship seen in the graph. Then write the equation in slope-intercept form to represent your line. **Describe your strategy.**

(c) How does the domain of the arithmetic sequence compare to the domain of the graph of the linear model?

You just wrote an equation to represent the graph of an arithmetic sequence. You can rewrite the explicit form of an arithmetic sequence to make connections to forms of linear equations.

WORKED EXAMPLE

You can derive the slope-intercept and point-slope forms from the explicit form of an arithmetic sequence.

First, rewrite the explicit form, and then interpret the structure.

Connection to Slope-Intercept Form

$a_n = a_1 + d(n - 1)$

$a_n = a_1 + dn - d$

$a_n = dn + a_1 - d$

$a_n = dn + (a_1 - d)$

$y = mx + b$

Connection to Point-Slope Form

$a_n = a_1 + d(n - 1)$

$a_n - a_1 = d(n - 1)$

$y - y_1 = m(x - x_1)$

THINK ABOUT...

All sequences and non-vertical lines are functions. So, n and x are input values, and a_n and y are output values.

4 Compare the common difference with the slope. **What do you notice?**

5 Explain why Hank's reasoning is not correct.

Hank

The y-intercept of a linear function is the same as the first term of an arithmetic sequence.

6 Complete the table to summarize the connections between arithmetic sequences and linear equations.

Arithmetic Sequence	Linear Equation		
$a_n = a_1 + d(n - 1)$	$y = mx + b$	$y - y_1 = m(x - x_1)$	**Mathematical Meaning**
a_n			
d			
n			
$a_1 - d$			

Consider the remaining graphs and explicit formulas from the beginning of the activity.

7 Write the equation of each line. Then verify that the slope is the same between any two points.

(a)

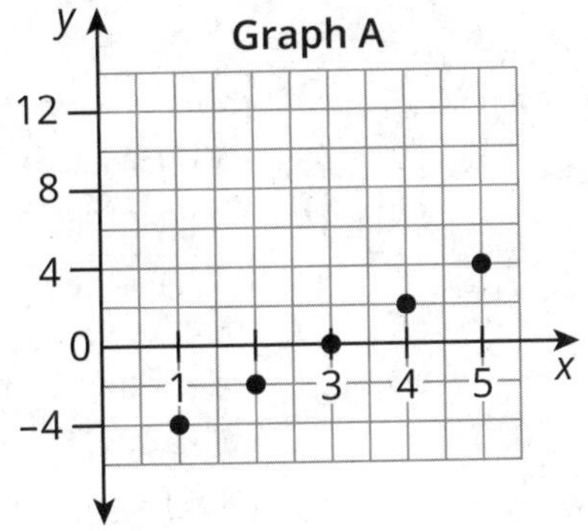

$a_n = -4 + 2(n - 1)$

(b)

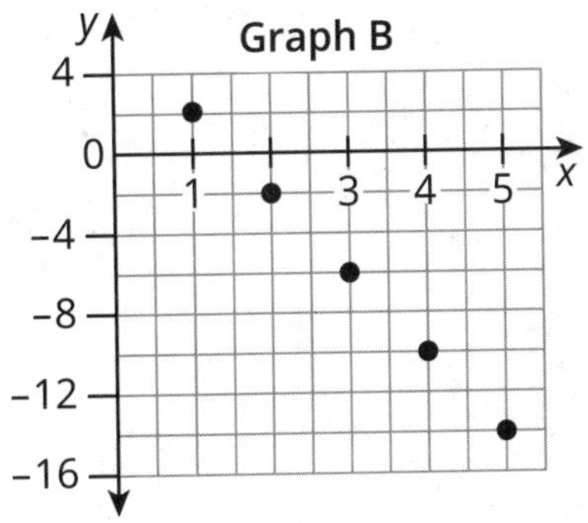

$a_n = 2 - 4(n - 1)$

(c)

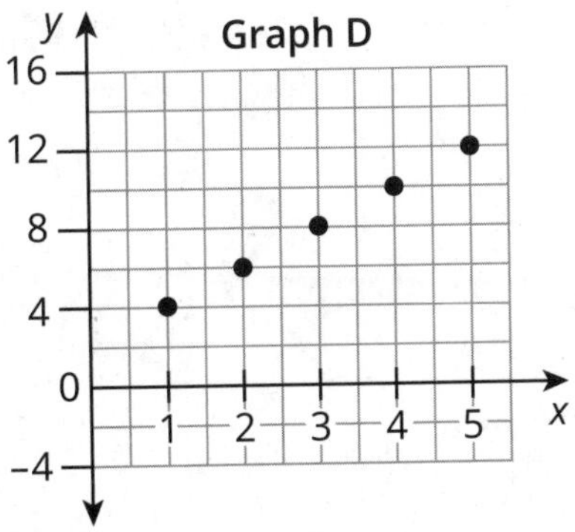

$a_n = 4 + 2(n - 1)$

Verifying that Slope Is Constant

You know that the slope of a line is constant between any two points on the line, not just consecutive points.

HABITS OF MIND
- Reason abstractly and quantitatively.
- Construct viable arguments and critique the reasoning of others.

> Consider the graph represented by the linear function $y = mx + b$ with slope m.

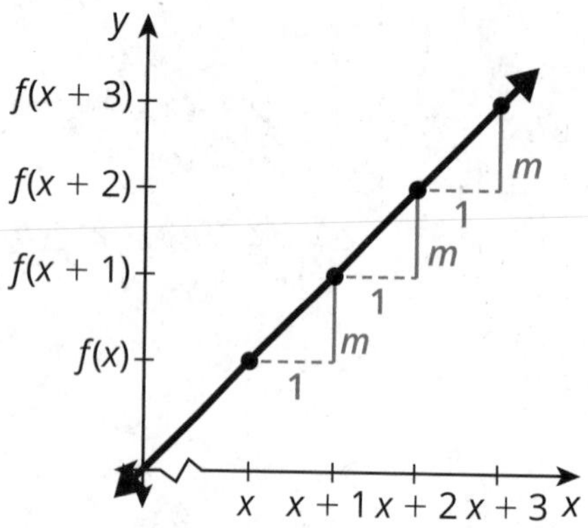

REMEMBER...
The expression $y = f(x)$ means that the value of y depends on the value of x. That is, for different values of x, there is a function f which determines the value of y.

1 Complete the table.

Input	Output	
x	$f(x)$	$m(x) + b$
$x + 1$	$f(x + 1)$	$m(x + 1) + b$
$x + 2$		
$x + 3$		

2 Select two non-consecutive points from the table and verify that the slope between those two points is m.

REMEMBER...
The slope formula is $m = \frac{y_2 - y_1}{x_2 - x_1}$.

Another name for the slope of a linear function is **average rate of change**. The formula for the average rate of change is $\frac{f(t) - f(s)}{t - s}$. This represents the change in the output as the input changes from s to t.

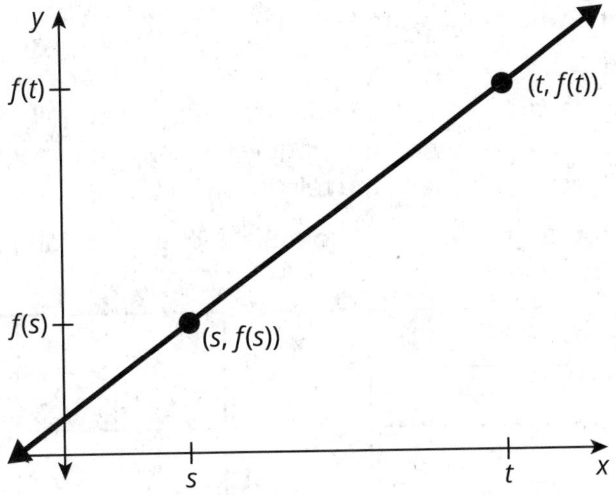

3 Show that the slope formula and the average rate of change formula represent the same ratio.

Analyzing Tables of Values

HABITS OF MIND
- Look for and make use of structure.
- Look for and express regularity in repeated reasoning.

When you see a graph, it is apparent that it represents a linear function. However, the structure of a table requires other strategies to determine whether it represents a linear function.

One strategy is to examine *first differences*. **First differences** are the values determined by subtracting consecutive output values when the input values have an interval of 1. If the first differences of a table of values are constant, the relationship is linear.

> Consider the tables that represent the explicit formula and function form of Graph C from the first activity.

n	$a_n = 2 + 4(n - 1)$
1	2
2	6
3	10
4	14

x	$y = 4x - 2$
0	−2
1	2
2	6
3	10

1 Determine the first differences in each table to verify they both represent a linear relationship.

2 Parks and Eva Cate agree that the table shown represents a linear relationship because there is a constant difference between consecutive points. Parks claims the slope is 5 and Eva Cate claims the slope is −5. Who's correct? **Explain your reasoning.**

x	y
1	22
2	17
3	12
4	7

22 − 17 = 5

17 − 12 = 5

12 − 7 = 5

THINK ABOUT...
What does slope describe?

3 Use first differences to determine whether each table represents a linear function. If so, write the equation for the relationship.

ⓐ

x	y
5	12
6	15
7	21
8	30

ⓑ

x	y
−2	12
−1	15
7	21
8	30

ⓒ

x	y
10	1
11	4
12	9
13	16

ⓓ

x	y
1	3
2	3
3	3
4	3

THINK ABOUT...

When the values of the dependent variable of a function remain constant over the entire domain, then the function is a constant function.

Making It Plain and Clear

> Create a table of values to represent a linear function. Then create a graph and verify that the slope is the same between any two points on the line.

x	y

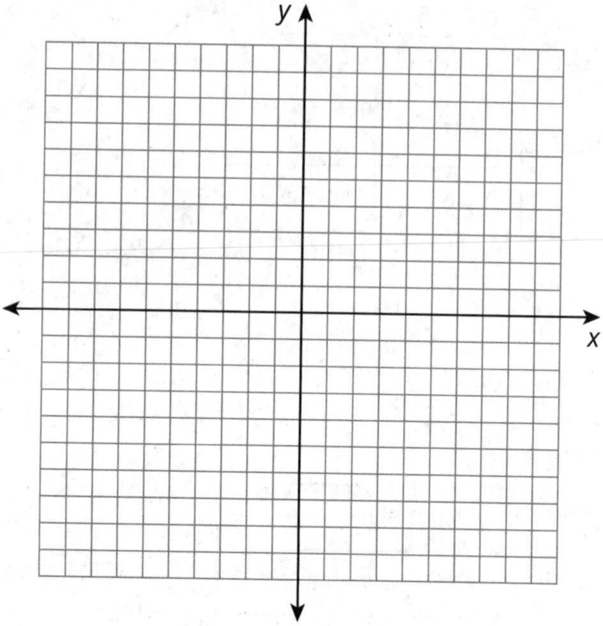

LESSON 1 ASSIGNMENT

> Use a separate piece of paper for your Journal entry.

JOURNAL

Describe the relationship between the terms *constant difference*, *slope*, and *average rate of change*.

REMEMBER

All arithmetic sequences are linear functions.

The average rate of change of any linear relationship is constant between any two points on that line.

PRACTICE

1 Rakesha claims that $y = 5x - 7$ is the linear function for the sequence that is represented by the explicit formula $a_n = -2 + 5(n - 1)$. James doesn't understand how this can be the case.

(a) Help James by rewriting the explicit formula of the given sequence in the form $y = mx + b$. Provide a rationale for each step.

(b) Graph the function. Label the first 5 values of the sequence on the graph.

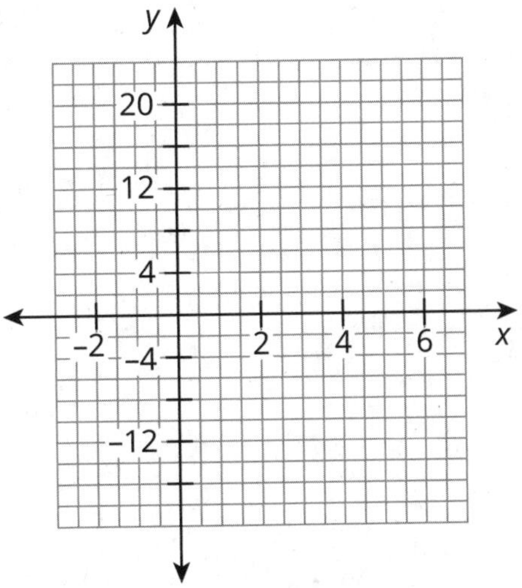

Go to LiveHint.com for help on the PRACTICE questions.

2 Determine whether each table of values represents a linear function. For those that represent linear functions, write the function. For those that do not, explain why not.

ⓐ

x	*y*
5	12
6	15
7	21
8	30

ⓑ

x	*y*
−2	8
−1	5
0	2
1	−1

ⓒ

x	*y*
1	11
2	16
3	21
4	26

STRETCH Optional

Craig left his house at noon and drove 50 miles per hour until 3 P.M. Then he drove the next 5 hours at 70 miles per hour.

1 Graph Craig's driving trip and calculate the average rate of change for the entire trip.

LESSON 2

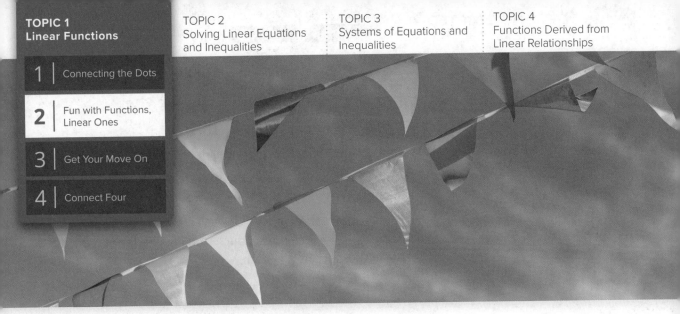

Fun with Functions, Linear Ones

Making Sense of Different Representations of a Linear Function

Learning Goals

- Determine whether a scenario, equation, table, or graph represents a linear relationship.
- Calculate the average rate of change from a table.
- Write functions given a table of values.
- Interpret expressions that represent different quantities in terms of a context and a graph.
- Compare different equation representations of linear functions.

KEY TERMS

polynomial

degree

leading coefficient

zero of a function

REVIEW (1–2 minutes)

> Determine the slope of the line between each pair of points.

1. (0, 10) and (3, 12)
2. (−1, 4.5) and (1, −4.5)
3. (−1, 0) and (0, 12)

You know how to determine whether a relationship represents a linear function, and you know how to write an equation for the function.

How can you use the structure of the equation to identify characteristics of the function?

Well, Are Ya or Aren't Ya?

You have represented linear functions in various ways.

1 Determine whether each representation models a linear or nonlinear function.

Scenario A

A tree grows 3.5 inches each year.

Scenario B

The strength of a medication decreases by 50% each hour it is in the patient's system.

Scenario C

The area of a square depends on its side length.

Equation A

$y = 14 - 9x$

Equation B

$y = 2^x + 1$

Equation C

$y = \frac{1}{4}(x + 7) - 1$

Table A

x	y
1	3
1	4
1	5

Table B

x	y
3	1
4	1
5	1

Table C

x	y
−9	45
−8	30
−7	15

Graph A

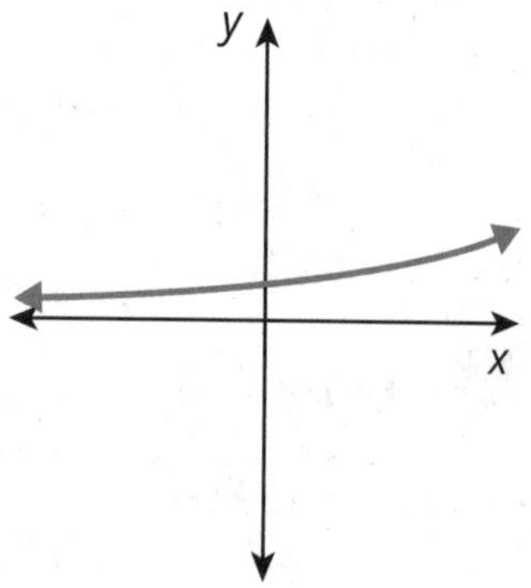

Graph B

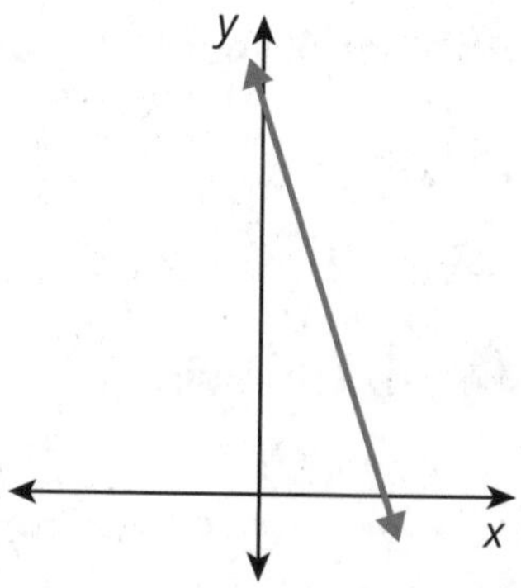

Graph C

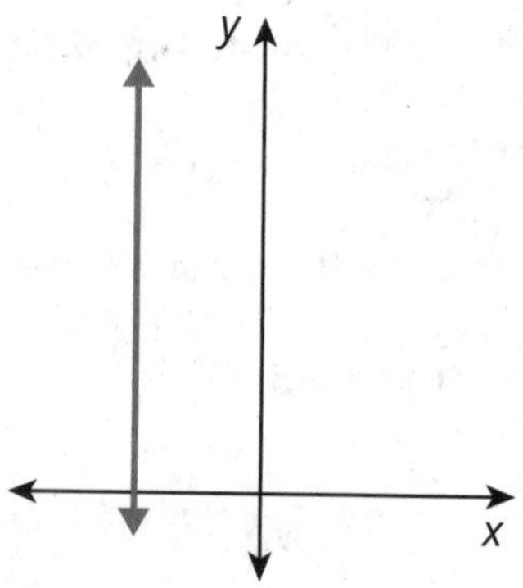

MATHia CONNECTION

- Multiple Representations of Linear Equations

Interpreting Linear Functions

HABITS OF MIND

- Look for and make use of structure.
- Look for and express regularity in repeated reasoning.

Each table of values in the previous activity had consecutive input values. Tables in that format allow you to use differences to determine whether the representation is linear.

Often, input values are in intervals other than 1, and sometimes the input values are in random order. To determine whether these tables represent linear functions, you need to make sure the slope, or average rate of change, is constant between all given points.

1 Determine whether each table represents a linear function. If so, write the function.

ⓐ

x	*y*
−2	5.5
1	4.75
4	4
7	3.25

ⓑ

x	*y*
0	5
2	13
4	21
8	29

ASK YOURSELF...

Is there a pattern in the input values?

> Analyze each situation represented as a table of values.

Dillan sells pretzels at festivals on weekends and records his past sales.

Number of Pretzels Sold	Amount of Money Earned (dollars)
15	37.5
42	105
58	145
29	72.5

2 What does this table tell you about his sales?

3 How much money would Dillan earn if he sold 75 pretzels?

Delany and her friends recently went to the community fair. They had to pay an entrance fee and then purchase 1 ticket for each ride. Dakota is going to the fair tomorrow and wants to know the cost of each ride ticket. Delany and her friends help Dakota by writing down how much money they spent and the number of tickets they purchased.

4 What does this table tell you about the cost to go to the fair and ride the rides?

5 If Dakota has $20 to spend, how many ride tickets can she buy?

Number of Ride Tickets	Amount of Money Spent (dollars)
2	7.5
4	9
6	10.5
11	14.25

The local pet store has a fish tank on display at the community fair. Darren is responsible for draining the tank at the end of the fair. The pet store manager provides him with this information from when they drained the same tank at the end of the fair last year.

6 How many gallons of water were in the fish tank when they began to drain it?

7 How long did it take to empty the tank?

Time (hours)	Amount of Water Remaining (gallons)
$\frac{1}{4}$	169
$\frac{1}{2}$	163
$\frac{3}{4}$	157
1	151

Interpreting Graphs of Linear Functions

HABITS OF MIND
- Model with mathematics.
- Use appropriate tools strategically.

You have interpreted linear functions in the form of tables. Now let's interpret the graphs of linear functions.

Marilynn sells silk screened T-shirts for her mom at local festivals. After each festival, she returns whatever money she earns to her mom.

> Consider the graph representing Marilynn's potential earnings based on the number of T-shirts she sells.

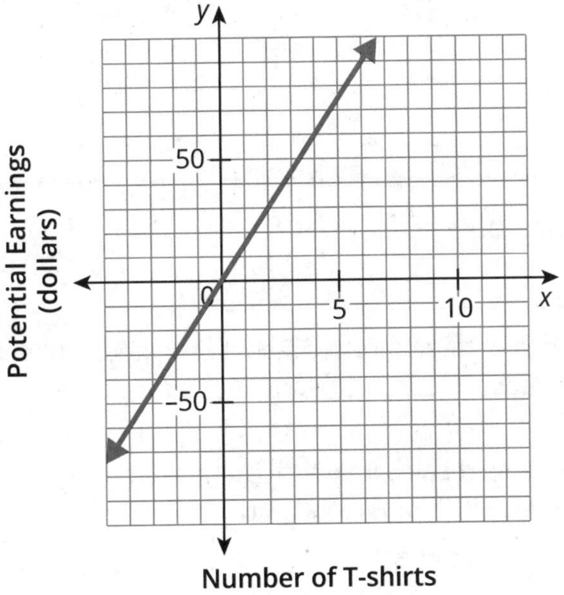

1 Analyze and interpret the graph. List as many facts as you can about the scenario based on what you see in the graph. **Describe how the facts relate to the scenario**.

ASK YOURSELF...
What is the meaning of the slope, x- and y-intercepts, domain, and range in terms of this situation?

2 Interpret the meaning of the origin.

3 Write a function, $E(t)$, to model Marilynn's potential earnings given the number of T-shirts she sells.

4 What does (t, $E(t)$) represent in terms of the function and the graph?

5 Evaluate each and interpret the meaning in terms of the equation, the graph, and the scenario.

(a) $E(2)$

(b) $E(5)$

(c) $E(2.75)$

Marilynn has a goal to earn $100 at the festival.

> Let's consider how to determine the number of T-shirts she needs to sell to meet her goal.

WORKED EXAMPLE

To determine the number of T-shirt sales it takes to earn $100 using the function, $E(t) = 15t$, substitute 100 for $E(t)$ and solve.

$$E(t) = 15t$$

$$100 = 15t$$

$$\frac{100}{15} = t$$

$$6.67 = t$$

6 Consider the worked example.

(a) Interpret the meaning of $t = 6.67$.

(b) Why can you substitute 100 for $E(t)$?

You can also use the graph to determine the number of T-shirts Marilynn needs to sell to earn $100.

WORKED EXAMPLE

To determine the number of T-shirt sales it takes to earn $100 using your graph, you need to determine the intersection of the two lines represented by the equation $100 = 15t$.

First, graph the function defined by each side of the equation, and then determine the intersection point of the two graphs.

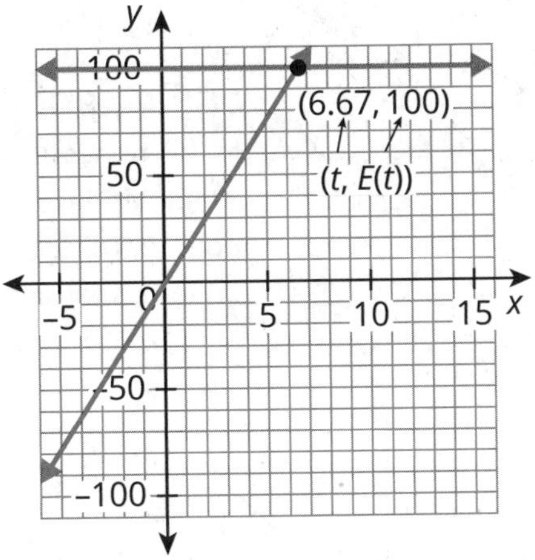

$E(t) = 15t$

$100 = 15t$

$y = 100$ $\quad$ $y = 15x$

Solution: (6.67, 100)

In terms of the graph, Marilynn needs to sell 6.67 T-shirts to earn $100. In terms of the context, she needs to sell 7 T-shirts.

REMEMBER...

The graph of an equation plotted on the coordinate plane represents the set of all its solutions.

TOPIC 1

7 Consider the equation and graphical representations. What are the limitations of using each to answer questions about the number of T-shirts sold or the amount of money earned?

(a) Equation

(b) Graph

Interpreting Changes to the Graph of a Linear Function

HABITS OF MIND
- Look for and make use of structure.
- Look for and express regularity in repeated reasoning.

How do the different representations of a linear function change when its graph changes?

For the next festival, Marilynn's mom suggests that she still sells each T-shirt for $15, but should give away 3 T-shirts in a raffle.

> Consider the graph of this new relationship, $G(t)$.

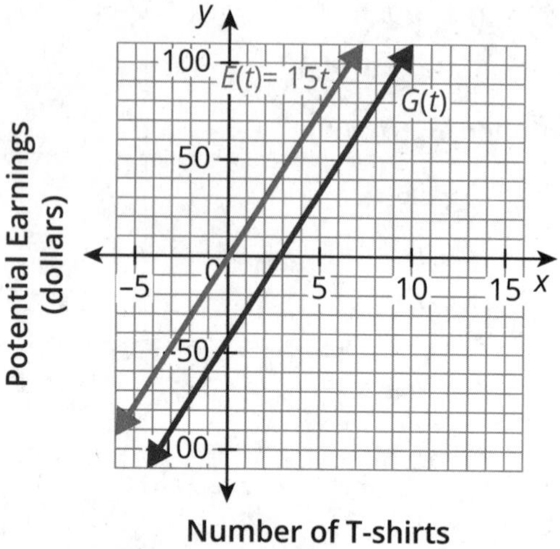

THINK ABOUT...
In this relationship, $y = E(t)$ and $y = G(t)$ both represent potential earnings.

1. Compare the two graphs. **What do you notice?**

(a) How do the graphs show the selling price per T-shirt remains the same?

(b) Determine and interpret the meaning of $y = G(0)$ in terms of the graph and this scenario. Label the point on the graph.

(c) Determine and interpret the meaning of $G(t) = 0$ in terms of the graph and this scenario. Label the point on the graph.

Michelle and Myra each wrote an equation to describe the effect of giving away three T-shirts.

Michelle

Marilynn is giving away 3 T-shirts, so she has 3 fewer shirts to sell.

$G(t) = 15(t - 3)$

Myra

The cost of giving away three shirts is $45.

$G(t) = 15t - 45$

2 Verify the two equation representations are equivalent.

3 How many T-shirts will Marilynn need to sell to earn $100? **Use the graph and an equation.**

4 Consider the expressions in the first two rows that define the quantities of the function and then the parts of each equation written by Michelle and Myra to complete the table. First, determine the unit of measure for each expression. **Then describe the contextual meaning and the mathematical meaning of each part of the function.**

		What It Means	
Expression	**Unit**	**Contextual Meaning**	**Mathematical Meaning**
t			
$G(t)$			
15			
$(t - 3)$			
$15t$			
-45			

The linear functions that Michelle and Myra each wrote are equivalent; however, they are in different forms. The linear function $G(t) = 15(t - 3)$ is in factored form and $G(t) = 15t - 45$ is in general form.

You can refer to a linear function as a *polynomial* function. A **polynomial** is a mathematical expression involving the sum of powers in one or more variables multiplied by coefficients.

- The **degree** of a polynomial is the greatest variable exponent in the expression.
- The **leading coefficient** of a polynomial is the numeric coefficient of the term with the greatest power.

DID YOU KNOW?
Polynomial comes from *poly-* meaning "many" and *-nomial* meaning "term," so it means "many terms."

WORKED EXAMPLE

A few examples of polynomial functions.

Polynomial Functions		Degree
Constant	$P(x) = 7$	0
Linear	$P(x) = 2x - 5$	1
Quadratic	$P(x) = 3x^2 - 2x + 4$	2
Cubic	$P(x) = 4x^3 - 2$	3

TAKE NOTE...
When you graph a polynomial, the degree tells you the maximum number of times the graph can cross the *x*-axis

The structure of each linear function tells you important information about the graph. Let's consider the general form of a linear function, $f(x) = ax + b$, where a and b are real numbers and $a \neq 0$.

You know the form $y = mx + b$ as slope-intercept form, where m represents the slope and b represents the y-intercept. Notice that the general form has the same structure. The general form shows that a linear equation is a polynomial of degree 1.

You will learn more about polynomials as you progress through high school mathematics.

THINK ABOUT...
The variables used to represent any real number in the general linear form are irrelevant. Think about the position of the number as either the leading coefficient or a constant and the potential effect on the function.

5 Consider the general form of the linear function $G(t)$.

(a) Identify the a-value (slope) on the graph.

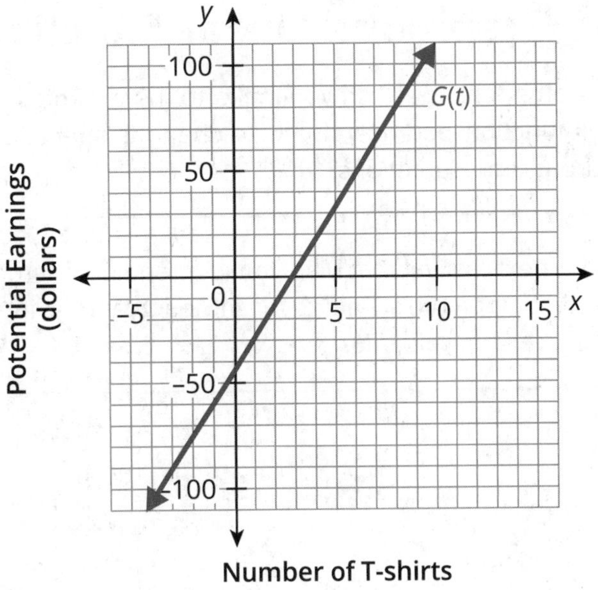

(b) Label the b-value (y-intercept) on the graph.

Next, consider the factored form of a linear function, $f(x) = a(x - c)$, where a and c are real numbers and $a \neq 0$. When a polynomial is in factored form, the value of x that makes the factor $(x - c)$ equal to zero is the x-intercept. This value is called the zero of the function. A **zero of a function** is a real number that makes the value of the function equal to zero, or $f(x) = 0$.

You can set $(x - c)$ equal to zero and determine the point where the graph crosses the x-axis.

6 Consider the factored form of the linear function $G(t)$.

(a) Identify the a-value (slope) on the graph.

(b) Label the c-value (x-intercept) on the graph.

7 What is the zero of $G(t)$? **Explain your reasoning.**

Interpreting More Changes to the Graph of a Linear Function

HABITS OF MIND
- Look for and make use of structure.
- Look for and express regularity in repeated reasoning.

What other changes can you make to the graph of a linear function, and how do those changes affect its different representations?

The next festival that Marilynn is attending charges a $35 fee to rent a booth. She is still selling her mom's T-shirts for $15 each and giving 3 away in a raffle. The graph shows this new relationship, *F*(*t*).

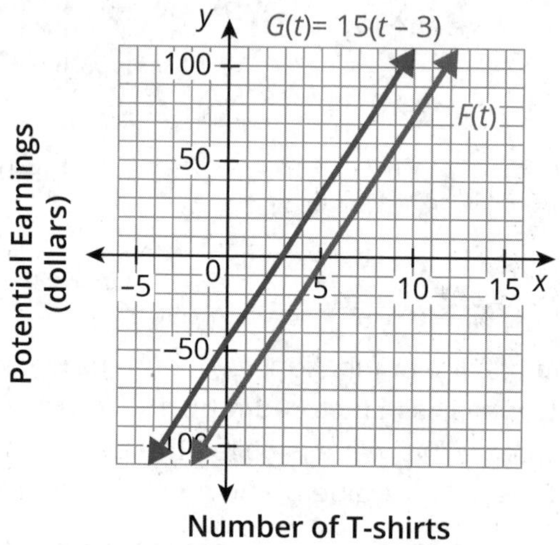

1 Consider the relationship between the graphs of *G*(*t*) and *F*(*t*).

(a) How do the graphs show that the selling price per T-shirt remains the same?

(b) How did the new booth fee of $35 change the graph?

(c) How many T-shirts will Marilynn need to sell before she will have any money to return to her mom? **Explain your reasoning**.

(d) How many T-shirts will Marilynn need to sell to earn $100?

2 Consider the relationship between the equations of $G(t)$ and $F(t)$.

(a) Write the function $F(t)$ in terms of $G(t)$.

(b) Rewrite $F(t)$ in general form. Then describe how the a- and b-values are represented on the graph.

THINK ABOUT...

The general form of a linear function is $f(x) = ax + b$.

The factored form of a linear function is $f(x) = a(x - c)$.

The values a, b, and c are real numbers and $a \neq 0$.

(c) Rewrite $F(t)$ in factored form. Use a fraction to represent the c-value. **Then describe how the a- and c-values are represented on the graph.**

Reading Between the Lines

> Complete each "I can" sentence using *always*, *sometimes*, or *never*.

1 Suppose you are given a dependent value and need to calculate an independent value of a linear function.

ⓐ I can ______________________________ use a table to determine an *approximate* value.

ⓑ I can ______________________________ use a table to calculate an *exact* value.

ⓒ I can ______________________________ use a graph to determine an *approximate* value.

ⓓ I can ______________________________ use a graph to calculate an *exact* value.

ⓔ I can ______________________________ use an equation to determine an *approximate* value.

ⓕ I can ______________________________ use an equation to calculate an *exact* value.

2 Write the function that models each table of values. Then evaluate the function for each independent and dependent value.

ⓐ

x	1	2	3	4	5
$f(x)$	−20	5	30	55	80

$f(x) =$

$f(12) =$

$f(x) = -145$

(b)

x	1	3	5	7	9
g(x)	18	6	−6	−18	−30

$g(x) =$

$g(-9) =$

$g(x) = -54$

3 Complete the graphic organizer located on page 218 for the linear function $f(x) = 2x - 8$.

(a) Write $f(x)$ in general form. **Describe the information given in this form.**

(b) Write $f(x)$ in factored form. **Describe the information given in this form.**

(c) Graph $f(x)$. **Describe how you know this graph can cross the *x*-axis only one time.**

(d) Create a table of values for $f(x)$.

Graphic Organizer

$f(x) = 2x - 8$

General Form

$f(x) = ax + b$, where a and b are real numbers and $a \neq 0$

Factored Form

$f(x) = a(x - c)$, where a and c are real numbers and $a \neq 0$

Graph

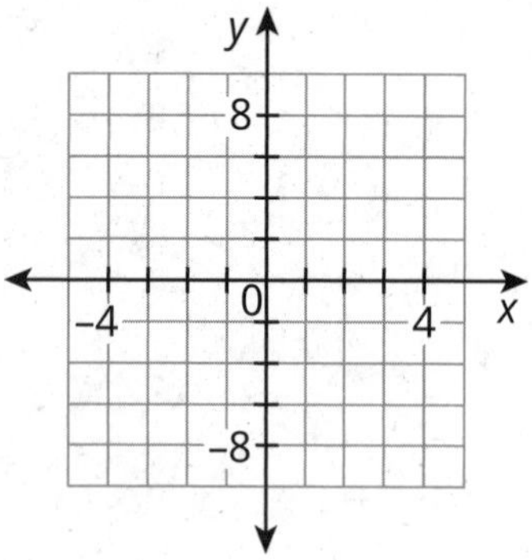

Table

x	y

LESSON 2 ASSIGNMENT

> Use a separate piece of paper for your Journal entry.

JOURNAL

Describe a zero of a function in your own words.

REMEMBER

The general form of a linear function is $f(x) = ax + b$, where a and b are real numbers and $a \neq 0$. In this form, the a-value is the leading coefficient which describes the steepness and direction of the line. The b-value describes the y-intercept.

The factored form of a linear function is $f(x) = a(x - c)$, where a and c are real numbers and $a \neq 0$. In this form, the a-value is the slope and the value of x that makes the factor $(x - c)$ equal to zero is the x-intercept.

PRACTICE

1 Determine whether the table of values represents a linear function. If so, write the function.

(a)

x	y
−2	$5\frac{2}{3}$
0	5
2	$4\frac{1}{3}$
4	$3\frac{2}{3}$

(b)

x	y
−5	−27
0	−2
5	20
10	48

2 For each scenario, write a linear function in factored form and in general form. Then sketch a graph and label the x- and y-intercepts. Finally, answer each question.

(a) Carlos prints and sells T-shirts for $14.99 each. Each month 5 T-shirts are misprinted and cannot be sold. What are his potential earnings when he prints 22 T-shirts? How many T-shirts does he need to sell to earn $200?

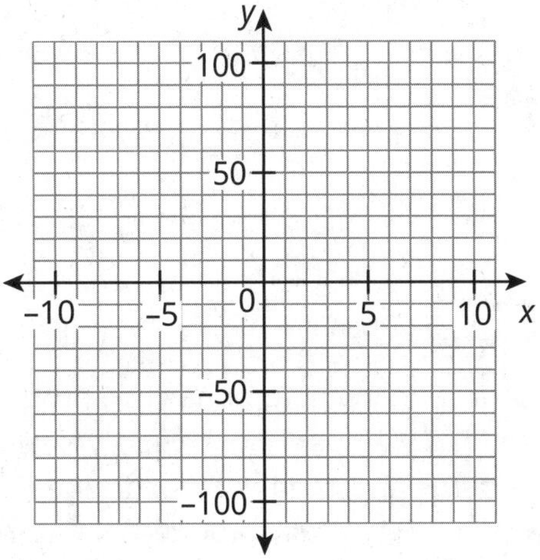

Go to LiveHint.com for help on the PRACTICE questions.

ⓑ Mei paints and sells ceramic vases for $35 each. Each month she typically breaks 3 vases in the kiln. What are her potential earnings when she sells 17 ceramic vases? How many ceramic vases does she need to sell to earn $600?

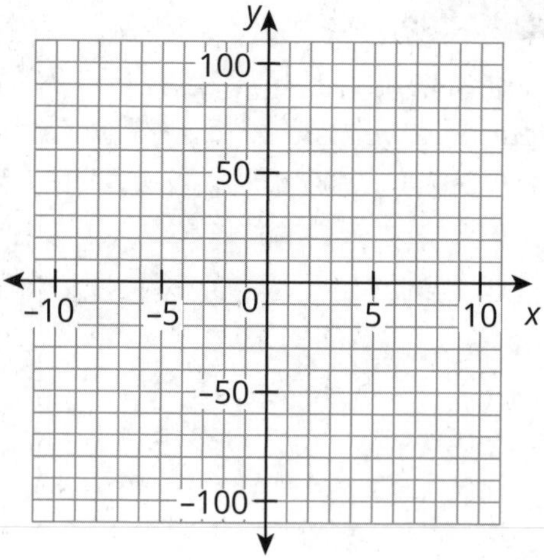

ⓒ Emilio builds and sells homemade wooden toys for $12 each. The festival he is attending charges $50 to set up his booth. How much money does he earn when sells 35 wooden toys? How many wooden toys does he need to sell to earn $250?

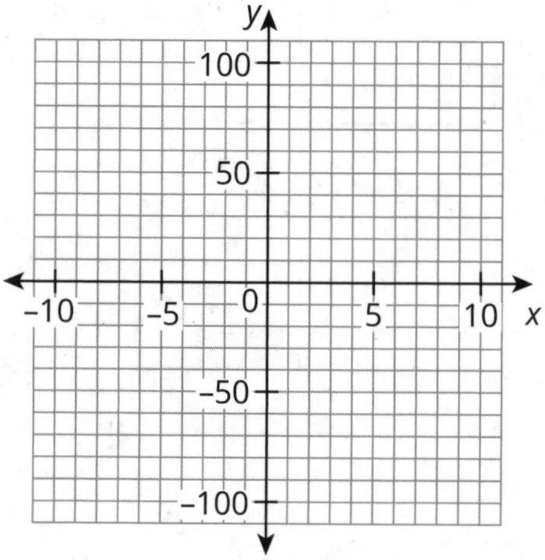

STRETCH Optional

> A pretzel manufacturer has two production lines. Line A produces a variety of pretzel that is sold for $2.40 per bag. Line A typically produces 3 bags per day that do not meet company standards and cannot be sold. Line B produces a variety of pretzel that is sold for $3.60 per bag. Line B typically produces 4 bags per day that do not meet company standards and cannot be sold. Line A produces 3 times as many bags as Line B each day.

1. Write a linear function that represents the total number of bags the lines can produce combined.

LESSON 3

Get Your Move On

Transforming Linear Functions

KEY TERM

basic function

Learning Goals

- Determine the effects on the graph of a linear function when $f(x)$ is replaced by $f(x) + D$ or $A \cdot f(x)$.
- Graph linear function transformations expressed symbolically and show intercepts.
- Identify key characteristics of the graphs of linear functions, such as slope and y-intercept, in terms of quantities from a verbal description.

REVIEW (1–2 minutes)

> Given the function $h(x) = -2x - 5$, evaluate each expression.

1. $h(3)$

2. $2 \cdot h(-2)$

3. $-1 \cdot h(1) + 5$

4. $5 \cdot h(0) + 5$

You have learned about linear functions and their characteristics, including slope and y-intercept.

What effects do different transformations have on the characteristics of linear functions?

Returning to Transformation Station

> Consider $\overline{AB}$ with coordinates A (−5, −5) and B (5, 5).

Follow your teacher's instructions to copy this line segment on a coordinate plane on the floor of your classroom, with different students standing at different points of the line segment.

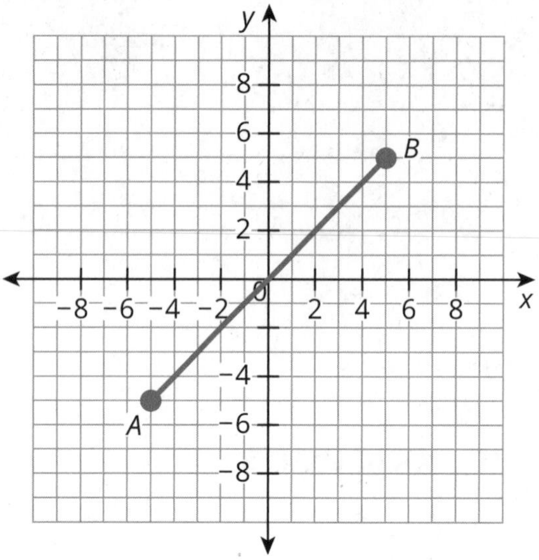

1 Move on the coordinate plane to translate the entire line segment up 4 units and then down 4 units. **Describe how the student "points" move.**

2 How do the translations affect the coordinates of the figure?

Original Point	4 units up	4 units down
(x, y)		

3 Draw $\overline{CD}$ on the coordinate plane so that it is a vertical translation of $\overline{AB}$ up 4 units. Compare the two line segments. **Describe the relationship between them.**

4 Move back to where you started. Then, multiply all the y-coordinates by 2 and then by −2. **Describe how the student "points" move.**

5 Draw $\overline{EF}$ on the coordinate plane by multiplying all the y-coordinates of $\overline{AB}$ by 2. Compare the two line segments. **Describe the relationship between them.**

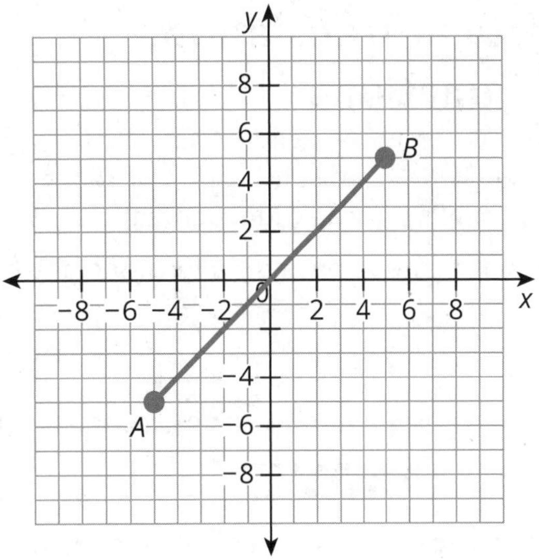

6 Draw $\overline{GH}$ on the coordinate plane by multiplying all the y-coordinates of $\overline{AB}$ by −2. Compare the two line segments. **Describe the relationship between them.**

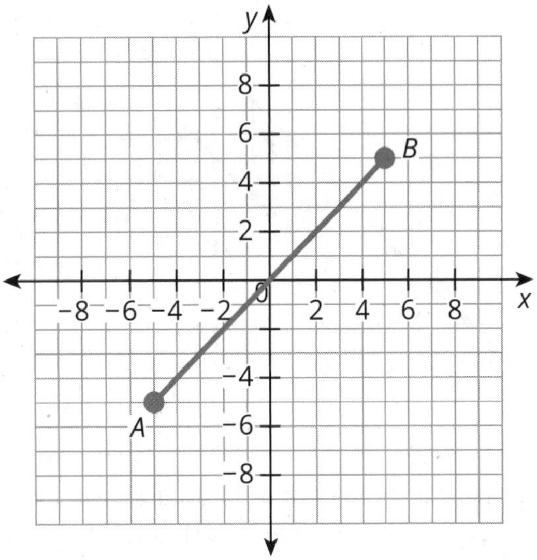

MATHia CONNECTION
- Exploring Graphs of Linear Functions
- Vertically Translating Linear Functions

Vertical Translations of Functions

HABITS OF MIND
- Look for and make use of structure.
- Look for and express regularity in repeated reasoning.

The function $f(x) = x$ is the *basic function* for the linear function family. A **basic function** is the simplest function of its type.

1 Identify the slope and y-intercept of the basic linear function.

Let's determine how translations impact the graph of the linear function $f(x) = x$.

WORKED EXAMPLE

You can translate the graph of $f(x)$ down 5 units by moving each point 5 units down. The transformed graph is $m(x)$.

To translate the point (−2, −2) on $f(x)$, subtract 5 units from the output value, or y-value. The input value, or x-value, remains unchanged. The coordinates of the translated point on $m(x)$ are (−2, −7). The coordinates of four additional points on $f(x)$ are translated for you.

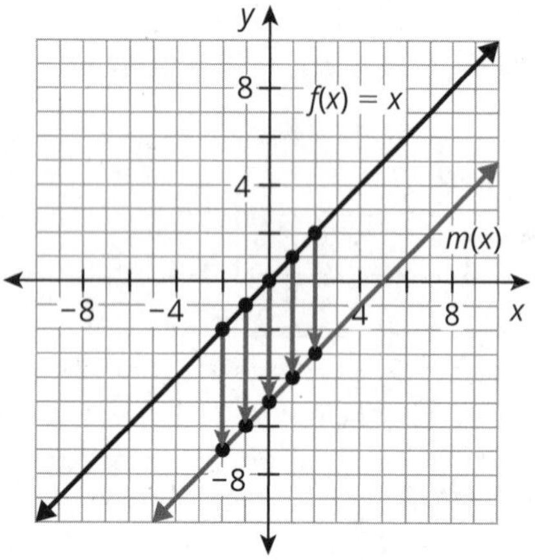

Original Graph	
x	***f*(x)**
−2	−2
−1	−1
0	0
1	1
2	2

Transformed Graph	
x	***m*(x)**
−2	−7
−1	−6
0	−5
1	−4
2	−3

2 Consider the translated function, $m(x)$. Identify the slope and y-intercept of the graph of the function. Then, write the equation for the function in general form.

3 Translate $f(x)$ again to create a new function, $p(x)$.

ⓐ Translate the graph of $f(x)$ up 5 units. Label your graph as $p(x)$. Complete the table of corresponding points on $p(x)$.

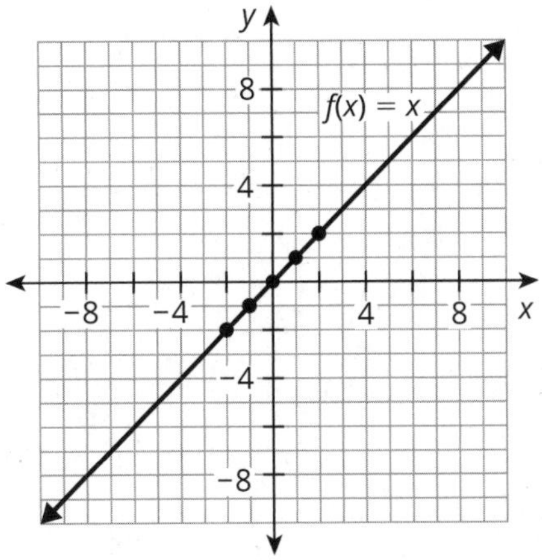

Original Graph		Transformed Graph	
x	$f(x)$	x	$p(x)$
−2	−2		
−1	−1		
0	0		
1	1		
2	2		

ⓑ Identify the slope and y-intercept of the graph of the function. Then, write the equation for the function in general form.

For the basic function $f(x) = x$, the transformed function $y = f(x) + D$ shows a vertical translation of the function. This translation affects the output values, or y-values, of the function.

- For $D > 0$, the resulting graph vertically shifts up.
- For $D < 0$, the resulting graph vertically shifts down.
- The distance the graph shifts is the absolute value of D, or $|D|$.

4 Compare the values of $f(2)$ and $p(2)$. **How did the transformation of the function affect the value of the function at $x = 2$?**

5 Consider the graph of $j(x) = 2x - 1$.

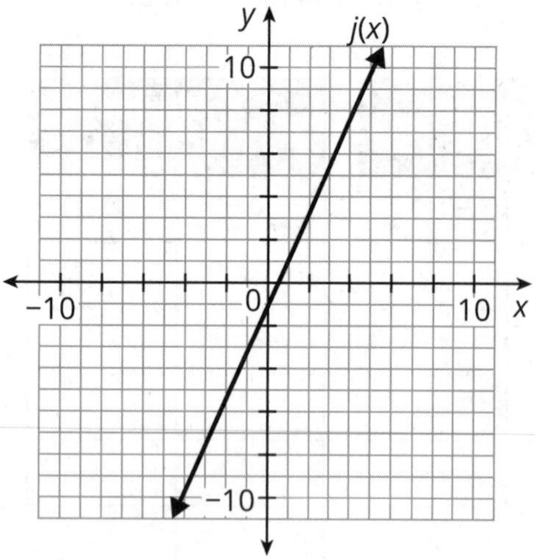

ASK YOURSELF...
What tools do you need to be precise?

ⓐ Translate the graph of $j(x)$ up 4 units. Label the graph as $q(x)$. Then, write an equation for $q(x)$ in terms of $j(x)$.

ⓑ Translate the graph of $j(x)$ down 4 units. Label the graph as $r(x)$. Then, write an equation for $r(x)$ in terms of $j(x)$.

ⓒ Rewrite $q(x)$ and $r(x)$ in terms of x.

ⓓ Compare the equations and graphs of $j(x)$, $q(x)$, and $r(x)$.
What do you notice?

THINK ABOUT...
Will the graphs of $j(x)$, $q(x)$ and $r(x)$ ever intersect?

Vertical Dilations of Functions

HABITS OF MIND

- Look for and make use of structure.
- Look for and express regularity in repeated reasoning.

In this activity, let's consider how vertical dilations impact the graph of the linear function $f(x) = x$.

1 Suppose the output values of $f(x)$ change by a factor of 4 to create $a(x)$.

(a) Sketch the graph of $a(x)$ and complete the table of values.

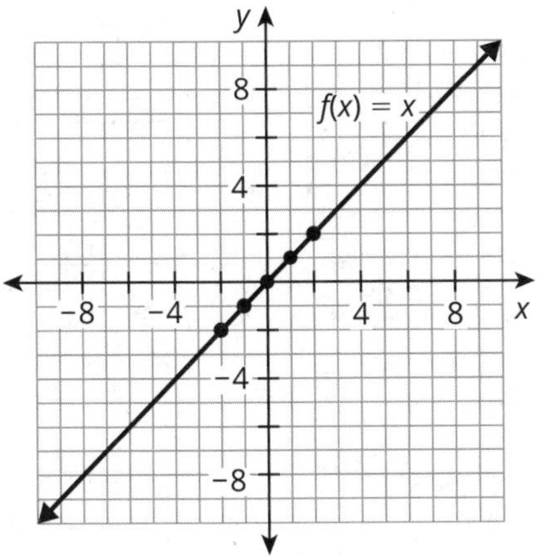

Original Graph		Transformed Graph	
x	***f*(x)**	**x**	***p*(x)**
−2	−2	−2	
−1	−1	−1	
0	0	0	
1	1	1	
2	2	2	

(b) Identify the slope and y-intercept of the function $a(x)$.
Then, write the equation for the function $a(x)$ in general form.

2 Suppose the output values of $f(x)$ are changed by a factor of $\frac{2}{3}$ to create $b(x)$.

ⓐ Sketch the graph of $b(x)$ and complete the table of values.

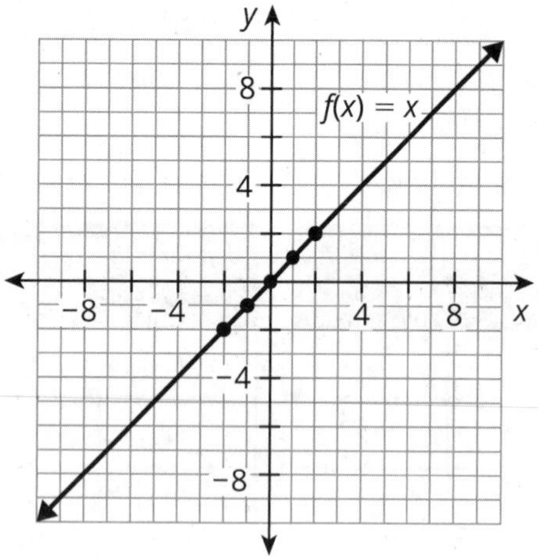

Original Graph	
x	**f(x)**
−2	−2
−1	−1
0	0
1	1
2	2

Transformed Graph	
x	**b(x)**
−2	
−1	
0	
1	
2	

ⓑ Identify the slope and y-intercept of the function $b(x)$. Then, write the equation for the function $b(x)$ in general form.

3 Suppose the output values of $f(x)$ are changed by a factor of -4 to create $c(x)$.

(a) Sketch the graph of $c(x)$ and complete the table of values.

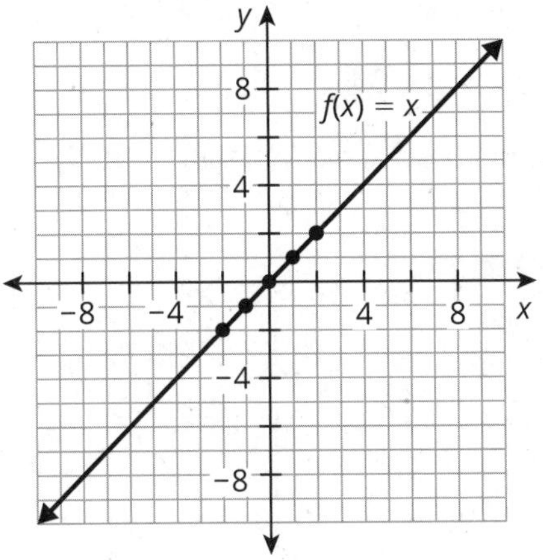

Original Graph		Transformed Graph	
x	***f*(x)**	**x**	**c(x)**
−2	−2		
−1	−1		
0	0		
1	1		
2	2		

(b) Identify the slope and *y*-intercept of the function $c(x)$. Then, write the equation for the function $c(x)$ in general form.

For the basic function $f(x) = x$, the transformed function $y = A \cdot f(x)$ shows a vertical dilation of the function. This dilation affects the output values, or *y*-values, of the function.

- For $|A| > 1$, the resulting graph vertically stretches by a factor of A units.
- For $0 < |A| < 1$, the resulting graph vertically compresses by a factor of A units.
- For $A < 0$, the resulting graph is vertically stretched or compressed and is reflected across the *x*-axis.

4 Compare the values $f(-1)$ and $c(-1)$. **How did the transformation of the function affect the value of the function at $x = -1$?**

Vertical Dilations and Vertical Translations of Functions

HABITS OF MIND
- Look for and make use of structure.
- Look for and express regularity in repeated reasoning.

Let's consider more transformations of the basic function $f(x) = x$.

1 Describe the transformations performed on $f(x)$ to produce $g(x)$. Then, graph $g(x)$. Write the function equation in general form.

ⓐ $g(x) = 2 \cdot f(x) + 7$

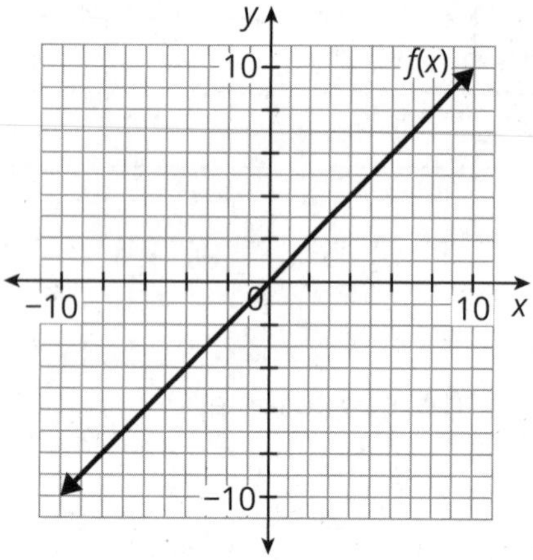

ⓑ $g(x) = 3 \cdot f(x) - 1$

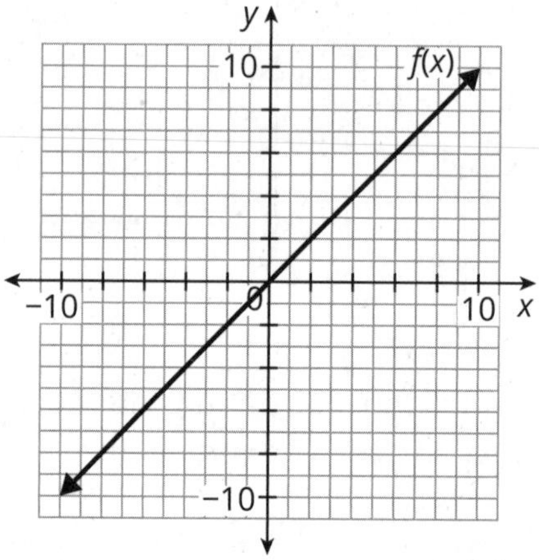

ⓒ $g(x) = \frac{1}{3} \cdot f(x) + 2$

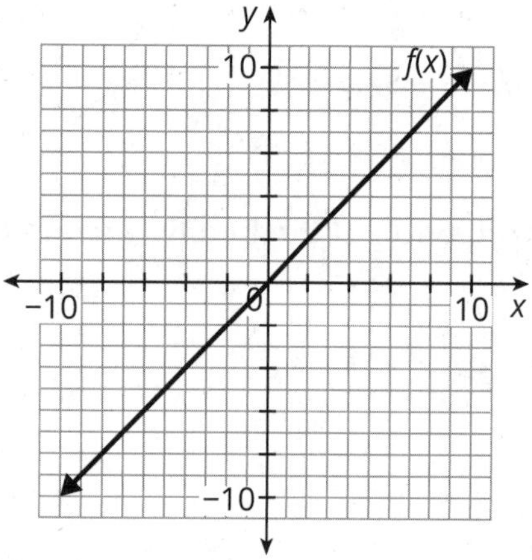

ⓓ $g(x) = \frac{1}{2} \cdot f(x) - 3$

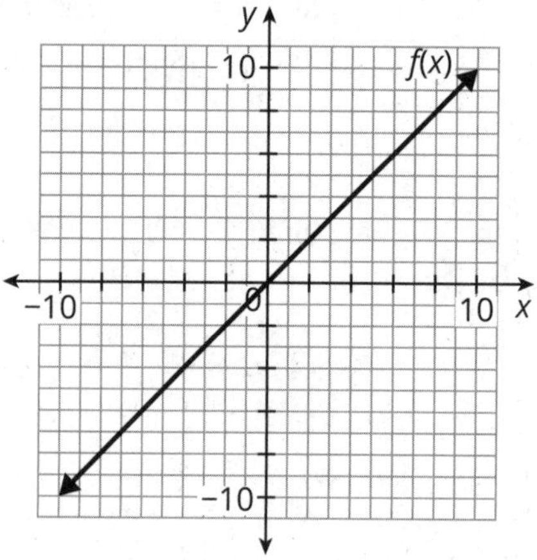

(e) $g(x) = -1 \cdot f(x) - 4$

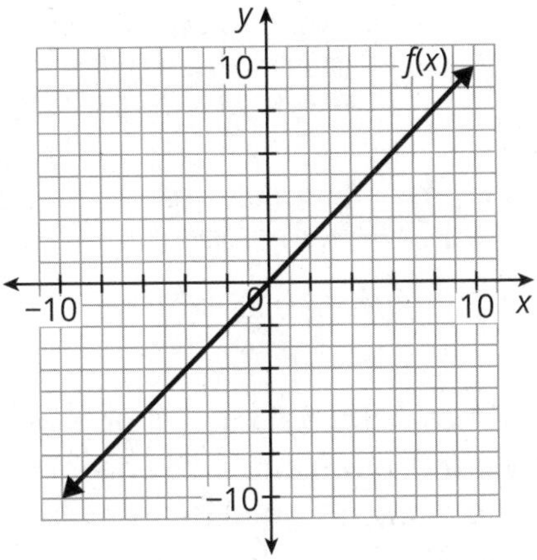

(f) $g(x) = -\frac{2}{3} \cdot f(x) + 5$

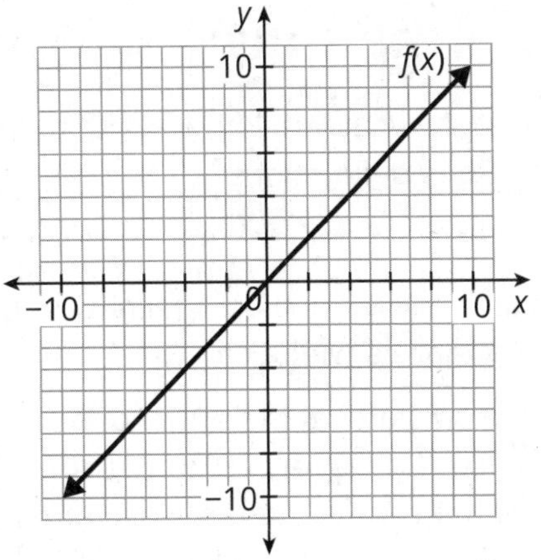

When a function is both translated and stretched vertically, you can write the resulting function in the form $A \cdot f(x) + D$, where D represents the vertical translation of $f(x)$ and A represents the vertical dilation of $f(x)$.

2 Consider the function $g(x) = A \cdot f(x) + D$.

(a) How does changing the A-value affect the slope of the function? The y-intercept of the function?

(b) How does changing the D-value affect the slope of the function? The y-intercept of the function?

Applying Linear Function Transformations

Now let's apply what you know about the transformations of functions.

HABITS OF MIND

- Reason abstractly and quantitatively.
- Construct viable arguments and critique the reasoning of others.

Your company is developing a new video game for kids, which involves scoring points by shooting targets with a cannon.

The cannon starts at the origin of a coordinate system as shown. By default it shoots along the line $f(x) = x$. Players can move the cannon up and down the y-axis and also change the angle of the cannon. When a player shoots the cannon, the game program determines the values of A and D for the linear function $A \cdot f(x) = x$. If the target is on that line, the program will show an animation of the cannonball hitting the target.

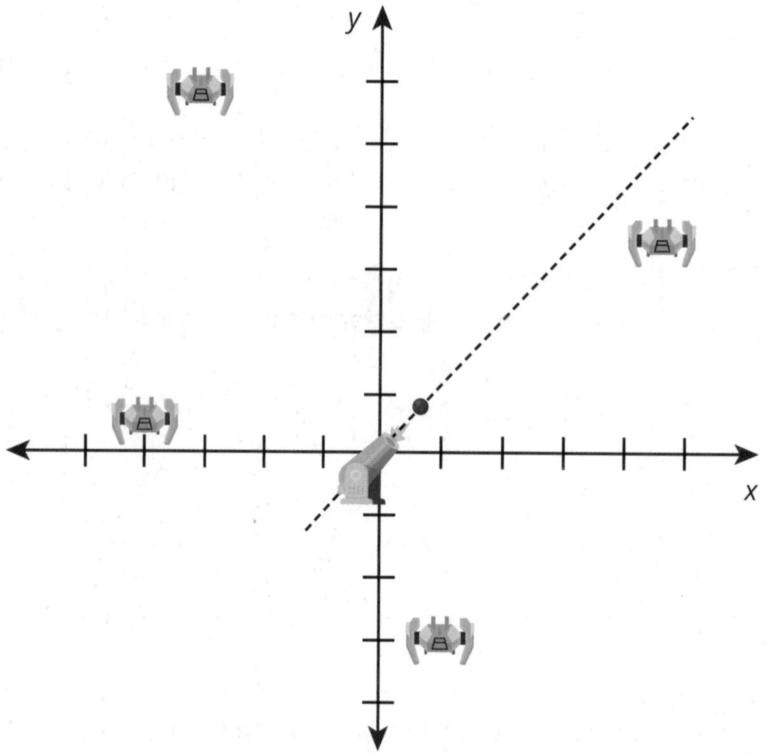

1 Test the program. Determine values for A and D for 4 linear functions that should hit the targets shown.

ASK YOURSELF...
The cannon can shoot in only one direction. Does that affect the domain or range of the linear function?

2 Identify the domain on which each graph hits the target.

The game developer is also testing two other versions of the game, with different abilities for the cannon.

Version B

The cannon can only shoot along a line parallel to $f(x) = x$ or $f(x) = -x$. It can move up and down the y-axis.

Version C

The cannon can change angles, but remains fixed at the origin.

3 Determine values for A and D, along with their corresponding domains, for 4 linear functions that can hit the targets in each version of the game. **Show your work.**

Function Matching

> Consider the graph of the linear function $f(x) = x$ and four transformations of $f(x)$.

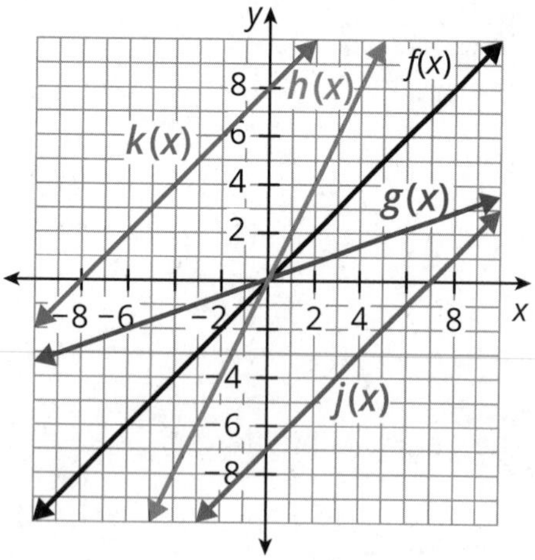

TRANSFORMATIONS
$\frac{1}{3} \cdot f(x)$
$2 \cdot f(x)$
$f(x) - 7$
$f(x) + 8$

1. Match each transformed graph to one of the transformations in the table. **Explain your reasoning.**

   (a) $k(x) =$ ____________

   (b) $h(x) =$ ____________

   (c) $g(x) =$ ____________

   (d) $j(x) =$ ____________

LESSON 3 ASSIGNMENT

> Use a separate piece of paper for your Journal entry.

JOURNAL

Describe the term *basic function* in the context of transformations using your own words.

REMEMBER

For the basic function $f(x) = x$, the transformed function $y = f(x) + D$ shows a vertical translation of the function.

- For $D > 0$, the resulting graph vertically shifts up.
- For $D < 0$, the resulting graph vertically shifts down.

The transformed function $y = Af(x)$ shows a vertical dilation of the function. For $|A| > 1$, the resulting graph vertically stretches by a factor of A units.

- For $0 < |A| < 1$, the resulting graph vertically compresses by a factor of A units.
- For $A < 0$, the resulting graph is vertically stretched or compressed and is reflected across the x-axis.

PRACTICE

1. Given $w(x) = 4x$.

   a) Graph $r(x) = \frac{1}{2} \cdot w(x)$. Then complete the table of corresponding points on $r(x)$.

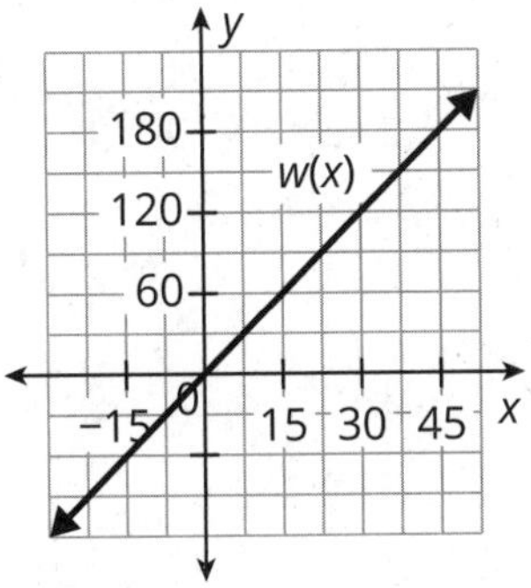

x	w(x)	r(x)
0		
15		
30		
45		

   b) Describe the transformation performed on $w(x)$ to produce $r(x)$.

   c) Write the equation for the function $r(x)$ in general form.

2 Given $f(x) = 10x$.

ⓐ Graph $b(x) = f(x) - 30$. Then complete the table of corresponding points for $b(x)$.

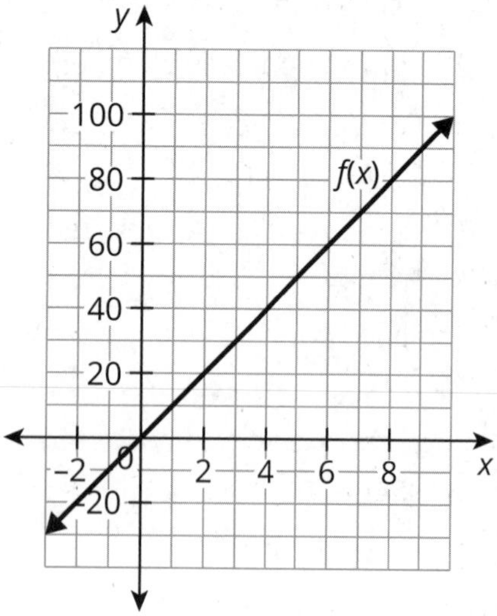

x	f(x)	b(x)
1		
2		
4		
6		
8		
9		

ⓑ Write the equation for the function $b(x)$ in general form.

ⓒ Describe the transformation performed on $f(x)$ to produce $b(x)$.

STRETCH Optional

› Consider the graphs of the functions $f(x)$ and $g(x)$.

1 Write an equation for each function in general form.

2 Write an equation for $g(x)$ in terms of $f(x)$.

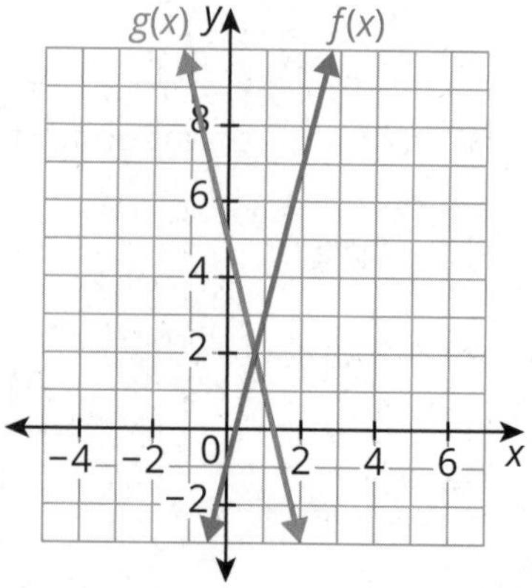

LESSON 4

Connect Four

Comparing Linear Functions in Different Forms

Learning Goals

- Compare linear functions represented algebraically, graphically, in tables, or with verbal descriptions.
- Choose and interpret appropriate units to represent independent and dependent quantities in situations modeled by linear functions.
- Choose and interpret appropriate scales and origins for graphs of linear functions.

REVIEW (1–2 minutes)

> Determine whether each set of ordered pairs represents a function.
Explain your reasoning.

1. $\{(-1, -1), (0, 0), (1, 1), (2, 2)\}$

2. $\{(-1, -2), (0, 0), (1, 2), (2, 4)\}$

3. $\{(-1, -1), (0, -1), (1, -1), (2, -1)\}$

4. $\{(-1, -1), (-1, 0), (-1, 1), (-1, 2)\}$

You have represented linear functions in a variety of different ways.

How does each linear function representation compare with the others?

Odd One Out

1 Choose the function that does not belong with the others and justify your choice.

Function A

x	*y*
−5	10
−1.5	3
0	0
2.5	−5

Function B

During one year at Bellefield High School, the ratio of boys to girls was 1 : 1.

Function C

$c(x) = \frac{1}{5}x$

Function D

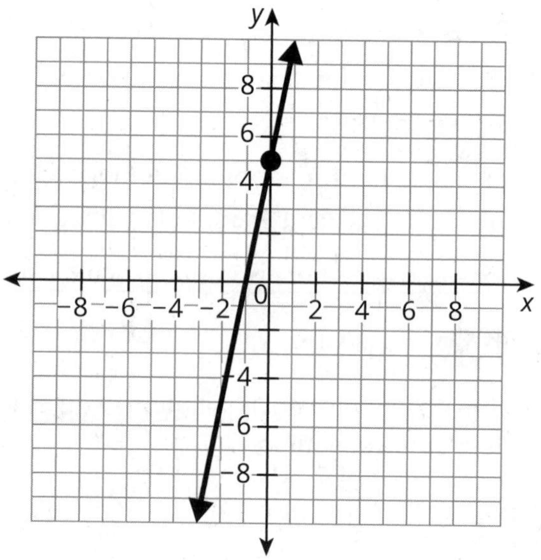

Comparing Tables and Graphs

Let's look at linear functions represented in tables and in graphs.

HABITS OF MIND
- Reason abstractly and quantitatively.
- Construct viable arguments and critique the reasoning of others.

Large recycling centers pay out different amounts per ton of cardboard recycled. Washington County Recycling Center lists its payout amounts in a table, and Jackson County uses a graph to advertise its payout amounts. The two centers' payout amounts are close but not equal.

Washington County Recycling

0.5	$7.50
1	$15
1.5	$22.50
2	$30

Jackson County Recycling

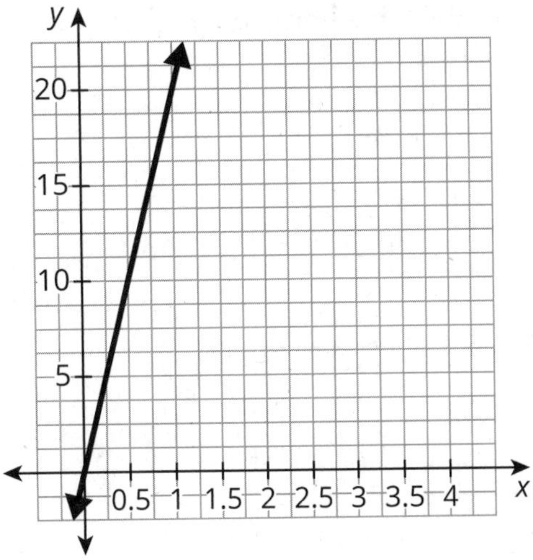

1 Each representation shows a functional relationship between quantities. Label the quantities and their units in the table and on the graph.

2 Let $w(x)$ represent the function for Washington County, and let $j(x)$ represent the function for Jackson County. Use >, <, or = to complete each statement.

(a) $w(0.5)$ ______ $j(0.5)$ (b) $w(1)$ ______ $j(1)$ (c) $w(3)$ ______ $j(3)$

3 Compare the y-intercepts of each relationship. What does each y-intercept mean in terms of the relationship between the quantities?

4 Which recycling center would you choose? **Provide evidence to justify your choice.**

Comparing Equations and Tables

Now look at linear functions represented in tables and in equations.

HABITS OF MIND
- Reason abstractly and quantitatively.
- Construct viable arguments and critique the reasoning of others.

Beto and Lydia are friends who live in different countries. When they chat online and talk about the weather, one of them always uses temperature in degrees Celsius while the other talks about temperature using degrees Fahrenheit.

Beto uses an equation to convert Lydia's temperatures, and Lydia looks at a table to convert Beto's temperatures. Here are the equation and part of the table.

Beto

10	−12.2
30	−1.1
50	10
75	23.9

Lydia

$j(x) = \frac{9}{5}x + 32$

REMEMBER...
0°C = 32°F

1 Identify quantities in the table and equation. Who is converting from °C to °F, and who is converting from °F to °C? **Explain your reasoning.**

2 Compare the given characteristics for each function in terms of the quantities.

(a) Slope

(b) *y*-intercept

THINK ABOUT...
The units of the quantities are very important.

MATHia CONNECTION

- Comparing Linear Functions in Different Forms

Comparing Descriptions and Graphs

HABITS OF MIND

- Reason abstractly and quantitatively.
- Construct viable arguments and critique the reasoning of others.

Finally, let's look at linear functions represented in scenarios and in graphs.

Michelle and D'Andre both opened bank accounts at the same time. D'Andre started with \$0 and deposited the same amount each month. In the 4th month, he had \$80 saved.

D'Andre

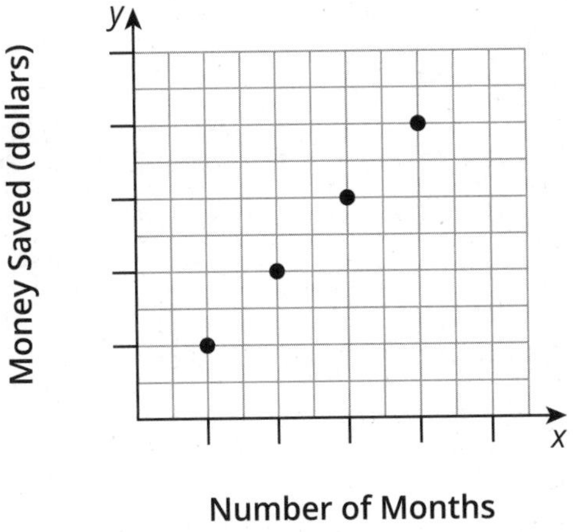

Michelle

Michelle opened her bank account on September 1st with \$25 and continues to deposit \$25 each month.

1. Use what you know about D'Andre's account to determine the scale of each axis and interpret the origin on the graph. **Explain your reasoning.**

2. Compare the given characteristics for each function in terms of the quantities.

   (a) Slope

   (b) y-intercept

Function Maker Space

> Consider the table of values.

x	−10	10	20	25
y	0	5	7.5	8.75

1. Create a situation to represent the table of values.

2. Write an equation that has a slope that is less steep than the relationship in the table.

3. How does the slope of the graph shown compare to the slope from the table of values and your equation?

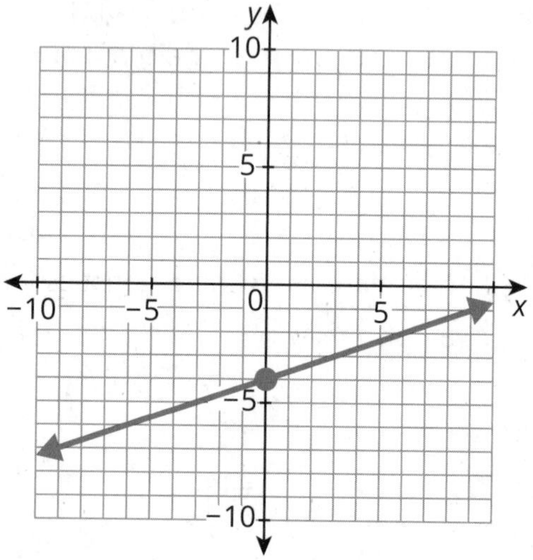

4. What strategies did you use to create your linear functions and to compare the slopes?

LESSON 4 ASSIGNMENT

> Use a separate piece of paper for your Journal entry.

JOURNAL

Describe how to compare the slopes and *y*-intercepts of two linear functions if one is a graph and one is a table.

REMEMBER

You can represent a linear function using an equation, a table, a graph, or with a verbal description. You can understand characteristics of linear functions, such as slope, *y*-intercepts, and independent and dependent quantities from different representations of functions.

PRACTICE

1 Bookstores specializing in selling used books award different amounts of points to customers who supply them with used books. People use the points toward the purchase of other books in the store. BookTraders lists its point values in a table, and Round the Block Books uses a graph to post its point values.

BookTraders Reward Points

2	12
4	24
6	36
8	48

Round the Block Books Reward Points

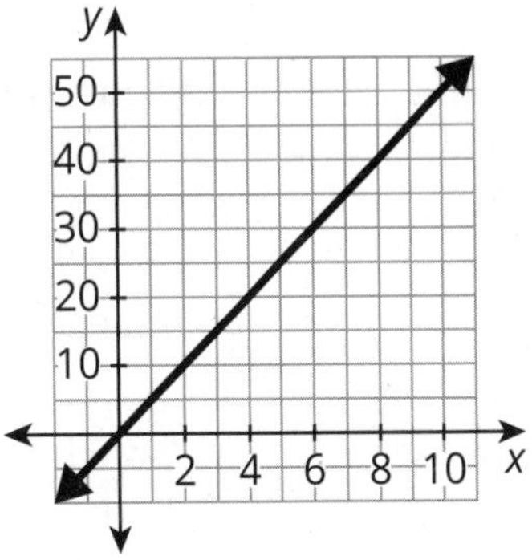

(a) Label each column of values in the table and label the *x*-axis and *y*-axis on the graph with the appropriate variable quantities.

(b) Compare the slope of each function and explain what each represents in context.

(c) Compare the *y*-intercepts of each function and explain what each represents in context.

Go to LiveHint.com for help on the PRACTICE questions.

2 Alejandro and Maria collect movies. Maria's movie collection is shown in the graph. She started with 0 movies and added the same number of movies to her collection each month. In the 5th month, she had 15 movies.

Maria

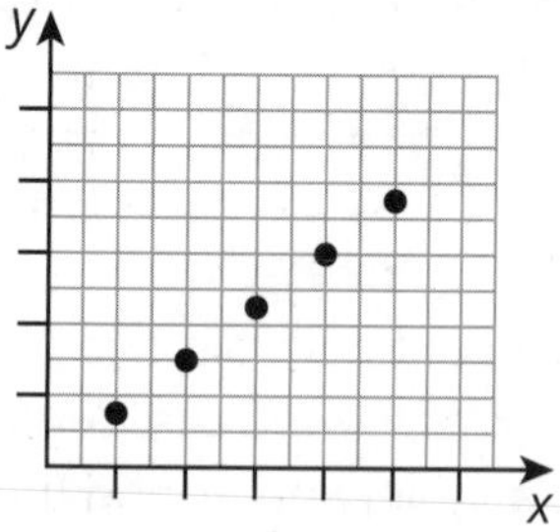

Alejandro

Alejandro started his collection with 27 movies he inherited from his uncle and continues to buy 2 movies each month.

a) Use what you know about Maria's movie collection to determine the scale of her graph. Label the *x*- and *y*-axis, the origin, and the intervals on both axes. Explain your reasoning.

b) Compare the slope for each function. Explain what each represents in context.

c) Compare the *y*-intercepts of each function and explain what each represents in context.

STRETCH Optional

> Tim and Tom are twins. Their parents track their height every year between the ages of 5 and 15.

1 Which twin is growing faster? Justify your answer.

2 At what age does one twin surpass the other in height? Explain your reasoning.

Tim

$y = 3.1x + 40.6$

Tom

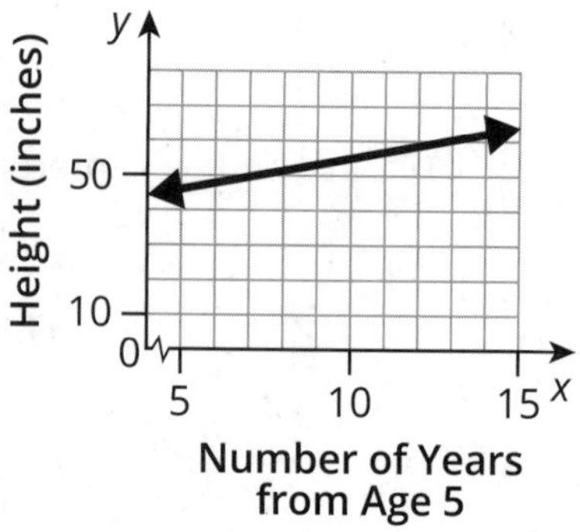

MIXED PRACTICE

> This Mixed Practice worksheet includes two sections: Spaced Review and End-of-Topic Review. **Use a separate piece of paper to show your work.**

Spaced Review

> Practice concepts from previous topics.

1 For each situation decide whether the correlation implies causation. List reasons why or why not.

ⓐ The number of winter coats sold at department stores is highly correlated to average low temperatures in the area.

ⓑ The number of concessions sold at a concert is highly correlated to the number of people in attendance at the concert.

2 Describe the pattern of association between the two quantities in each scatter plot.

ⓐ

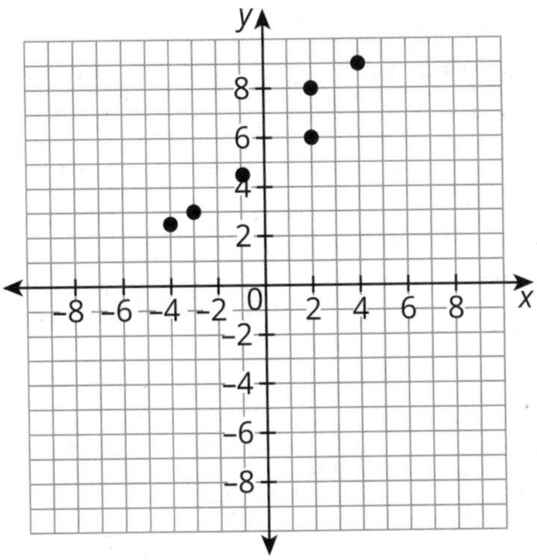

ⓑ

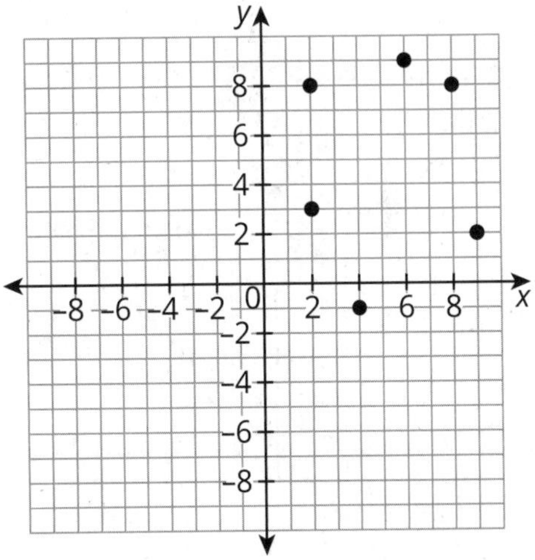

3 Determine the function family to which each equation belongs. Explain your reasoning.

ⓐ $f(x) = 4 \cdot 9^x$

ⓑ $g(x) = |8x - 3|$

4 Determine the slope, *x*-intercept, and *y*-intercept for each linear representation.

ⓐ

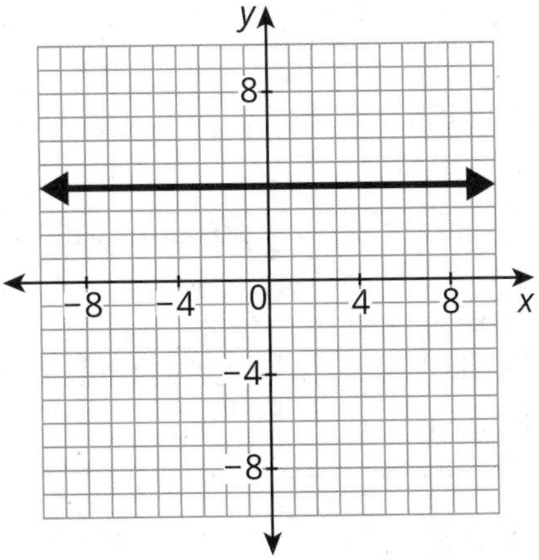

ⓑ

x	*y*
−20	8
−10	10
0	12
10	14
20	16

5 Solve each equation.

ⓐ $2(9n - 6) + 52 = 2(7n + 8)$

ⓑ $68 = -7 - 15b$

End-of-Topic Review

AVAILABLE ONLINE

1. A **Topic Summary** reviews the main concepts for the topic.
2. A video of the **Worked Example** is provided.

> Practice concepts you learned in **Linear Functions**.

6 Determine whether each relationship shows a constant difference. If so, write the linear function that represents the relationship.

(a)

x	y
2	9
3	11
4	13
5	15

(b)

x	y
1	2
2	1
3	$\frac{1}{2}$
4	$\frac{7}{2}$

7 The graph represents the basic function $f(x) = x$. The equation for the transformed function $g(x)$ is $g(x) = \frac{2}{3} \cdot f(x) - 2$.

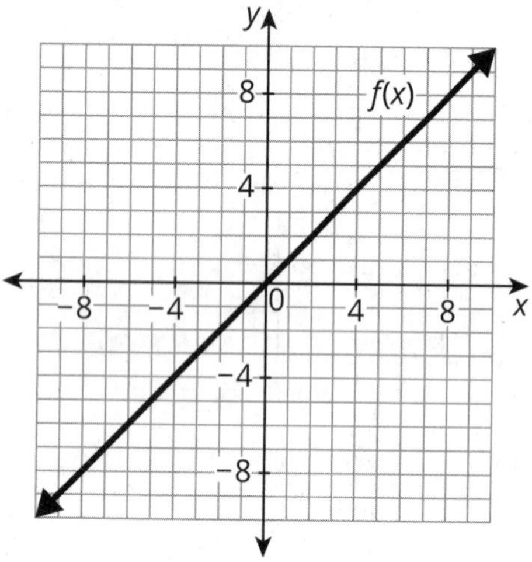

(a) Describe the transformations performed on $f(x)$ to produce $g(x)$.

(b) Graph $g(x)$.

(c) Write the equation of $g(x)$ in general form and identify the slope and y-intercept.

8 Determine whether each table of values represents a linear function. If so, write the function. If not, explain why.

(a)

x	y
2	3
4	4
6	5
8	6

(b)

x	y
−4	−17
−2	−9
2	7
4	17

LESSON 1

Strike a Balance

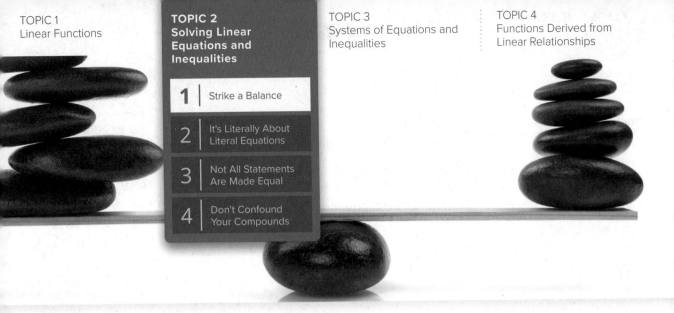

Solving Linear Equations

KEY TERMS

solution
no solution
infinite solutions

Learning Goals

- Write equivalent equations using Properties of Equality.
- Use Properties of Equality to solve linear equations and justify a solution method.
- Determine whether an equation has one solution, no solution, or infinite solutions.
- Solve linear equations with variables on both sides.

REVIEW (1–2 minutes)

> Solve each equation for *x*.

1. $\frac{1}{3}x = 8$

2. $5 + x = 12.7$

3. $2x - 9 = 6$

4. $12 + 2x = 3x - 1$

You know that equations are one way to represent a linear function, and you have used equations to evaluate linear functions for a given input value.

How can you use equations to solve for unknown input values of a function?

Equation Creation

An equation is a mathematical sentence that uses an equals sign to show that two expressions are equivalent. When one of those expressions contains a variable, you can solve the equation.

Consider the equation $x = 2$. You can substitute the value 2 for x to create the true statement $2 = 2$. Because this is the only value that makes the statement true, 2 is the only solution to the equation $x = 2$.

By performing the same operation on each side of an equation, you can create more complex equations that have the same solution.

TAKE NOTE...
A **solution** to an equation is a value for the variable that makes the equation a true statement.

1. Consider the equation $x = 2$.

   a. Choose any constant. Add that constant to each side of the equation and rewrite each side with the fewest terms.

   b. Choose any constant other than 0. Multiply each side of the equation you created in part (a) by that constant and rewrite each side with the fewest terms.

   c. Choose any number other than 0 to represent a in the expression ax. Subtract the term ax from each side of the equation you created in part (b) and rewrite each side with the fewest terms.

   d. Choose any constant other than 0. Divide each side of the equation you created in part (c) by that constant and rewrite each side with the fewest terms.

2. Have a partner solve the equation you created in Question 1 to verify that $x = 2$ is the solution.

THINK ABOUT...
What strategies can you use to verify a solution?

Using Properties to Justify Solutions

HABITS OF MIND
- Reason abstractly and quantitatively.
- Construct viable arguments and critique the reasoning of others.

Recall that the Properties of Equality are rules that allow you to rewrite equations to isolate the variable.

Properties of Equality	For all numbers *a*, *b*, and *c*
Addition Property of Equality	If $a = b$, then $a + c = b + c$.
Subtraction Property of Equality	If $a = b$, then $a - c = b - c$.
Multiplication Property of Equality	If $a = b$, then $ac = bc$.
Division Property of Equality	If $a = b$ and $c \neq 0$, then $\frac{a}{c} = \frac{b}{c}$.

Sara and Ethan both created new equations starting from the solution statement $x = 2$.

Sara

$-3x + 14 = 18 - 5x$

Ethan

$2x = 5 - \frac{1}{2}x$

1 Verify that both equations are equivalent to $x = 2$ using the given strategy.

(a) Substitution

(b) Properties of Equality

There are also basic number properties you can use to justify your steps when solving equations.

Number Properties	**For all numbers *a*, *b*, and *c***
Commutative Property	$a + b = b + a$ $ab = ba$
Associative Property	$a + (b + c) = (a + b) + c$ $a(bc) = (ab)c$
Distributive Property	$a(b + c) = ab + ac$

2 Solve each equation. Write the properties that justify each step of your solving strategy.

(a) $3(2x + 1) = 4x + 6$

(b) $\frac{1}{2}x - 6 = 2 + (2x + 1)$

3 Compare the solution strategies used by Kaleigh and Destiny. **What do you notice about the properties each student used?**

Kaleigh

$4(3x + 2) = 8x + 4$

$12x + 8 = 8x + 4$

$4x = -4$

$x = -1$

Destiny

$4(3x + 2) = 8x + 4$

$\frac{4(3x + 2)}{4} = \frac{8x + 4}{4}$

$3x + 2 = 2x + 1$

$x = -1$

Solutions to Linear Equations

In the Getting Started, you built equations from $x = 2$. In this activity, you will build equations from two mathematical sentences and compare your results.

HABITS OF MIND
- Look for and make use of structure.
- Look for and express regularity in repeated reasoning.

1 Consider the mathematical sentence $2 = 2$.

Is there any variable or constant that you could add to or subtract from both sides, or multiply or divide both sides by using the Properties of Equality to make this true sentence false? **Choose variables and constants to create new mathematical sentences to justify your conclusion.**

2 Consider the mathematical sentence $2 \neq 3$.

Is there any variable or constant that you could add to or subtract from both sides, or multiply or divide both sides by using the Properties of Equality to make both sides equal? **Choose variables and constants to create new mathematical sentences to justify your conclusion.**

A linear equation can have one solution, *no solution*, or *infinite solutions*.

- The equations you solved in the previous activity are examples of linear equations with one solution.
- A linear equation with **no solution** means that there is no value for the variable that makes the equation true.
- A linear equation with **infinite solutions** means that any value for the variable makes the equation true.

3 Consider the equations you created in this activity.

(a) Explain whether the equation(s) you created in Question 1 have one solution, no solution, or infinite solutions.

(b) Explain whether the equation(s) you created in Question 2 have one solution, no solution, or infinite solutions.

4 Consider the equation $2x = 3x$. Does this equation have one solution, no solution, or infinite solutions? **Explain your reasoning**.

ACTIVITY 3

MATHia CONNECTION
- Solving Linear Equations in a Variety of Forms

Tic-Tac-Bingo

HABITS OF MIND
- Reason abstractly and quantitatively.
- Construct viable arguments and critique the reasoning of others.

In this activity, you are going to play a game called Tic-Tac-Bingo. The object of the game is to match two expressions to create an equation with specific solution types.

> Tear out the Tic-Tac-Bingo board located on page 255.

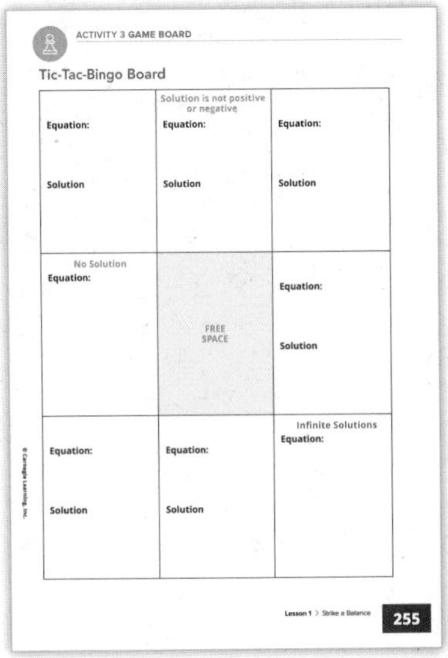
ACTIVITY 3 GAME BOARD

Tic-Tac-Bingo Board

Equation: Solution	Solution is not positive or negative Equation: Solution	Equation: Solution
No Solution Equation:	FREE SPACE	Equation: Solution
Equation: Solution	Equation: Solution	Infinite Solutions Equation:

Lesson 1 > Strike a Balance 255

STEP 1 Prepare the board.

The board has 9 spaces. Three spaces are already designated. Fill each remaining space with one of the solution types from the word bank. You must use each option at least once.

WORD BANK

SOLUTION TYPES

positive rational solution

negative rational solution

non-zero integer solution

STEP 2 Play the game.

Your teacher will assign you an expression. When you and a classmate have created an equation with one of the solution types, write your equation in the corresponding box.

Try to be the first person to fill three spaces in a row. Then, try to be the first person to fill your board with equations.

1. Reflect on the equations you created.

   a. How can you look at an equation and determine that it has no solution?

   b. How can you look at an equation and determine that it has infinite solutions?

TOPIC 2

One Step at a Time

1. Write the property that justifies each step to solve the given equation.

$-\frac{1}{3}(6x - 21) = -5(x + 1)$

$-2x + 7 = -5x - 5$ ____________________

$-2x + 5x + 7 = -5x + 5x - 5$ ____________________

$3x + 7 - 7 = -5 - 7$ ____________________

$\frac{3x}{3} = \frac{-12}{3}$ ____________________

$x = -4$

2. Solve the equation using the justification given for each step.

$5x + 7 = \frac{-15x - 1}{3} + \frac{4}{3}$

____________________ Multiplication Property of Equality

____________________ Distributive Property

____________________ Associative Property

____________________ Subtraction Property of Equality

____________________ Addition Property of Equality

____________________ Division Property of Equality

$x = -\frac{3}{5}$

Tic-Tac-Bingo Board

Equation: **Solution**	Solution is not positive or negative **Equation:** **Solution**	**Equation:** **Solution**
No Solution **Equation:**	FREE SPACE	**Equation:** **Solution**
Equation: **Solution**	**Equation:** **Solution**	Infinite Solutions **Equation:**

Why is this page blank?

So you can tear out the tic-tac-bingo board on the other side.

LESSON 1 ASSIGNMENT

> Use a separate piece of paper for your Journal entry.

JOURNAL

Explain how you know when an equation has no solution and when it has infinite solutions.

REMEMBER

To solve an equation, use the Properties of Equality to isolate the variable. A linear equation can have one solution, no solution, or infinite solutions.

PRACTICE

1 Solve each equation. Write the properties that justify each step of your solution.

(a) $3x - 8 = -7x + 18$

(b) $-2(4 - x) = 12x - 3$

(c) $\frac{1}{2}(-10x + 4) = -4(-3 + 2x) + 8$

(d) $\frac{-2x - 4}{5} + \frac{8}{5} = 3(x - 1)$

Go to LiveHint.com for help on the PRACTICE questions.

(e) $\frac{4}{3}x - 2\left(9 - \frac{1}{3}x\right) = -\frac{7}{3}x + 9$

2 Determine whether each equation has one solution, no solution, or infinite solutions. Explain your reasoning.

(a) $-2(x + 5) = -6x + 4(x - 2)$

(b) $4(0.2x - 1.2) = -0.5x + 3.4$

(c) $\frac{\frac{1}{2}x - 7}{2} = -3x + 4$

(d) $2(x - 4) + x = 3(x - 2) - 2$

(e) $3 - \frac{2}{5}x - \frac{12}{5} = \frac{10 - 2x}{5}$

(f) $6(x - 1) + 21 = 6x + 15$

STRETCH Optional

> Consider the equation $2x - 5(x - 1) = 50$.

1 Solve the equation for x.

2 Chen was asked to solve the inequality: $2x - 5(x - 1) < 50$. She gave an answer of $x < -15$. Substitute in any value for x less than -15 to determine whether Chen is correct. If not, determine the correct solution.

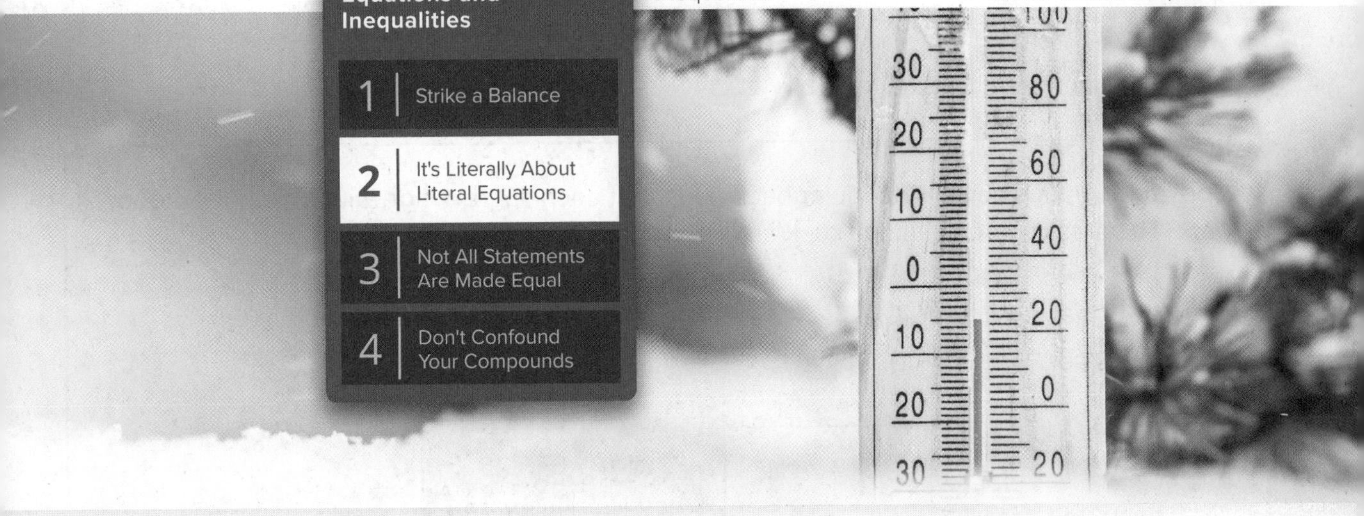

LESSON 2

It's Literally About Literal Equations

Literal Equations

KEY TERM

literal equation

Learning Goals

- Rewrite linear equations in different forms.
- Analyze the structure of different forms of linear equations.
- Recognize and use literal equations.
- Rearrange literal equations to highlight quantities of interest.

REVIEW (1–2 minutes)

> The formula for the circumference of a circle is $C = 2\pi r$. Determine the radius for each circle with the given circumference. Use 3.14 for π and round to the nearest tenth of a unit, if necessary.

1. $C = 62.8$ in.
2. $C = 10$ cm
3. $C = 15.7$ ft
4. $C = 48$ mm

You have used different properties to solve linear equations to determine which value makes the equation true.

How can you use those same properties to solve for one specific variable in an equation that has multiple variables?

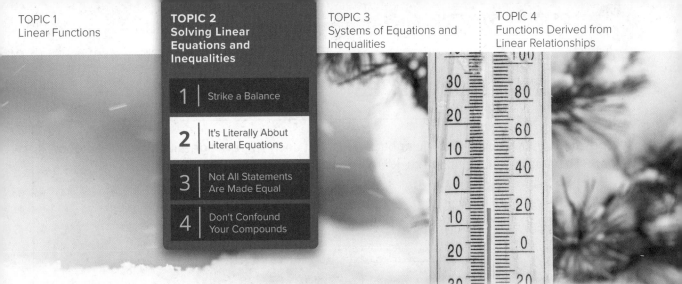

Perimeter Perspectives

Cody and Jessica have rectangular backyards that each share a side with a neighborhood park. The sides shared with the park are adjacent to each other as shown.

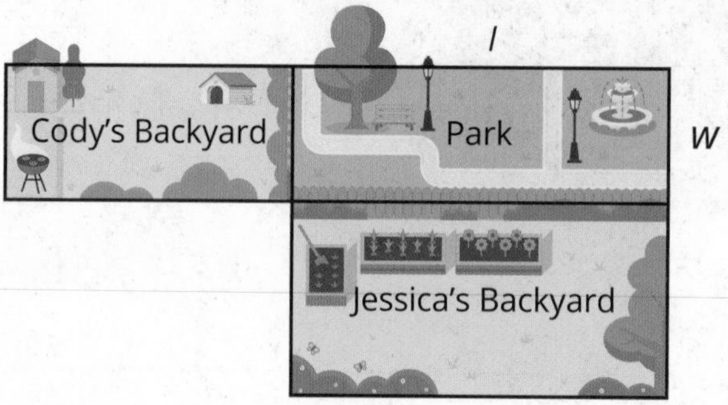

Cody and Jessica are each responsible for constructing their own fence to separate their yard from the park. The city gives them the measure of the perimeter of the park in feet. So that each knows how much fencing to buy, Cody needs to determine the park's width, and Jessica needs to determine the length of the park.

1. How can you write an equation for the park's perimeter from each person's perspective to help them determine the information they need?

REMEMBER...
The formula for the perimeter of a rectangle is $P = 2l + 2w$.

2. Show that the two equations are equivalent.

Equations in Different Forms

HABITS OF MIND
- Look for and make use of structure.
- Look for and express regularity in repeated reasoning.

The slope, *x*-intercept, and *y*-intercept are each important characteristics of linear functions. The structure of equations can reveal these characteristics of a function.

> Consider each equation. **Determine each characteristic and then explain your work.**

1 $y = -\frac{2}{3}x + 4$

(a) slope

(b) *y*-intercept

(c) *x*-intercept

(d) **How did you determine each characteristic?**

2 $y = 4(x - 2)$

(a) slope

(b) *y*-intercept

(c) *x*-intercept

(d) **How did you determine each characteristic?**

3 $3x - 2y = 8$

(a) slope

(b) *y*-intercept

(c) *x*-intercept

(d) **How did you determine each characteristic?**

There are three useful forms of linear equations.

General Form	Factored Form	Standard Form
$y = ax + b$	$y = a(x - c)$	$Ax + By = C$

4 Identify the form for each equation in Questions 1 through 3.

TAKE NOTE...
In general and factored form, the values of a, b, and c can be any real numbers. In standard form, however, there are constraints on the variables: A must be a positive integer, and A and B cannot both be 0.

> Consider how the structure of the standard form of a linear function reveals its key characteristics.

5 For the equation $Ax + By = C$, determine the slope, x-intercept, and y-intercept.

6 Which form of a linear equation is more efficient for determining each characteristic?

(a) Slope

(b) x-intercept

(c) y-intercept

7 If you want to use your calculator to graph an equation, which form is more efficient? **Explain your reasoning.**

ACTIVITY 2

MATHia CONNECTION

- Extending Equations to Literal Equations
- Solving Literal Equations

Rewriting Literal Equations

HABITS OF MIND

- Look for and make use of structure.
- Look for and express regularity in repeated reasoning.

Literal equations are equations in which the variables represent specific measures. You most often see literal equations when you study formulas. You can manipulate these literal equations to allow you to solve for one specific variable.

You have used a common literal equation, the formula for converting degrees Fahrenheit to degrees Celsius.

$$C = \frac{5}{9}(F - 32)$$

> Josh is talking on the phone to his friend Greg who lives in Europe. Greg is used to describing temperatures in °C, while Josh is used to describing temperatures in °F. Greg can use the formula above to quickly convert the temperatures Josh describes to °C.

1. How can you rewrite the formula so that Josh can quickly convert the temperatures that Greg describes to °F? **Justify your solution method.**

2. Josh tells Greg that the temperature where he lives is currently 77°F. Greg tells Josh that the temperature where he lives is currently 30°C. Josh says it is warmer where he lives, and Greg says it is warmer where he lives. Who is correct? **Explain your reasoning**.

3 Maya, Sherry, and Brian each convert the given formula to degrees Fahrenheit.

Maya

$$C = \frac{5}{9}(F - 32)$$
$$C = \frac{5}{9}F - \frac{160}{9}$$
$$9(C) = 9\left(\frac{5}{9}F - \frac{160}{9}\right)$$
$$9C = 5F - 160$$
$$9C + 160 = 5F$$
$$\frac{9C}{5} + \frac{160}{5} = \frac{5F}{5}$$
$$\frac{9}{5}C + 32 = F$$

ⓐ Explain Maya's reasoning.

Sherry

$$C = \frac{5}{9}(F - 32)$$
$$C = \frac{5}{9}F - 32$$
$$9(C) = 9\left(\frac{5}{9}F - 32\right)$$
$$9C = 5F - 288$$
$$9C + 288 = 5F$$
$$\frac{9C}{5} + \frac{288}{5} = \frac{5F}{5}$$
$$\frac{9}{5}C + 57.6 = F$$

Brian

$$C = \frac{5}{9}(F - 32)$$
$$C = \frac{5}{9}F - \frac{160}{9}$$
$$9(C) = 9\left(\frac{5}{9}F - \frac{160}{9}\right)$$
$$9C = 45F - 1440$$
$$9C + 1440 = 45F$$
$$\frac{9C}{45} + \frac{1440}{45} = \frac{45F}{45}$$
$$\frac{1}{5}C + 32 = F$$

ⓑ Explain the error in Sherry's work.

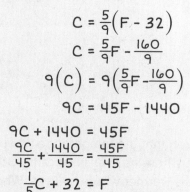

ⓒ Explain the error in Brian's work.

4 Carlos and Mikala do not like working with fractions. Each rewrites the equation so that it does not have fractions.

Carlos

$$F = \frac{9}{5}C + 32$$
$$(5)F = 5\left(\frac{9}{5}C + 32\right)$$
$$5F = 9C + 160$$
$$5F - 9C = 160$$

Mikala

$$C = \frac{5}{9}(F - 32)$$
$$(9)C = (9)\left(\frac{5}{9}(F - 32)\right)$$
$$9C = 5(F - 32)$$
$$9C = 5F - 160$$
$$9C - 5F = -160$$

Carlos and Mikala got two different equations. Who is correct? **Explain your reasoning**.

5 In the original equations, the coefficients $\frac{9}{5}$ and $\frac{5}{9}$ as well as the constant 32 had meaning based on temperature. What do the coefficients, 9 and 5, and the constant, 160, represent in Carlos's and Mikala's equations?

6 How is the literal equation $y = a(bx + c)$ similar to the equation for converting °F to °C? How would you solve this equation for the variable x?

Solving Literal Equations for Specific Variables

HABITS OF MIND
- Look for and make use of structure.
- Look for and express regularity in repeated reasoning.

> Rewrite each literal equation to solve for the given variable.

1 Think Inside the Box is manufacturing new boxes for You Pack' Em, We Ship 'Em (YPEWSE). YPEWSE told Think Inside the Box that the boxes must have a specific volume and base area. However, YPEWSE did not specify a height for the boxes.

(a) Write a literal equation to calculate the volume of a box. Then rewrite the volume formula to solve for height.

REMEMBER...
Volume is measured in cubic units since you calculate it using three dimensions. Height measures only one dimension.

(b) YPEWSE specified the box's volume must be 450 cubic inches, and the area of the base must be 75 square inches. Use your formula to determine the height of the new boxes.

2 The volume of an ice cream cone is the measure of how much ice cream fits inside the cone. An ice cream cone company wants to make an ice cream cone with a greater height that still holds the same amount of ice cream.

(a) Write an equation to calculate the volume of a cone. Then rewrite the equation to solve for the height.

TAKE NOTE...
The formula for the volume of a cone is $V = \pi r^2\left(\frac{h}{3}\right)$ where r is the radius and h is the height.

(b) Explain how your equation determines a linear measurement when the original equation determined a cubic measurement.

3 The formula for the area of a trapezoid is $A = \frac{1}{2}h(b_1 + b_2)$, where h is its height and b_1 and b_2 are the lengths of each base.

(a) Rewrite the area formula to solve for the height.

(b) Use your formula to determine the height of a trapezoid with an area of 24 cubic centimeters and base lengths of 9 cm and 7 cm.

4 For the given literal equation $Z = \frac{A}{B} + \frac{C}{D}$, solve for each variable given. **Justify your solution method.**

(a) A

(b) D

This Ought to Be Duck Soup

In this lesson, you rewrote literal equations to highlight specific variables.

1. The formula for the volume of a cylinder is $V = 2\pi rh$ where V is the volume, r is the length of the radius of the base, and h is the height. Rewrite the formula to solve for the height.

2. The volume of a can of soup is 37.68 cubic inches and the length of the radius of the base of the can is 1.5 inches. Use the formula to determine the height of the can of soup. Use 3.14 for π.

3. The formula for the surface area of a cylinder is $SA = 2\pi r^2 + 2\pi rh$ where SA is the surface area, r is the length of the radius of the base, and h is the height. Rewrite the formula to solve for the height.

4. The surface area of a can of soup is 51.81 square inches and the length of the radius of the base is 1.5 inches. Use your formula to determine the height of the can of soup. Use 3.14 for π.

LESSON 2 ASSIGNMENT

> Use a separate piece of paper for your Journal entry.

JOURNAL

Define the term *literal equation* in your own words.

REMEMBER

You can rewrite literal equations using Properties of Equality to isolate specific variables.

PRACTICE

1. In the USA, the shoe sizes for men are approximated by the equation $3f - s = 24$, where f represents the length of the foot in inches and s represents the shoe size.

   a. The average man's foot is 11.5 inches long. What is the average man's shoe size?

   b. Use the function to determine the x-and y-intercept. State the meaning of each in terms of this problem situation.

   c. Which form can you most easily use to determine the slope of this equation? Determine the slope of this equation and describe what it means in terms of the problem situation.

Go to LiveHint.com for help on the PRACTICE questions.

2 The boxes that shoes come in are often used in other capacities once the shopper has bought the shoes. Sometimes the boxes are used to hold other items, so it is helpful to know the volume of the box.

(a) Write the equation to solve for the volume of the shoe box.

(b) When the area of the base of the box is 112 square inches and the height is 3.5 inches, what is the box's volume?

(c) Rewrite the equation to solve for width. Show your work.

(d) A box has a volume of 456 cubic inches, with a length of 1 foot and a height of 4 inches. Determine the width of the box.

3 Solve each equation for the specified variable.

(a) $V = \frac{1}{3}Bh$ for B

(b) $I = Prt$ for r

(c) $\frac{x + y}{3} = 6$ for y

(d) $A + B + C = 180$ for C

STRETCH Optional

A simple pendulum is made of a long string and a small metal sphere. You can determine the period of oscillation using the formula $T = 2\pi\sqrt{\left(\frac{L}{g}\right)}$, where g is the acceleration due to gravity, and L is the length of the string.

1 Solve the formula for g, the acceleration due to gravity.

LESSON 3

Not All Statements Are Made Equal

Modeling Linear Inequalities

KEY TERM

solve an inequality

Learning Goals

- Write and solve inequalities.
- Analyze a graph on a coordinate plane to solve problems involving inequalities.
- Interpret how a negative rate affects how to solve an inequality.

REVIEW (1–2 minutes)

> Solve each equation or inequality for x.

1. $x + 1 = 6$

2. $x - 2 > 5$

3. $\frac{x}{3} \leq -1$

4. $-x > 4$

You have used horizontal lines on a graph and Properties of Equality with equations to solve problems that you can model with linear equations.

Can you use these same methods to solve problems involving linear inequalities?

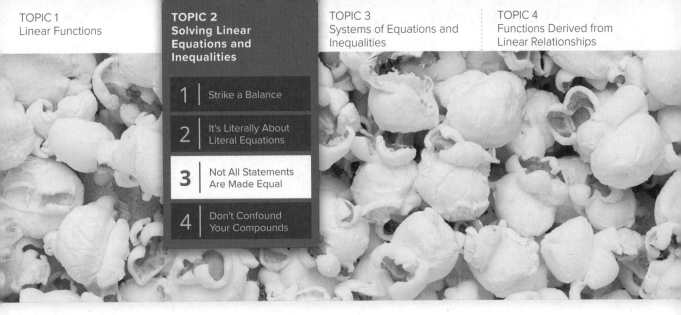

Fundraising Function

Alan's camping troop is selling popcorn to earn money for an upcoming camping trip. Each camper starts with a credit of $25 toward his sales, and each box of popcorn sells for $3.75.

1 Write a function, $f(b)$, to show Alan's total sales as a function of the number of boxes of popcorn he sells, b.

2 Analyze the function you wrote.

ⓐ Identify the independent and dependent quantities and their units.

ASK YOURSELF...
How will you represent $25 credit in your function?

ⓑ What is the slope of the function? **What does it represent in this problem situation?**

ⓒ What is the y-intercept? **What does it represent in this problem situation?**

MATHia CONNECTION

- Graphing Inequalities with Rational Numbers

Modeling Linear Inequalities

HABITS OF MIND

- Model with mathematics.
- Use appropriate tools strategically.

> Consider the graph that represents the function you wrote in the previous activity, $f(b) = 3.75b + 25$.

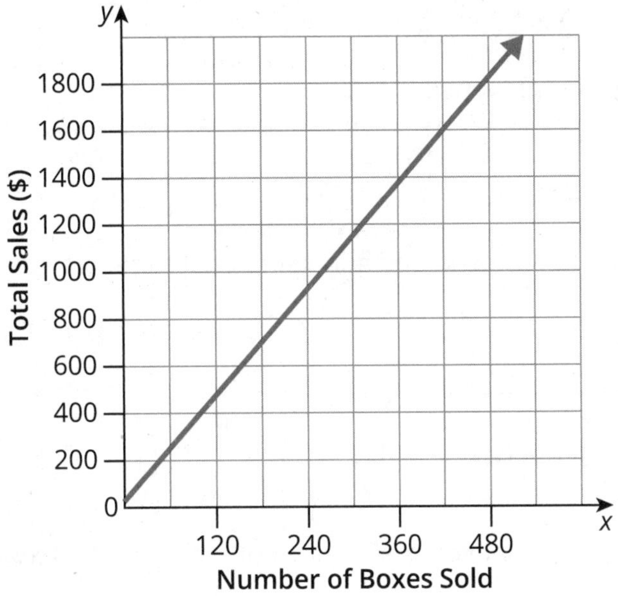

1 Suppose Alan has a sales goal of $1600.

(a) Draw a horizontal line from the y-axis until it intersects with the graphed function to determine the point on the graph that represents $1600 in total sales.

(b) How many boxes would Alan have to sell to make $1600 in total sales? **Explain your reasoning.**

(c) Use the number line to represent the number of boxes sold when the total sales are equal to $1600.

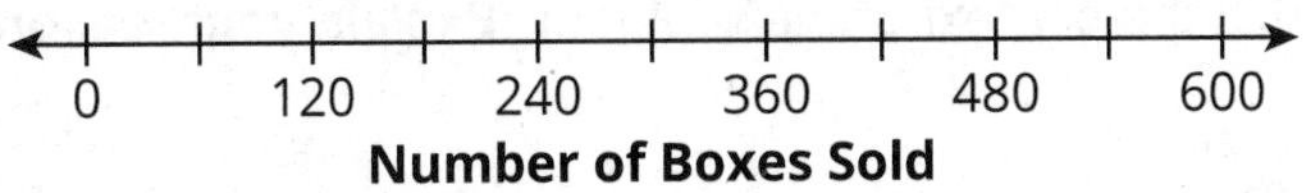

THINK ABOUT...

Are the points on your graph open or closed?

2 Analyze the region of the graph that lies below the horizontal line you drew, up to and including the point intersected by the line.

(a) What does this region of the graph represent?

(b) Write an inequality to represent this region.

(c) Use the number line to represent the number of boxes that are solutions to the inequality you wrote.

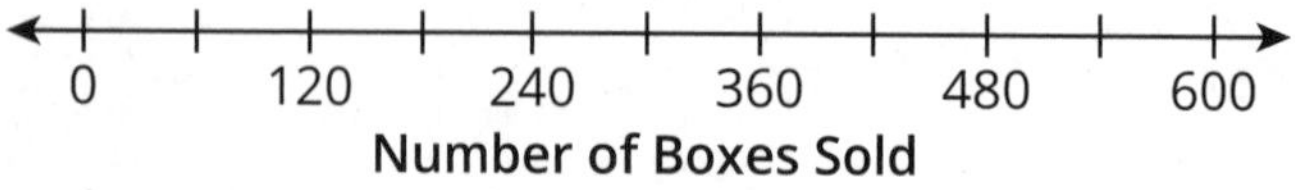

(d) Do all the solutions make sense in the context of the problem? **Explain your reasoning.**

3 Analyze the region of the graph of $f(b) = 3.75b + 25$ that lies above the horizontal line you drew, not including the point intersected by the line.

(a) What does this region of the graph represent?

(b) Write an inequality to represent this region.

(c) Use the number line to represent the number of boxes that are solutions to the inequality you wrote.

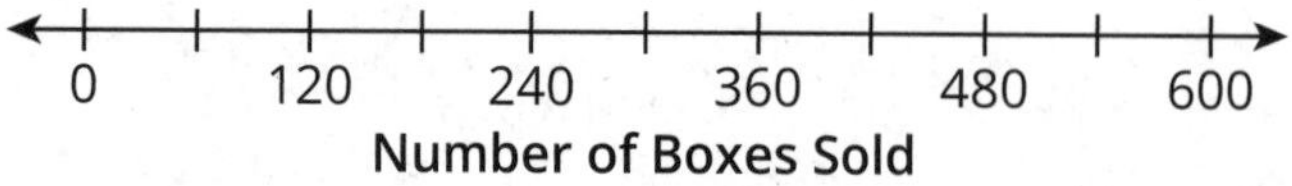

(d) Do all the solutions make sense in the context of the problem? **Explain your reasoning.**

4 Explain the difference between the open and closed circles on your number lines.

ASK YOURSELF...
How does the intersection point help you determine your answers?

5 Use the graph to answer each question. Write an equation or inequality statement for each.

(a) How many boxes would Alan have to sell to earn at least $925?

(b) How many boxes would Alan have to sell to earn less than $2050?

(c) How many boxes would Alan have to sell to earn exactly $700?

Solving Two-Step Linear Inequalities

HABITS OF MIND
- Reason abstractly and quantitatively.
- Construct viable arguments and critique the reasoning of others.

Another way to determine the solution set of any inequality is to solve it algebraically. The objective when solving an inequality is similar to the objective when solving an equation: You want to isolate the variable on one side of the inequality symbol.

> To make the first deposit on the trip, Alan's total sales, $f(b)$, need to be at least $1100.

TAKE NOTE...
To **solve an inequality** means to determine the values of the variable that make the inequality true.

WORKED EXAMPLE

You can set up an inequality and solve it to determine the number of boxes Alan needs to sell.

$$f(b) \geq 1100$$

$$3.75b + 25 \geq 1100$$

Solve the inequality in the same way you would solve an equation.

$$3.75b + 25 \geq 1100$$

$$3.75b + 25 - 25 \geq 1100 - 25$$

$$3.75b \geq 1075$$

$$\frac{3.75b}{3.75} \geq \frac{1075}{3.75}$$

$$b \geq 286.66...$$

1 How many boxes of popcorn does Alan need to sell to make the first deposit? **Explain your reasoning.**

THINK ABOUT...
How accurate does your answer need to be?

2 Write and solve an inequality for each. **Show your work.**

(a) What is the greatest number of boxes Alan could sell and still not have made $600 in sales?

(b) At least how many boxes would Alan have to sell to make $1500 in sales?

3 The worked example showed how to solve an inequality of the form, $y = ax + b$. How does your method change when the inequality is in a different form?

Reversing Inequality Signs

In this activity, you will consider what happens when you multiply or divide both sides of an inequality by a negative number.

HABITS OF MIND
- Reason abstractly and quantitatively.
- Construct viable arguments and critique the reasoning of others.

Alan's camping troop hikes down from their campsite at an elevation of 4800 feet to the base of the mountain, which is at sea level (an elevation of 0 feet). They hike down at a rate of 20 feet per minute.

1 Write a function, $h(m)$, to show the troop's elevation as a function of time in minutes. Label the function on the coordinate plane.

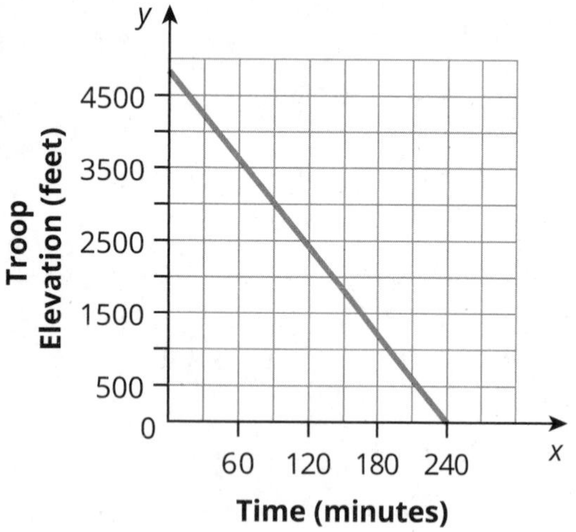

2 Identify the independent and dependent quantities and their units.

3 Analyze the function. Identify each characteristic and explain what it means in terms of this problem situation.

(a) Slope

(b) y-intercept

(c) x-intercept

(d) Domain of the function

4 Use the graph to determine how many minutes have passed when the troop is below 3200 feet. Draw an oval on the graph to represent this part of the function and write the corresponding inequality statement.

5 Write and solve an inequality to verify the solution set you interpreted from the graph.

6 Compare and contrast the solution sets you wrote using the graph and the function. **What do you notice?**

7 Analyze the relationship between the inequality statements representing $h(m)$ and m.

(a) Complete the table by writing the corresponding inequality statement that represents the number of minutes for each height.

$h(m)$	m
$h(m) > 3200$	
$h(m) \geq 3200$	
$h(m) = 3200$	
$h(m) < 3200$	
$h(m) \leq 3200$	

(b) Compare each row in the table shown. **What do you notice about the inequality signs?**

(c) Explain your answer from part (b). Use what you know about solving inequalities when you have to multiply or divide by a negative number.

Solving Other Linear Inequalities

The inequalities that you have solved in this lesson so far have all been two-step inequalities. Let's consider inequalities in different forms.

HABITS OF MIND
- Reason abstractly and quantitatively.
- Construct viable arguments and critique the reasoning of others.

Allison and John each solved the inequality $5x + 2 \geq 3x - 10$.

Allison

$$5x + 2 \geq 3x - 10$$
$$5x - 3x + 2 \geq 3x - 3x - 10$$
$$2x + 2 \geq -10$$
$$2x + 2 - 2 \geq -10 - 2$$
$$2x \geq -12$$
$$\frac{2x}{2} \geq \frac{-12}{2}$$
$$x \geq -6$$

John

$$5x + 2 \geq 3x - 10$$
$$5x - 5x + 2 \geq 3x - 5x - 10$$
$$2 \geq -2x - 10$$
$$2 + 10 \geq -2x - 10 + 10$$
$$12 \geq -2x$$
$$\frac{12}{-2} \leq \frac{-2x}{-2}$$
$$-6 \leq x$$

1. Describe the process each student used to solve the inequality.

   a. Allison

   b. John

2. How does the process of solving an inequality with variables on both sides compare to solving an equation with variables on both sides?

Curran and Ajani each solved the inequality $-4(x - 6) < 22$.

Curran

$$-4(x - 6) < 22$$
$$-4x + 24 < 22$$
$$-4x + 24 - 24 < 22 - 24$$
$$-4x < -2$$
$$\frac{-4x}{-4} > \frac{-2}{-4}$$
$$x > \frac{1}{2}$$

Ajani

$$-4(x - 6) < 22$$
$$\frac{-4(x - 6)}{-4} > \frac{22}{-4}$$
$$x - 6 > -5\frac{1}{2}$$
$$x > \frac{1}{2}$$

3 Describe the process each student used to solve the inequality.

(a) Curran

(b) Ajani

4 How does the process of solving an inequality using the Distributive Property compare to solving an equation using the Distributive Property?

It's About Solutions, More or Less

> Solve each inequality and graph the solution on the number line.

1 $-\frac{2}{3}x \geq 7$

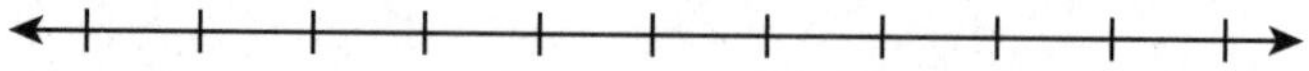

2 $32 > 23 - x$

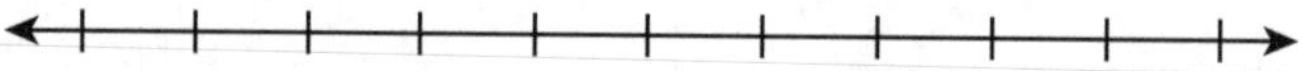

3 $2(x + 6) < 10$

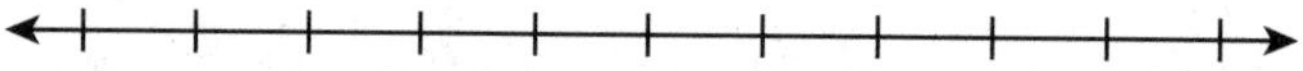

4 $15 - 4x \leq 3x - 6$

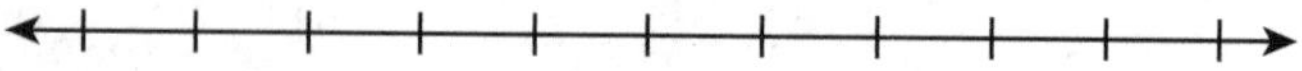

5 When $A < B$, identify the constraints to make eachstatement true.

ⓐ $A + C < B + C$

ⓑ $AC > BC$

ⓒ $-A < -B$

> Use a separate piece of paper for your Journal entry.

JOURNAL

Describe how to solve an inequality in your own words.

REMEMBER

The methods for solving linear inequalities are similar to the methods for solving linear equations. Be sure to reverse the direction of the inequality symbol when multiplying or dividing both sides by a negative number.

PRACTICE

1. Chang-Ho is going on a trip to visit some friends from summer camp. He will use $40 for food and entertainment. He will also need money to cover the cost of gas. The price of gas at the time of his trip is $3.25 per gallon.

   (a) Write a function to represent the total cost of the trip as a function of the number of gallons used.

   (b) Identify the independent and dependent quantities and their units.

   (c) Identify the rate of change and the *y*-intercept. Explain their meanings in terms of the problem situation.

   (d) Graph the function representing this situation on a coordinate plane.

   (e) Use the graph to determine how many gallons of gas Chang-Ho can buy if he has $170 saved for the trip. Draw an oval on the graph to represent the solution. Then write your answer in words and as an inequality.

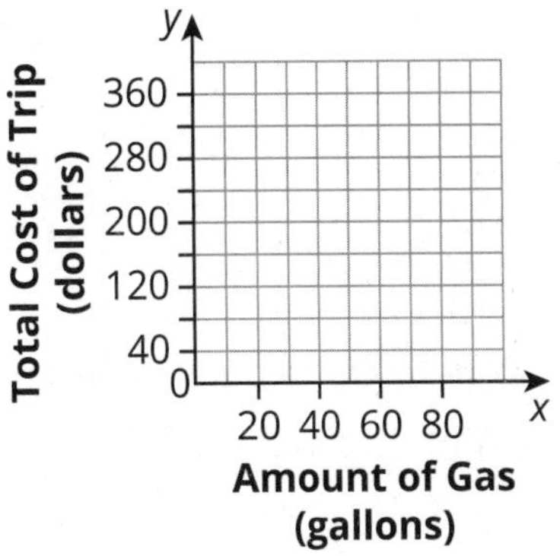

   (f) Verify the solution set you interpreted from the graph.

Go to LiveHint.com for help on the PRACTICE questions.

(g) Chang-Ho's mom gives him some money for his trip. He now has a total of $220 saved for the trip. What is the greatest number of gallons of gas he can buy before he runs out of money? Round your answer to the nearest hundredth, if necessary. Show your work and graph your solution on a number line.

2 Chang-Ho is on his way to visit his friends at camp. Halfway to his destination, he realizes there is as low leak in one of the tires. He checks the pressure, and it is at 26 psi. It appears to be losing 0.1 psi per minute.

(a) Write a function to represent the tire's pressure as a function of time in minutes.

(b) Chang-Ho knows that if the pressure in a tire goes below 22 psi, it may cause a tire blowout. What is the greatest amount of time that he can drive before the tire pressure hits 22 psi? Show your work and graph the solution.

3 Solve each inequality for the unknown value.

(a) $13 + 4x > 9$

(b) $99 - 5d \leq 4d$

(c) $3k - 9 \leq -6k - 225$

STRETCH Optional

The Crunch Yum Company orders its nut mixes every month from a distributor. The distributor charges $4.50 per pound of nut mix. There is a handling fee of $8.50 for every order. There is free shipping on any order between $100 and $400. Write a compound inequality to represent the number of pounds of nuts the company can order and get free shipping.

1 Solve the inequality and graph the solution on one number line.

LESSON 4

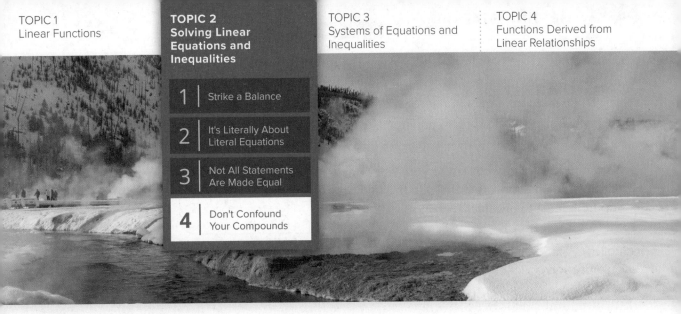

Don't Confound Your Compounds

Solving and Graphing Compound Inequalities

KEY TERMS

- **compound inequality**
- **solution of a compound inequality**
- **conjunction**
- **disjunction**

Learning Goals

- Write simple and compound inequalities.
- Graph compound inequalities.
- Solve compound inequalities.

REVIEW (1–2 minutes)

> Graph each inequality on the number line shown.

1. $x \geq -6$

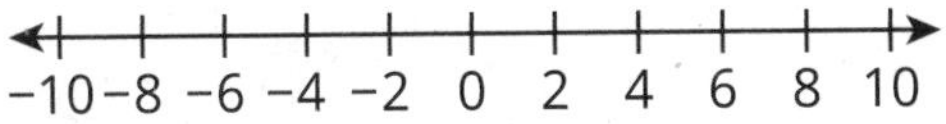

2. $x < 7$

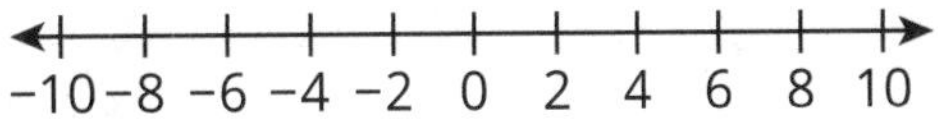

3. $-5 \leq x < 4$

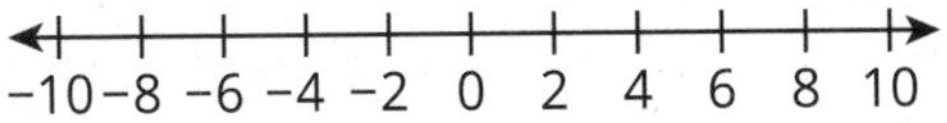

You have graphed and solved linear inequalities in two or more steps.

How can you determine the solution to a pair of inequalities joined by the words *and* or *or*?

Human Number Line

In this activity you will form a human number line with the other students in your class.

On the index card provided to you, write down the number of the day on which you were born. Use the numbers on your cards to line up from least to greatest.

ASK YOURSELF...
What numbers do you expect to see along the number line?

> Follow your teacher's directions to complete the activity. Then, reflect on what you noticed.

1. What patterns did you observe on the number line in response to the different directions?

2. Why do you think every student raised their card if they were born after the 10th or before the 20th?

3. Why do you think no student raised their card if they were born before the 10th and after the 20th?

Writing Compound Inequalities

You have explored some simple inequalities. Now let's look at inequalities that are more complex.

HABITS OF MIND
- Look for and make use of structure.
- Look for and express regularity in repeated reasoning.

When high schools buy sports equipment for their athletes from GoodSportsBuys.com, they must pay the cost of the items as well as a shipping fee. They add the shipping fee to each order based on the total cost of the items purchased.

Total Cost of Items	Shipping Fee
\$0.01 up to and including \$20	\$6.50
More than \$20 up to and including \$50	\$9.00
Between \$50 and \$75	\$11.00
From \$75 up to, but not including, \$100	\$12.25
\$100 or more	\$13.10

You can use inequalities to represent the various shipping fee categories at GoodSportsBuys.com. If you let x represent the total cost of items purchased, you can write an inequality to represent each shipping fee category.

1. Complete each inequality using an inequality symbol.

   a) \$6.50 shipping fees: x _______ \$0.01 and x _______ \$20

   b) \$9.00 shipping fees: x _______ \$20 and x _______ \$50

   c) \$11.00 shipping fees: x _______ \$50 and x _______ \$75

   d) \$12.25 shipping fees: x _______ \$75 and x _______ \$100

   e) \$13.10 shipping fees: x _______ \$100

2. Identify the inequalities in Question 1 that are compound inequalities.

TAKE NOTE...
A **compound inequality** is an inequality formed by the union *or*, or the intersection *and*, of two simple inequalities.

Let's consider two examples of compound inequalities. First, consider a compound inequality conjoined by *and*.

WORKED EXAMPLE

$$x > 2 \text{ and } x \leq 7.$$

Read this inequality as "all numbers greater than 2 and less than or equal to 7."

You can also write the inequality in the compact form of

$$2 < x \leq 7.$$

Now, let's consider a compound inequality conjoined by *or*.

WORKED EXAMPLE

$$x \leq -4 \text{ or } x > 2$$

Read this inequality as "all numbers less than or equal to −4 or greater than 2."

You can only write compound inequalities containing *and* in compact form.

3 Write the compound inequalities from Question 1 in compact form.

(a) \$6.50 shipping fees: ______________________________

(b) \$9.00 shipping fees: ______________________________

(c) \$11.00 shipping fees: ______________________________

(d) \$12.25 shipping fees: ______________________________

Problems with More than One Solution

HABITS OF MIND

- Reason abstractly and quantitatively.
- Construct viable arguments and critique the reasoning of others.

Now you can apply what you know about compound inequalities to help you solve some problems.

Water becomes non-liquid when it is 32°F or below, or when it is at least 212°F.

1. Represent this information on the number line.

2. Write a compound inequality to represent the same information. **Define your variable.**

3. Is your inequality always true, sometimes true, or never true? **Explain your reasoning.**

Luke and Logan play for the same baseball team. They practice at the Lions Park baseball field. Luke lives 3 miles from the field, and Logan lives 2 miles from the field.

4. What is the shortest distance, *d*, that could separate their homes? The longest distance, *d*?

ASK YOURSELF...
Would a diagram be helpful?

5. Write a compound inequality to represent all the possible distances that could separate their homes. Then represent the solution on the number line.

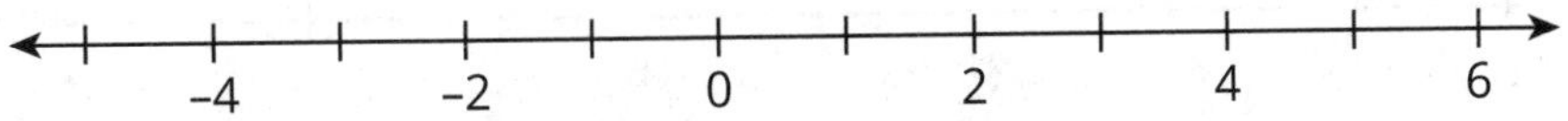

6. Luke bikes to Logan's house. He has been biking for 0.5 mile. What is the greatest number of miles he may have left to bike to reach Logan's house?

THINK ABOUT...
How accurate does your answer need to be?

Jodi bought a new car with a 14-gallon gas tank. Around town, she is able to drive 336 miles on one tank of gas. On her first trip traveling on highways, she drives 448 miles on one tank of gas.

7 Write a compound inequality in compact form that represents how many miles Jodi can drive on a tank of gas. Let *m* represent the number of miles per gallon of gas.

8 Rewrite the compound inequality as two simple inequalities separated by either *and* or *or*.

ASK YOURSELF...
How can you solve the compound inequality without rewriting it as two simple inequalities?

9 Solve each simple inequality. Then write the solution in compact form.

10 Explain your solution in terms of the problem situation.

11 Represent the solution on the number line. **Describe the shaded region in terms of the problem situation.**

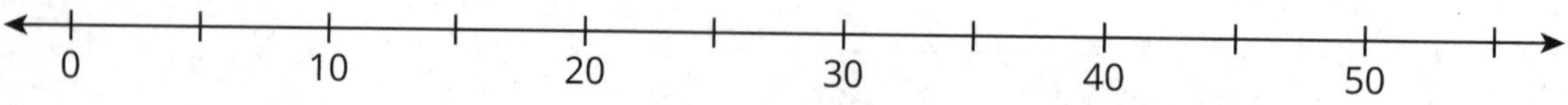

Solving Compound Inequalities

HABITS OF MIND

- Look for and make use of structure.
- Look for and express regularity in repeated reasoning.

Remember, a compound inequality is an inequality formed by the union *or*, or the intersection *and*, of two simple inequalities.

The **solution of a compound inequality** in the form $a < x < b$, where a and b are any real numbers, is the part or parts of the solutions that satisfy both inequalities. This type of compound inequality is a **conjunction**. The solution of a compound inequality in the form $x < a$ or $x > b$, where a and b are any real numbers, is the part or parts of the solution that satisfy either inequality. This type of compound inequality is a **disjunction**.

1. Classify each solution to all the questions in the previous activity as either a conjunction or disjunction.

Let's consider two examples for representing the solution of a compound inequality on a number line.

WORKED EXAMPLE

The compound inequality shown involves *and* and is a conjunction.

$$x \leq 1 \text{ and } x > -3$$

Represent each part above the number line.

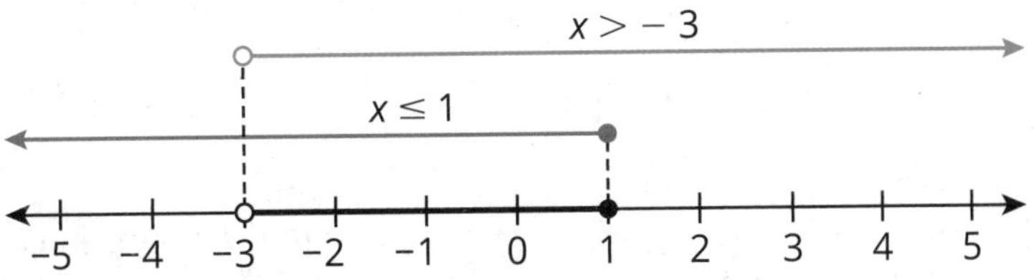

$$x \leq 1 \text{ and } x > -3$$

$$-3 < x \leq 1$$

The solution is the region that satisfies both inequalities. Graphically, the solution is the overlapping, or the intersection, of the separate inequalities.

WORKED EXAMPLE

The compound inequality shown involves *or* and is a disjunction.

$$x < -2 \text{ or } x > 1$$

Represent each part above the number line.

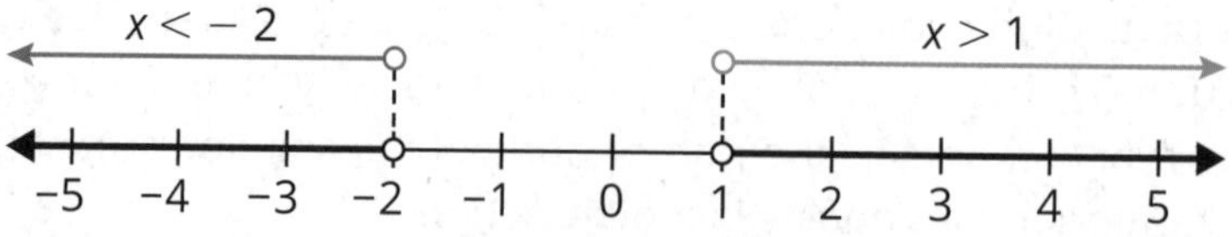

$$x < -2 \text{ or } x > 1$$

The solution is the region that satisfies either inequality. Graphically, the solution is the union, or all the regions, of the separate inequalities.

2 Consider the two worked examples in a different way.

(a) If the compound inequality in the first worked example, $x \leq 1$ and $x > -3$, was changed to the disjunction, $x \leq 1$ or $x > -3$, how would the solution set change? **Explain your reasoning.**

THINK ABOUT...
How might sketching a graph of the inequality on a number line help you visualize the differences?

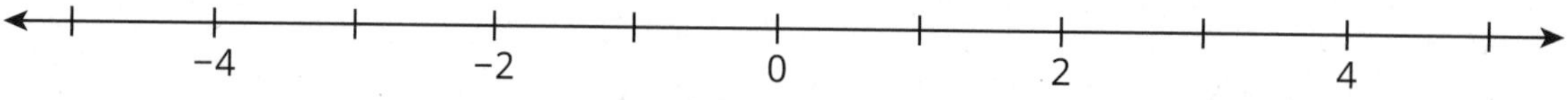

(b) If the compound inequality in the second worked example, $x < -2$ or $x > 1$, was changed to the conjunction, $x < -2$ and $x > 1$, how would the solution set change? **Explain your reasoning.**

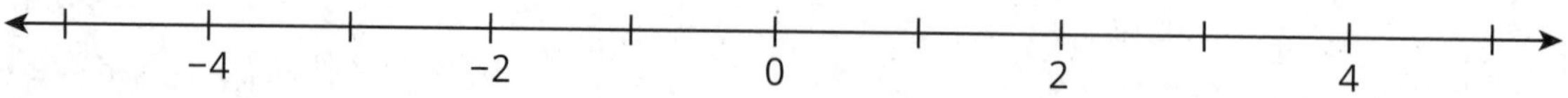

3 Represent the solution to each compound inequality on the number line shown. Then, write the final solution that represents the graph.

(a) $x < 2$ or $x > 3$

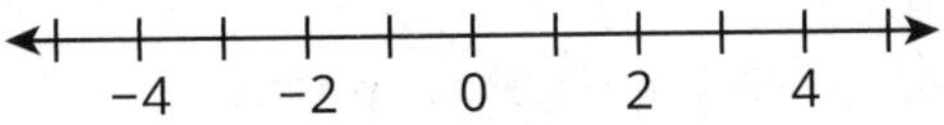

THINK ABOUT...
Pay attention to whether the inequality uses *and* or *or*.

(b) $-1 \geq x \geq -1$

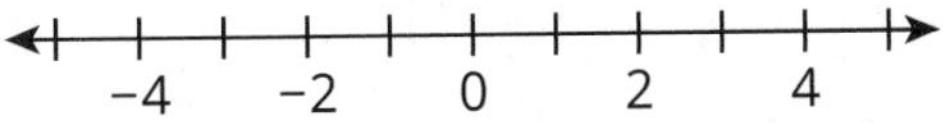

(c) $x < 0$ or $x < 2$

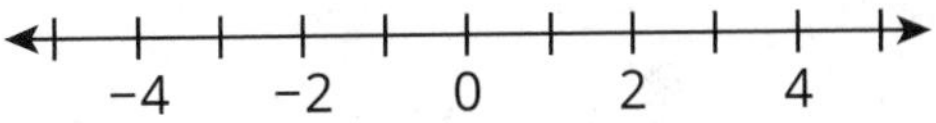

(d) $x > 1$ and $x < -2$

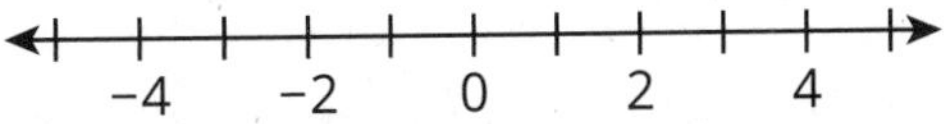

(e) $x < 3$ and $x > 2$

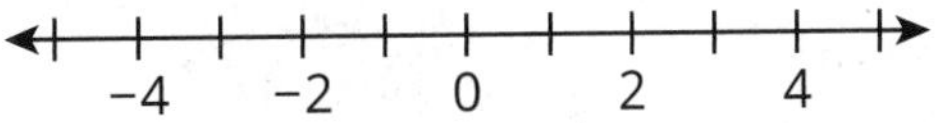

(f) $x < 2$ and $x < -1$

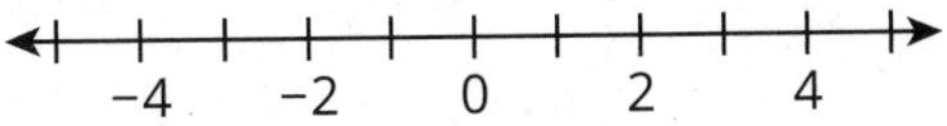

(g) $x > -1$ or $x < 0$

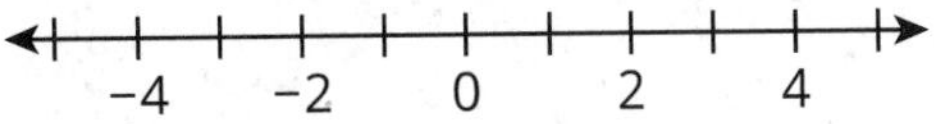

Solving Inequalities in Compact Form

HABITS OF MIND

- Look for and make use of structure.
- Look for and express regularity in repeated reasoning.

To solve a conjunction written in compact form, isolate the variable between the two inequality signs and then graph the resulting statement. To solve a disjunction, solve each inequality separately, keeping the word *or* between them, and then graph the resulting statements.

WORKED EXAMPLE

Consider the compound inequality $-3 \le 2x + 7 < 11$.
You can solve this equation in compact form by isolating the variable.

$$-3 \le 2x + 7 < 11$$
$$\underline{-7 \qquad -7 \quad -7}$$
$$-10 \le 2x < 4$$
$$-\frac{10}{2} \le \frac{2x}{2} < \frac{4}{2}$$
$$-5 \le x < 2$$

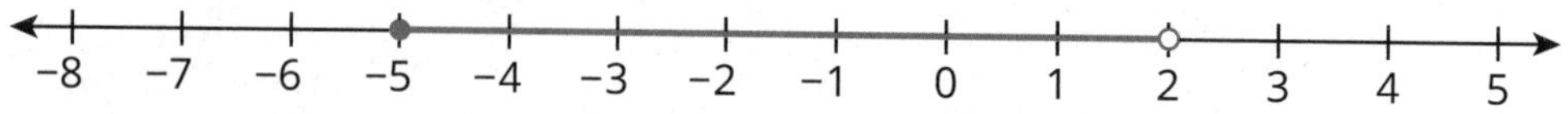

1 How is solving a compound inequality in compact form similar to solving a simple inequality? How is it different?

2 Solve and graph each compound inequality showing the steps you performed. Then, write the final solution that represents the graph.

ⓐ $6 < x - 6 \leq 9$

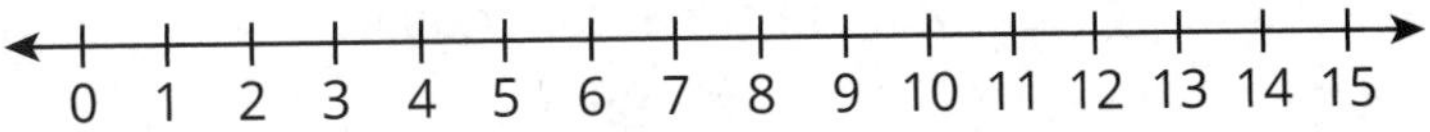

ⓑ $-2 < -x < 6$

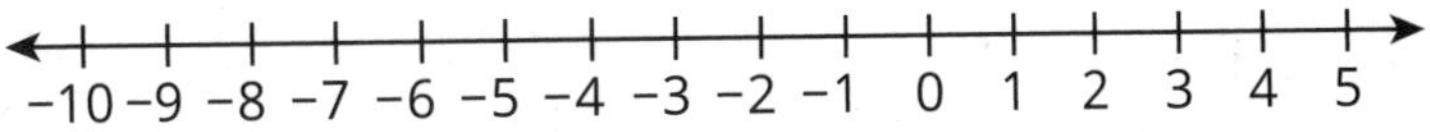

ⓒ $-4 \leq -3x + 1 \leq 12$

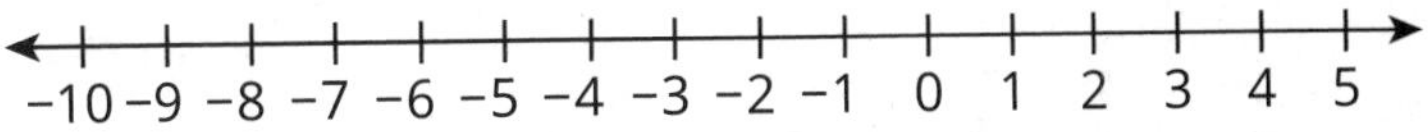

ⓓ $2x + 7 < 10$ or
$-2x + 7 > 10$

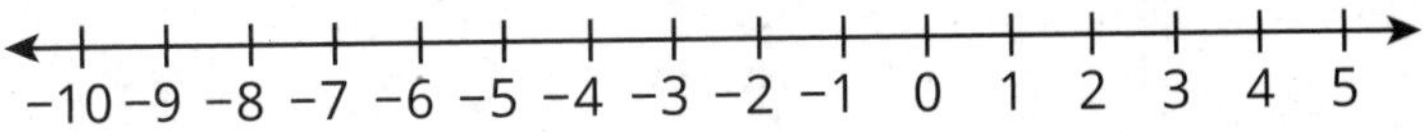

ⓔ $\frac{1}{2}x + 3 > 4$ or $-x < 3$

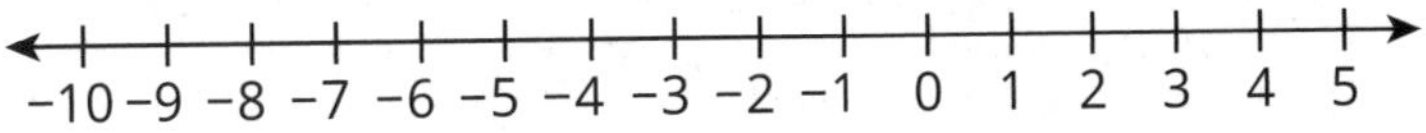

ⓕ $1 + 6x > 11$ or
$x - 4 < -5$

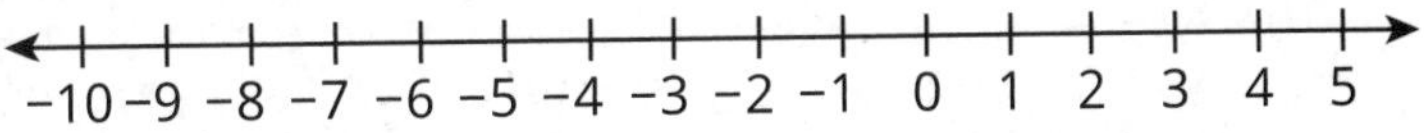

Make a Match

> Match each graph with the correct inequality.

Graph	Inequality
1 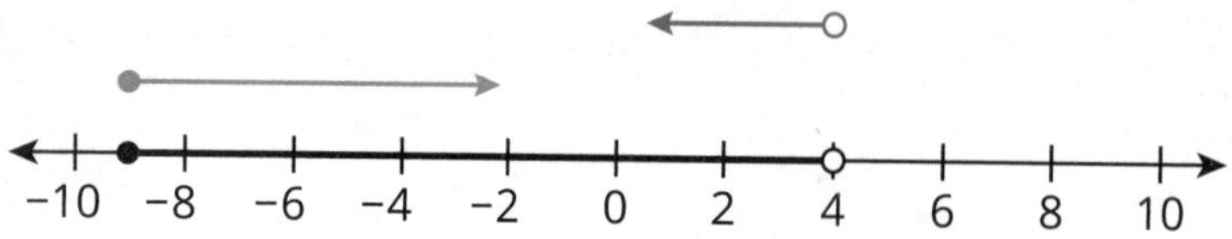	A. $2x + 8 \le 12$ and $3x + 9 > -6$
2 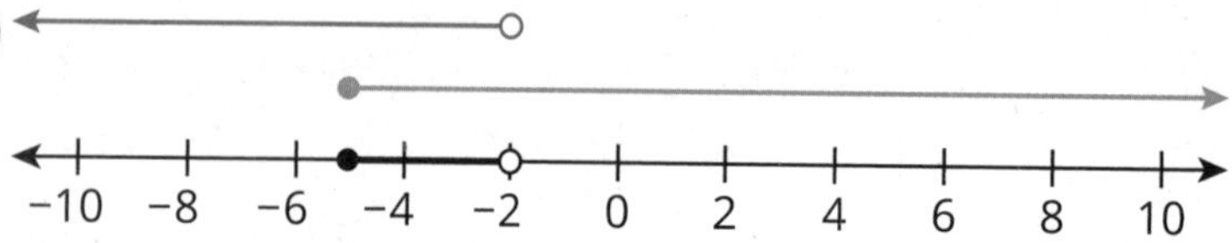	B. $-2x - 14 \le 4$ or $-2x - 3 > -11$
3 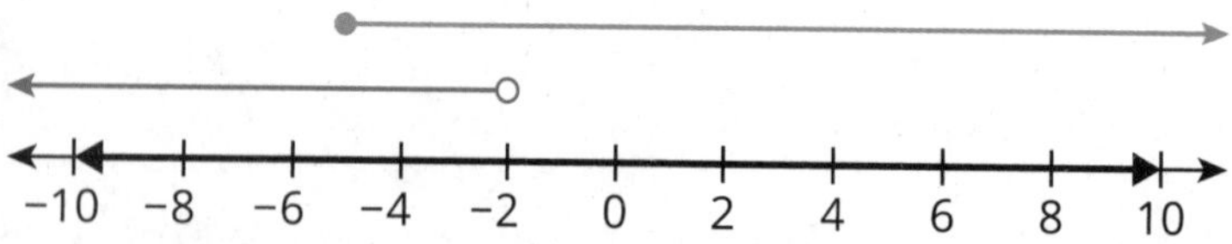	C. $-2x - 14 \le 4$ and $-2x - 3 > -11$
4 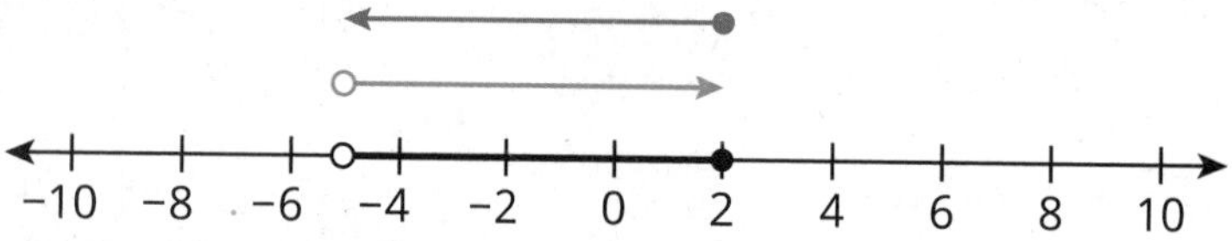	D. $12 < -3x + 6$ or $5x + 8 \ge -17$
5 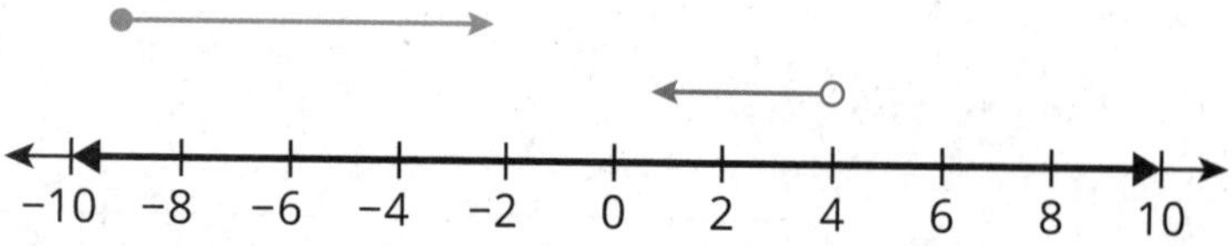	E. $12 < -3x + 6$ and $5x + 8 \ge -17$

LESSON 4 ASSIGNMENT

> Use a separate piece of paper for your Journal entry.

REMEMBER

The solution of a compound inequality in the form $a < x < b$, where a and b are any real numbers, is the part or parts of the solutions that satisfy both inequalities.

The solution of a compound inequality in the form $x < a$ or $x > b$, where a and b are any real numbers, is the part or parts of the solution that satisfy either inequality.

JOURNAL

Match each definition to its corresponding term.

1. compound inequality
2. conjunction
3. disjunction

(a) A solution of a compound inequality in the form $a < x < b$, where a and b are any real numbers

(b) An inequality formed by the union or, or the intersection and, of two simple inequalities

(c) A solution of a compound inequality in the form $x < a$ or $x > b$, where a and b are any real numbers

PRACTICE

1. Taneisha's family has signed up for a new cell phone plan. Taneisha now has a limit on the number of texts she can send or receive each month. She can text no more than 300 times per month.

   (a) Write a compound inequality to represent the number of texts, n, that Taneisha can send in a month.

   (b) Write the compound inequality in compact form.

   (c) Graph the inequality. Describe your number line representation.

2. John owns a 50-acre apple orchard. Unfavorable conditions such as drought and flooding will affect tree production. John does not want rainfall amounts to be less than 10 inches or more than 50 inches.

   (a) Represent the undesirable rainfall amounts on a number line.

Go to LiveHint.com for help on the PRACTICE questions.

(b) Write a compound inequality to represent the same information. Define your variable.

3 At John's apple orchard, the profit he will make depends on the number of bushels he grows and sells. He makes \$25 per bushel but must subtract \$300,000 for costs associated with growing the trees to calculate his profit.

(a) Write an expression to represent the profit John will make. Let b represent the number of bushels he will produce and sell.

(b) John must make at least \$80,000 to pay the bills, but he does not want to make more than \$250,000 because it will put him in a higher tax bracket. Write a compound inequality that represents the amount of profit John can make.

(c) Solve the compound inequality. Show your work.

(d) Graph the solution to the compound inequality. Describe the solution region in terms of the problem situation.

4 Solve each compound inequality.

(a) $-6x + 1 > -5$ and $3x + 4 \geq 1$

(b) $1 \leq 3j + 4 < 13$

(c) $2k - 4 \geq 2$ or $-4k + 6 > 3$

(d) $-10 < 4t - 2 \leq 10$

STRETCH Optional

A company produces T-shirts. There is a fixed monthly cost of \$500 to produce the T-shirts and a cost of \$4.50 per T-shirt for production. The company plans on selling the T-shirts for \$11.50 each. Write an expression to determine the cost to produce x t-shirts in a month. The company would like the profit next month to be at least \$2,000 but no more than \$10,000 for tax purposes.

1 Write and solve a compound inequality that represents the amount of profit the company can make.

2 Describe the solution region in terms of the problem situation.

MIXED PRACTICE

> This Mixed Practice worksheet includes two sections: Spaced Review and End-of-Topic Review. **Use a separate piece of paper to show your work.**

Spaced Review

> Practice concepts from previous topics.

1 Determine whether each relation shown is a function. Explain your reasoning.

(a)

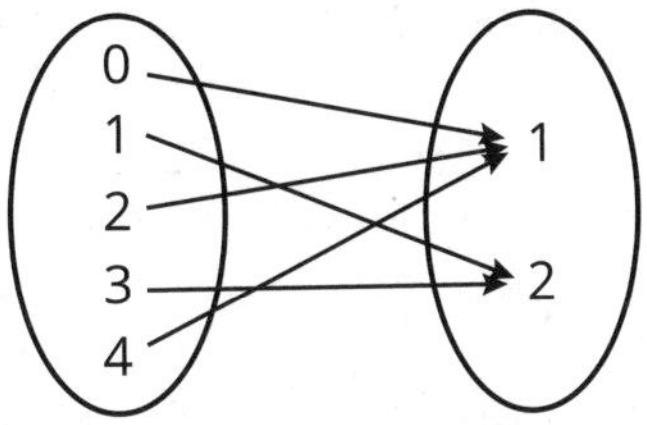

(b)

x	*y*
–5	6
–4	7
–5	8
–5	9

(c) {(–3, 10), (0, 8), (–1, 10), (9, 2)}

2 Draw a graph to represent the each linear relationship. Then, write an equation to represent the relationship.

(a) Linear proportional relationship

(b) Linear non-proportional relationship

3 Identify the slope and *y*-intercept of each equation.

(a) $y = 4x$

(b) $y = x - 4$

4 Calculate the slope of the line represented by each table.

(a)

x	*y*
4	8
10	11
16	14
20	16

(b)

x	*y*
2	5
4	3
5	2
8	–1

5 Evaluate $f(x) = 3x - 10$ for the given values.

(a) $f(0)$

(b) $f(5)$

6 The Peters Creek restaurant has an all-you-can eat shrimp deal. Currently, the cost of the deal is 50 cents per shrimp, with free soft drinks. The cost for the shrimp deal is modeled by the function $c(x) = 0.50x$, where x represents the number of shrimp eaten. A new manager decides to change the cost of the deal to 25 cents per shrimp, but a $5.00 charge for soft drinks. Let $p(x)$ be the function that represents the new cost for the all-you-can-eat shrimp deal.

(a) Write an equation for $p(x)$ in terms of $c(x)$. Describe the transformation performed on $c(x)$ to produce $p(x)$.

(b) Sketch the graph of $c(x)$ and $p(x)$ on the same coordinate plane.

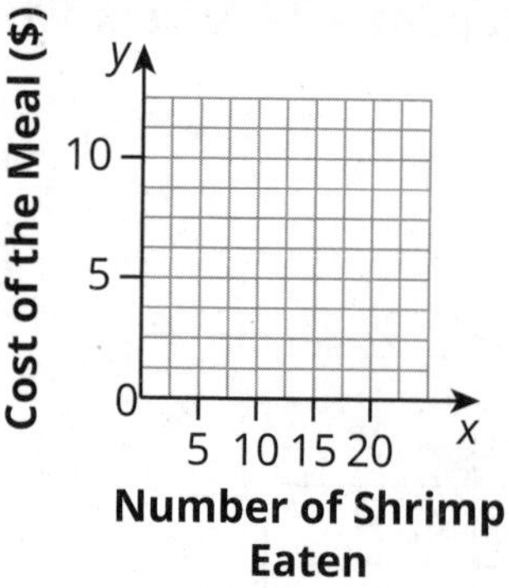

(c) Write the equation for the function $p(x)$ in general form.

7 Write a recursive formula for each sequence.

(a) 3, −6, 12, −24, 48, ...

(b) 180, 160, 140, 120, 100, ...

End-of-Topic Review

AVAILABLE ONLINE

1. A **Topic Summary** reviews the main concepts for the topic.
2. A video of the **Worked Example** is provided.

> Practice concepts you learned in **Solving Linear Equations and Inequalities.**

8 Joan received $100 in gift cards for an online music store. Each time she buys a new song it costs $1.29. She has already bought 10 songs. Write an inequality that models this situation. Then determine the number of songs she can buy and not run out of gift card money.

9 Solve the equation. Write the properties that justify each step.

$-\frac{2}{3}x(-9x + 24) = 2x - 4$

10 Solve each equation.

(a) $8(2m - 7) = 10m - 2$

(b) $-3(y + 20) = -9y$

11 Solve the equation and check your solution.

$\frac{3}{4}x - 11 = 4 + \left(-\frac{3}{4}x + 3\right)$

12 Determine whether the equation has one solution, no solution, or infinite solutions.

$3\left(2 + \frac{2}{3}x\right) = 5 + 2(x + 1)$

13 The formula for the area of a trapezoid is $A = \frac{1}{2}h(b_1 + b_2)$, where h is its height and b_1 and b_2 are the lengths of each base.

(a) Rewrite the equation to solve for b_1.

(b) Determine the length of the other base of a trapezoid when one base measures 10 m, the height is 20 m, and the area of the trapezoid is 600 square meters.

14 Solve each compound inequality. Graph the final solution on a number line.

(a) $-4 \le 3x + 2 \le 14$

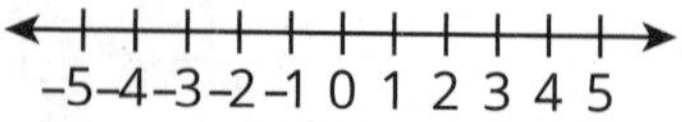

(b) $\frac{1}{3}x + 3 \ge 4$ or $-x < 2$

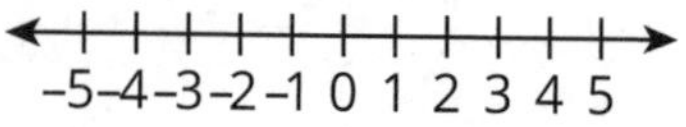

LESSON 1

Double the Fun

Introduction to Systems of Equations

KEY TERMS

system of linear equations

consistent systems

inconsistent systems

Learning Goals

- Write equations in standard form.
- Determine the intercepts of an equation in standard form.
- Use intercepts to graph an equation.
- Write a system of equations to represent a problem context.
- Solve systems of linear equations exactly and approximately.
- Interpret the solution to a system of equations in terms of a problem situation.
- Use slope and *y*-intercept to determine whether the system of two linear equations has one solution, no solution, or infinite solutions.

REVIEW (1–2 minutes)

> Determine an ordered pair that represents a solution to each equation.

1. $4x + 7y = 24$

2. $5x - 2y = -6$

3. $\frac{1}{2}x + \frac{3}{4}y = 10$

You have examined different linear functions and solved for unknown values.

How many solutions exist when you consider two functions at the same time?

Ticket Tabulation

The Marshall High School Athletic Association sells tickets for the weekly football games. Students pay $5 and adults pay $10 for a ticket. The athletic association needs to raise $3000 selling tickets to send the team to an out-of-town tournament.

1. Write an equation to represent this situation.

2. What combination of student and adult ticket sales would achieve the athletic association's goal?

3. Compare your combination of ticket sales with your classmates'. Did you all get the same answer? **Explain why or why not.**

MATHia CONNECTION
- Representing Systems of Linear Functions

Analyzing the Graph of an Equation in Standard Form

HABITS OF MIND
- Reason abstractly and quantitatively.
- Construct viable arguments and critique the reasoning of others.

> Consider the goal of the athletic association described in the previous activity.

Let *s* represent the number of student tickets sold, and let *a* represent the number of adult tickets sold. You can write an equation for this situation in standard form as $5s + 10a = 3000$.

One efficient way to graph a linear function in standard form is to use *x*- and *y*-intercepts.

- Calculate the *x*-intercept by substituting $y = 0$ and solving for *x*.
- Calculate the *y*-intercept by substituting $x = 0$ and solving for *y*.

REMEMBER...
The standard form of a linear equation is $Ax + By = C$ where *A*, *B*, and *C* are constants and *A* and *B* are not both zero.

1. Use the *x*-intercept and *y*-intercept to graph the equation.

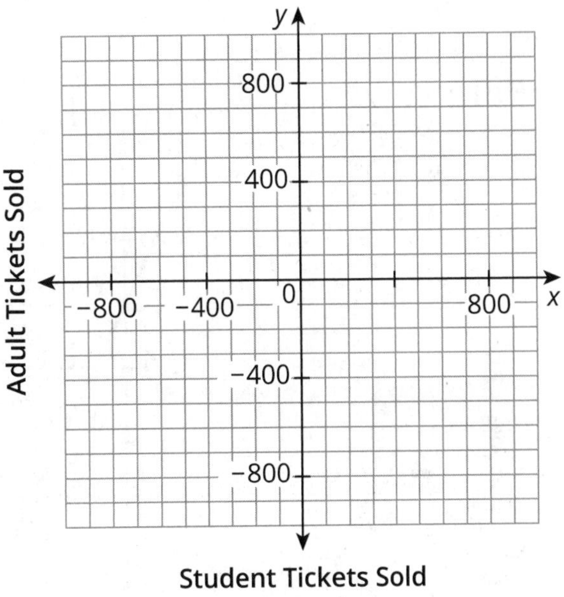

2. Determine the domain and range of each.

   (a) The mathematical function

   (b) The function modeling the real-world situation

3. Explain what each intercept means in terms of the problem situation.

4 Identify the slope of the function. Interpret its meaning in terms of the problem situation.

5 How can you use the graph to determine a combination of ticket sales to meet the goal of $3000?

ASK YOURSELF...
What does each point on the graph of an equation represent?

6 Felino graphed the equation $5s + 10a = 3000$ in a different way.
Explain why Felino's graph is correct.

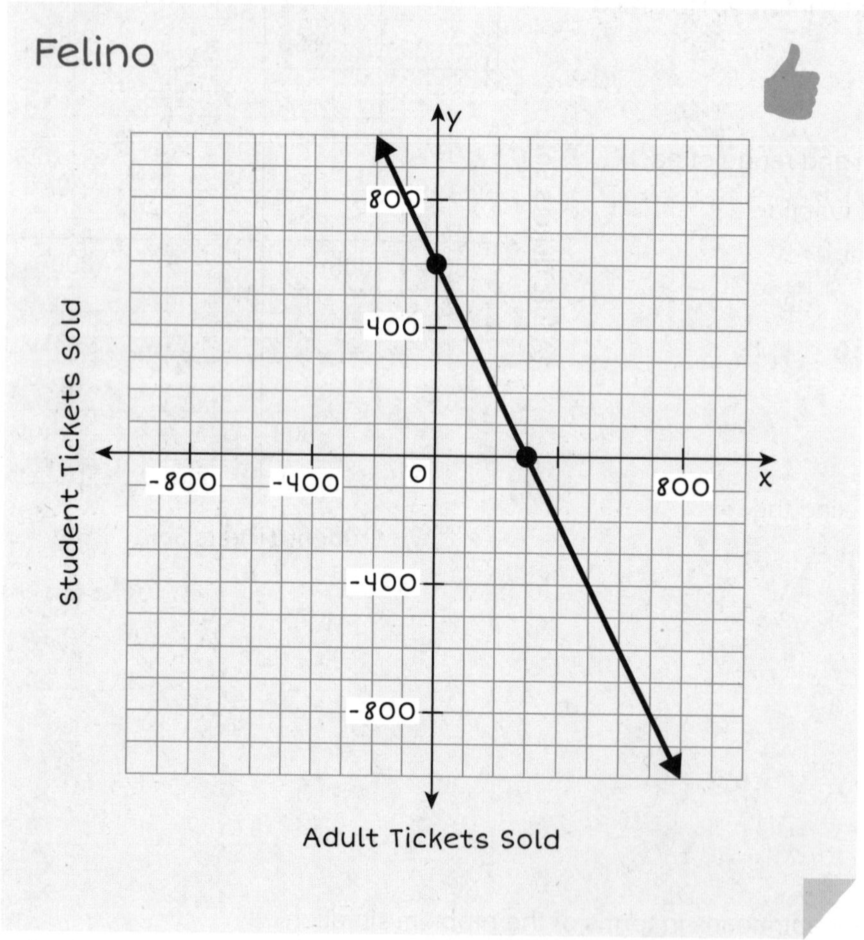

7 Use Felino's graph to describe the domain and range of each.

(a) The mathematical function

(b) The function modeling the real-world situation

8 Explain what each intercept means in terms of the problem situation.

9 Identify the slope of the function. Interpret its meaning in terms of the problem situation.

10 Compare the domain and range of the two functions that model the real-world situation. **What do you notice?**

11 Compare the *x*-intercepts and the *y*-intercepts of the two graphs. **What do you notice?**

12 Is there a way to determine the total amount of money collected from either graph? **Explain why or why not.**

MATHia CONNECTION
- Review of Modeling Linear Systems Involving Integers
- Solving Linear Systems Using Substitution

Determining the Solution to a System of Linear Equations

HABITS OF MIND
- Model with mathematics.
- Use appropriate tools strategically.

Lets's consider another equation relating the quantities from the Getting Started.

> The athletic director of the Marshall High School Athletic Association says that they sold 450 total tickets to the home game.

1 Write an equation that represents this situation. Let *s* represent the number of student tickets sold, and let *a* represent the number of adult tickets sold.

> Consider the coordinate planes that contain the function that models the earnings from ticket sales that you analyzed in the previous activity.

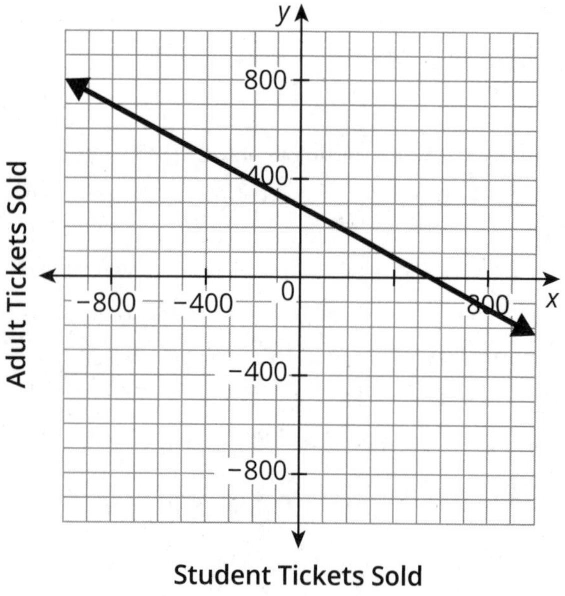

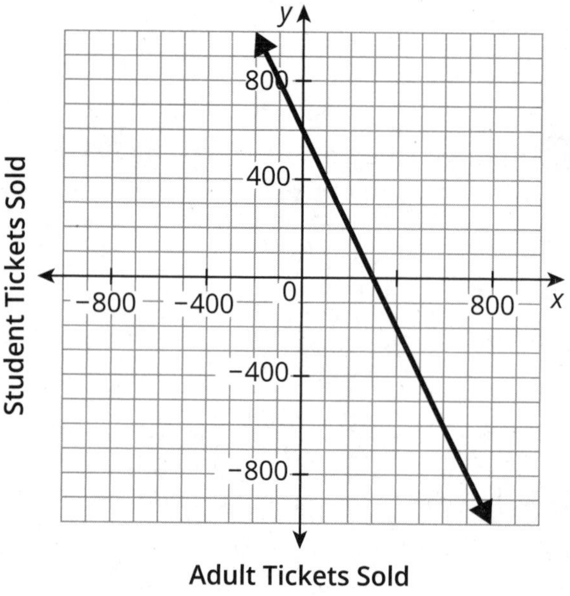

2 Use *x*- and *y*-intercepts to graph the function modeling the total number of tickets sold on each coordinate plane.

3 If the athletic association reached its goal of $3000 in ticket sales, how many of each type of ticket did they sell? Is there more than one solution?

REMEMBER...
According to the situation, they sold 450 tickets to the game.

4 Use technology to locate the exact point of intersection. **Explain the process you used.**

5 Justify algebraically that your solution is correct.

The two graphed equations share a relationship between quantities. Each equation describes a relationship between the number of adult tickets sold and the number of student tickets sold.

In one, the relationship is defined by the cost of each ticket and the total amount collected. In the second, the relationship is defined by the total number of tickets sold.

The two equations together form a *system of linear equations*. When two or more linear equations define a relationship between quantities, they form a **system of linear equations**.

Systems with No Solution, One Solution, or an Infinite Number of Solutions

HABITS OF MIND
- Look for and make use of structure.
- Look for and express regularity in repeated reasoning.

In this activity, you will consider the types of solutions to a system of linear equations.

Marcus and Phillip are in the Robotics Club. They are both saving money to buy materials to build a new robot.

Marcus opens a new bank account. He deposits $25 that he won at a robotics competition. He also plans on depositing $10 a week that he earns from tutoring.

Phillip decides he wants to save money as well. He already has $40 saved from mowing lawns over the summer. He plans to also save $10 a week from his allowance.

1 Write equations to represent the amount of money Marcus saves and the amount of money Phillip saves.

2 Use your equations to predict when Marcus and Phillip will have the same amount of money saved.

You can prove your prediction by solving and graphing a system of linear equations.

3 Analyze the equations in your system.

(a) How do the slopes compare? **Describe what this means in terms of this problem situation.**

(b) How do the *y*-intercepts compare? **Describe what this means in terms of this problem situation.**

4 Determine the solution of the system of linear equations algebraically and graphically.

(a) Use the substitution method to determine the intersection point. Then determine whether your solution makes sense. **Describe what it means in terms of the problem situation.**

(b) Predict what the graph of this system will look like. **Explain your reasoning**.

(c) Graph both equations on the coordinate plane.

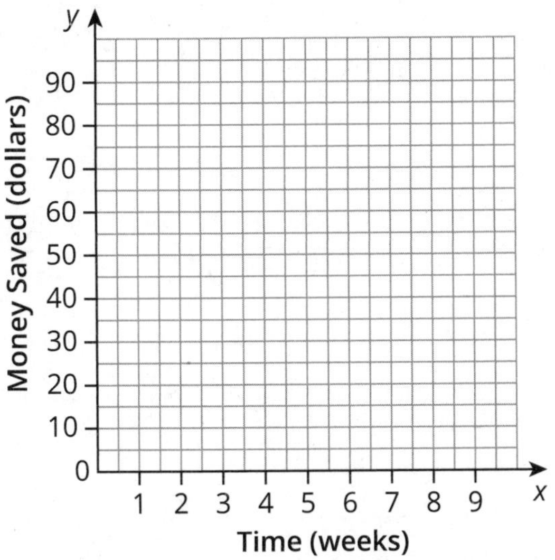

5 Analyze the graph you created.

(a) Describe the relationship between the graphs.

(b) Does this linear system have a solution? **Explain your reasoning**.

6 Was your prediction in Question 2 correct? **Explain how you algebraically and graphically proved your prediction.**

Tonya is also in the Robotics Club and has heard about Marcus's and Phillip's savings plans. She wants to be able to buy her new materials before Phillip, so she opens her own bank account. She is able to deposit $40 in her account that she has saved from her job as a waitress. Each week she also deposits $4 from her tips.

7 Use equations and graphs to determine when Tonya and Phillip have saved the same amount of money.

REMEMBER...
Define your variables!

ⓐ Write a linear system to represent the total amount of money Tonya and Phillip have saved after a certain amount of time.

ⓑ Graph the linear system on the coordinate plane.

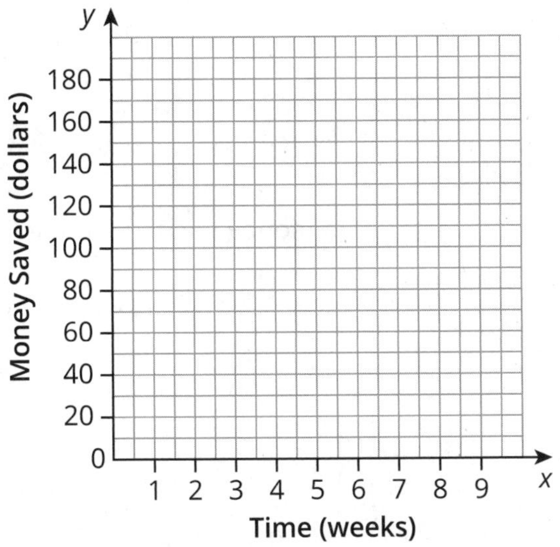

ⓒ Do the graphs intersect? **If so, describe the meaning in terms of this problem situation.**

Phillip and Tonya went on a shopping spree this weekend and spent all their savings except for $40 each. Phillip is still saving $10 a week from his allowance. Tonya now deposits her tips twice a week. On Tuesdays, she deposits $4, and on Saturdays, she deposits $6.

8 Phillip claims he is still saving more each week than Tonya.

(a) Do you think Phillip's claim is true? **Explain your reasoning**.

(b) How can you prove your prediction?

9 Prove your prediction algebraically and graphically.

(a) Write a new linear system to represent the total amount of money each friend has after a certain amount of time.

(b) Graph the linear system on the coordinate plane

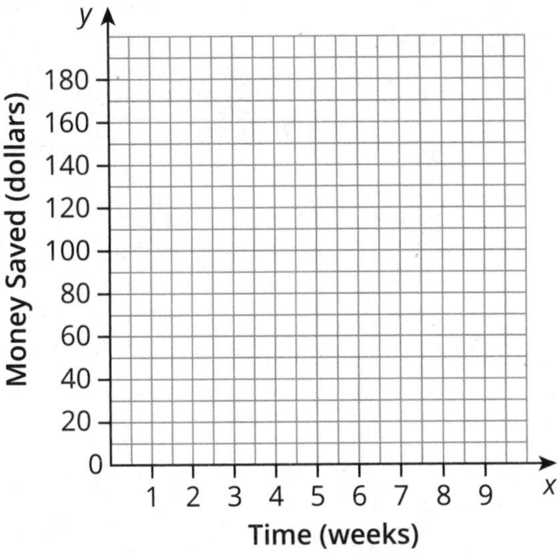

10 Analyze the graph.

(a) Describe the relationship between the graphs. **What does this mean in terms of this problem situation?**

(b) Algebraically prove the relationship you stated in part (a).

(c) How does this solution prove the relationship? **Explain your reasoning**.

11 Was Phillip's claim that he is still saving more than Tonya a true statement? **Explain why or why not.**

Beating the System

> Consider the systems you solved algebraically in this lesson.

1. How does solving a linear system in two variables compare to solving an equation in one variable?

A system of equations may have one unique solution, no solution, or infinite solutions. Systems that have one or an infinite number of solutions are **consistent systems**. Systems with no solution are **inconsistent systems**.

2. Complete the table.

System of Two Linear Equations	Consistent Systems		Inconsistent Systems
Description of *y*-Intercepts	*y*-intercepts can be the same or different	*y*-intercepts are the same	*y*-intercepts are different
Number of Solutions			
Description of Graph			

3. Explain why the *x*- and *y*-coordinates of the points where the graphs of a system intersect are solutions.

LESSON 1 ASSIGNMENT

> Use a separate piece of paper for your Journal entry.

JOURNAL

Define each term in your own words.

1. consistent systems
2. inconsistent systems

REMEMBER

When two or more equations define a relationship between quantities, they form a system of linear equations. The point of intersection of a graphed system of linear equations is the solution to both equations. A system of linear equations can have one solution, no solution, or infinite solutions.

PRACTICE

1. Mr. Johanssen gives his class 50-question multiple-choice tests. Each correct answer is worth 2 points, while a half point is deducted for each incorrect answer. If the student does not answer a question, that question does not get any points.

   (a) A student needs to earn 80 points on the test in order to keep an A grade for the semester. Write an equation in standard form that represents the situation. Identify 3 combinations of correct and incorrect answers that satisfy the equation.

   (b) Determine the *x*- and *y*-intercepts of the equation and use them to graph the equation. Explain what each intercept means in terms of the problem situation.

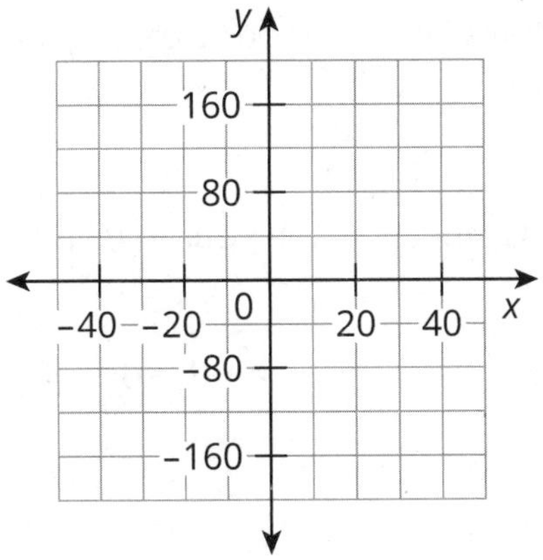

2 Wesley owns a dairy farm. In the morning, it takes him 0.3 hour to set up for milking the cows. Once he has set up, it takes Wesley 0.2 hour to milk each cow by hand. A milking machine he is considering will take 0.4 hour to set up each morning and takes 0.05 hour to milk each cow.

ⓐ Write a system of linear equations that represents the total amount of time Wesley will spend milking the cows using the two different methods.

ⓑ Graph both equations on the coordinate plane. Estimate the point of intersection and describe its meaning in context.

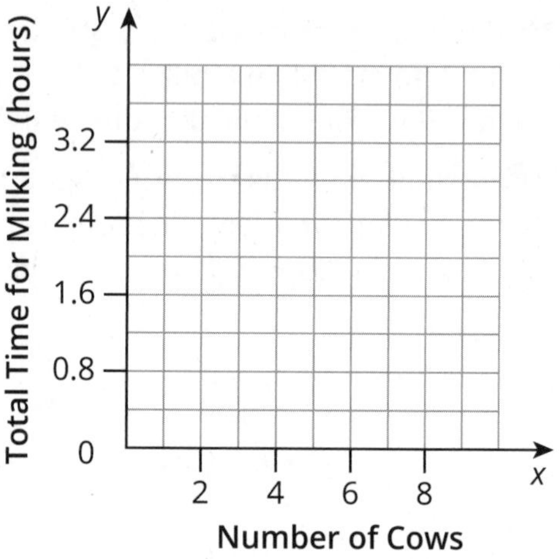

ⓒ Verify your answer to part (b) by solving the system algebraically.

ⓓ Does the solution make sense in terms of this problem situation? Explain your reasoning.

3 Identify whether each system is consistent or inconsistent. Explain your reasoning.

ⓐ $\begin{cases} -3x + 4y = 3 \\ -12x + 16y = 8 \end{cases}$

ⓑ $\begin{cases} 7x + 3y = 0 \\ 14x + 6y = 0 \end{cases}$

ⓒ $\begin{cases} 6x + y = 1 \\ -6y - 4y = -4 \end{cases}$

STRETCH Optional

> Solve the system of equations shown. Explain your reasoning.

$\begin{cases} 3x + 5y = 18 \\ y = |x - 4| \end{cases}$

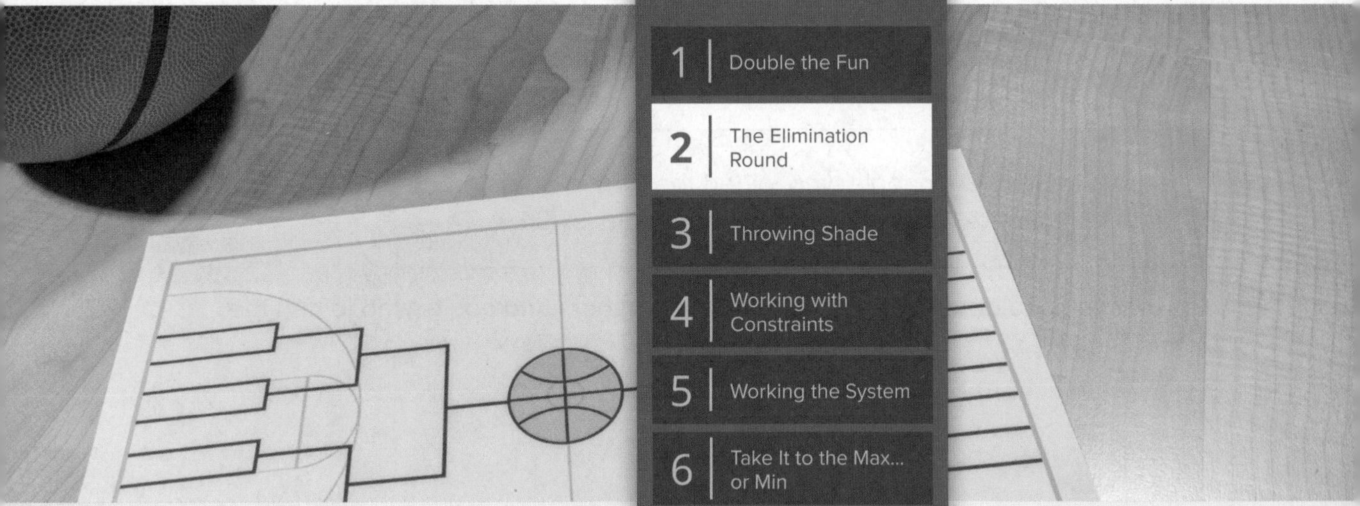

LESSON 2

The Elimination Round

Using Linear Combinations to Solve a System of Linear Equations

KEY TERM

linear combinations method

Learning Goals

- Write a system of equations to represent a problem context.
- Solve a system of equations algebraically using linear combinations.
- Interpret the solution to a system of equations in terms of a problem situation.

REVIEW (1–2 minutes)

> Determine the additive inverse for each expression.

1. 4

2. x

3. $20x$

4. $-9x$

5. $78.5x$

You have solved a system of linear equations graphically and algebraically, using the substitution method.

What are other algebraic strategies for solving systems of equations?

Comic-Con(line)

There are a total of 324 people who joined the Comic Gurus group on a social media site. Teenagers outnumber adults by 34.

1. Use reasoning to determine the number of teenagers and adults who joined the Comic Gurus.

2. How can you check that your solution is correct?

Combining Linear Systems

HABITS OF MIND
- Reason abstractly and quantitatively.
- Construct viable arguments and critique the reasoning of others.

> Consider the scenario from the Getting Started. Let's explore an algebraic strategy to determine a solution.

1 Write the system that represents the problem situation. Use x to represent the teenagers of the group, and use y to represent the adults of the group. Write the equations in standard form.

> Analyze Chloe's and Mara's strategies for solving the system of equations.

REMEMBER...
As long as you maintain equality, you can rewrite equations any way you want.

Chloe

I can use the substitution method to solve this system.

$$x + y = 324$$
$$x - y = 34 \longrightarrow x = y + 34$$
$$(y + 34) + y = 324$$
$$2y + 34 = 324$$
$$2y = 290$$
$$y = 145$$

$$x = 145 + 34$$
$$x = 179$$

Mara

You can eliminate one of the quantities by adding the two equations together.

$$\begin{array}{r} x + y = 324 \\ +\ \ x - y = 34 \\ \hline 2x = 358 \\ x = 179 \end{array}$$

$$179 + y = 324$$
$$y = 145$$

2 Explain why each student is correct in their reasoning.

3 Examine the structure of the system. Which characteristic of the system made Mara's strategy efficient?

4 Identify the solution to the linear system as an ordered pair. Then interpret the solution in terms of this problem situation.

The algebraic method used by Mara to solve the linear system is the **linear combinations method**. The linear combinations method is a process used to solve a system of equations by adding two equations together, resulting in an equation with one variable. You can then determine the value of that variable and use it to determine the value of the other variable.

5 Solve each system of equations using the linear combinations method.

(a) $\begin{cases} -4x + y = 10 \\ -2x - y = -1 \end{cases}$

(b) $\begin{cases} \frac{1}{2}x + 5y = -6 \\ \frac{1}{2}x + y = -6 \end{cases}$

Using Additive Inverses to Combine Linear Systems

HABITS OF MIND
- Look for and make use of structure.
- Look for and express regularity in repeated reasoning.

In the system of equations from the previous activity, one of the variables in both equations has coefficients that are additive inverses. What if a system doesn't have variables that are additive inverses?

Let's use the strategy of linear combinations to solve other systems.

WORKED EXAMPLE

Consider this system of equations: $\begin{cases} 7x + 2y = 24 \\ 4x + y = 15 \end{cases}$

$$\begin{aligned} 7x + 2y &= 24 \\ -2(4x + y) &= -2(15) \end{aligned}$$

Multiply the second equation by a constant that results in coefficients that are additive inverses for one of the variables.

$$\begin{array}{r} 7x + 2y = 24 \\ + \ -8x - 2y = -30 \\ \hline -x + 0 = -6 \\ x = 6 \end{array}$$

Now that the *y*-values are additive inverses, you can solve this linear system for *x*.

$$\begin{aligned} 7(6) + 2y &= 24 \\ 42 + 2y &= 24 \\ 2y &= -18 \\ y &= -9 \end{aligned}$$

Substitute the value for *x* into one of the equations to determine the value for *y*.

The solution to the system of linear equations is (6, −9)

REMEMBER...
Two numbers with a sum of zero are additive inverses.

1. In the worked example, you only need to rewrite one equation to solve using the linear combinations method. **Why?**

ASK YOURSELF...
How can you solve the system of equations by transforming the first equation instead of the second?

TOPIC 3

Now, let's consider a system where you need to rewrite both equations.

WORKED EXAMPLE

Consider this system of equations:

$$\begin{cases} 4x + 2y = 3 \\ 5x + 3y = 4 \end{cases}$$

$3(4x + 2y) = 3(3)$
$-2(5x + 3y) = -2(4)$

Multiply each equation by a constant that results in coefficients that are additive inverses for one of the variables

$12x + 6y = 9$
$-10x - 6y = -8$

2 Determine the solution for the linear system in the worked example.

3 How could you have solved this system by creating *x*-values that are additive inverses?

4 Describe the first step needed to solve each system using the linear combinations method. Identify which variable you will solve for when you add the equations.

ⓐ $\begin{cases} 5x + 2y = 10 \\ 3x + 2y = 6 \end{cases}$

ⓑ $\begin{cases} x + 3y = 15 \\ 5x + 2y = 7 \end{cases}$

ⓒ $\begin{cases} 4x + 3y = 12 \\ 3x + 2y = 4 \end{cases}$

5 Analyze each system. How would you rewrite the system to solve for one variable? **Explain your reasoning.**

ⓐ $\begin{cases} \frac{1}{2}x - 5y = -45 \\ -\frac{1}{2}x + 10y = -20 \end{cases}$

ⓑ $\begin{cases} 4x + 3y = 24 \\ 3x + y = -2 \end{cases}$

ⓒ $\begin{cases} 3x + 5y = 17 \\ 2x + 3y = 11 \end{cases}$

ⓓ $\begin{cases} 6x + 3y = 5 \\ 2x + y = 1 \end{cases}$

ⓔ $\begin{cases} x + 2y = -6 \\ 2x + 4y = -12 \end{cases}$

MATHia CONNECTION

- Solving Linear Systems Using Linear Combinations
- Solving Linear Systems Using Any Method

Applying the Linear Combinations Method

HABITS OF MIND

- Model with mathematics.
- Use appropriate tools strategically.

Let's use the linear combinations method to solve a problem.

Let It Snow Resort offers two winter specials: the Get-Away Special and the Extended Stay Special. The Get-Away Special offers two nights of lodging and four meals for $270. The Extended Stay Special offers three nights of lodging and eight meals for $435. Determine what Let It Snow charges per night of lodging and per meal.

1. Write the system of linear questions that represents the problem situation. Let *n* represent the cost for one night of lodging at the resort and *m* represent the cost for each meal. Write the equations in standard form.

2. How are these equations the same? How are these equations different?

3. Solve the system comparing the two winter specials.

4 Interpret the solution of the linear system in the problem situation.

5 Check your solution algebraically.

6 Is the Extended Stay Special the better deal? **Explain why or why not.**

Fractions and Linear Combinations

Now let's consider using the linear combinations method to solve a system of linear equations involving fractions.

HABITS OF MIND
- Model with mathematics.
- Use appropriate tools strategically.

The School Spirit Club is making beaded friendship bracelets with the school colors to sell in the school store. The bracelets are black and orange and come in two lengths: 5 inches and 7 inches. The club has enough beads to make a total of 84 bracelets. So far, they have made 49 bracelets, which represents $\frac{1}{2}$ the number of 5-inch bracelets plus $\frac{3}{4}$ the number of 7-inch bracelets they plan to make and sell. Determine how many 5-inch and 7-inch bracelets the club plans to make.

1. Let x represent the number of 5-inch bracelets, and let y represent the number of 7-inch bracelets. Write a system of equations in standard form to represent this problem situation.

2. Karyn says that the first step to solving this system is to multiply the second equation by the least common denominator (LCD) of the fractions. Jacob says that the first step is to multiply the first equation by $-\frac{1}{2}$. Who is correct? **Explain your reasoning.**

3 Rewrite the equation containing fractions as an equivalent equation without fractions.

4 Determine the solution to the system of equations by using linear combinations and check your answer.

TOPIC 3

5 Interpret the solution of the linear system in terms of this problem situation.

There's a Method in My Madness

You have used three different methods for solving systems of equations: graphing, substitution, and linear combinations.

1. Describe how to use each method and the characteristics of the system that makes this method most appropriate.

   a. Graphing Method

   b. Substitution Method

   c. Linear Combinations Method

LESSON 2 ASSIGNMENT

> Use a separate piece of paper for your Journal entry.

JOURNAL

Explain how you would combine the two equations to solve for x and y. Use the following terms in your explanation: *linear combination* and *additive inverses.*

$$\begin{cases} 3x + 2y = -25 \\ x - 4y = 5 \end{cases}$$

REMEMBER

You can use the linear combinations method to solve a system of equations by adding two equations together, resulting in an equation with one variable. You can then determine the value of that variable and use it to determine the value of the other variable.

PRACTICE

1. The two high schools, Jefferson Hills East and Jefferson Hills West, are taking field trips to the state capital. A total of 408 students from Jefferson Hills East will be riding in 3 vans and 6 buses. A total of 516 students from Jefferson Hills West will be riding in 6 vans and 7 buses. Each van has the same number of passengers, and each bus has the same number of passengers.

   a. Write a system of equations that represents this problem situation. Let x represent the number of students in each van, and let y represent the number of students in each bus.

   b. How are the equations in the system the same? How are they different?

   c. Describe the first step needed to solve the system using the linear combinations method. Identify the variable that you will eliminate and the variable that you will solve for when you add the equations.

Go to LiveHint.com for help on the PRACTICE questions.

(d) Solve the system of equations using the linear combinations method. Show your work.

(e) Interpret the solution of the linear system in terms of the problem situation.

(f) Check your solution algebraically.

2 Solve each system of linear equations.

(a) $\begin{cases} 3x + y = 9 \\ 7x + 1y = 32 \end{cases}$

(b) $\begin{cases} 5x - 8y = 25 \\ -x + 4y = -8 \end{cases}$

(c) $\begin{cases} \frac{2}{3}x + \frac{1}{4}y = 18 \\ \frac{1}{6}x - \frac{3}{8}y = -6 \end{cases}$

(d) $\begin{cases} 5x + 4y = -14 \\ 3x + 6y = 6 \end{cases}$

STRETCH Optional

> Use linear combinations to solve the given system of three equations in three variables. Show your work.

$$\begin{cases} 3x + y + 3z = -2 \\ 6x + 2y + 9z = 5 \\ -2x - y - z = 3 \end{cases}$$

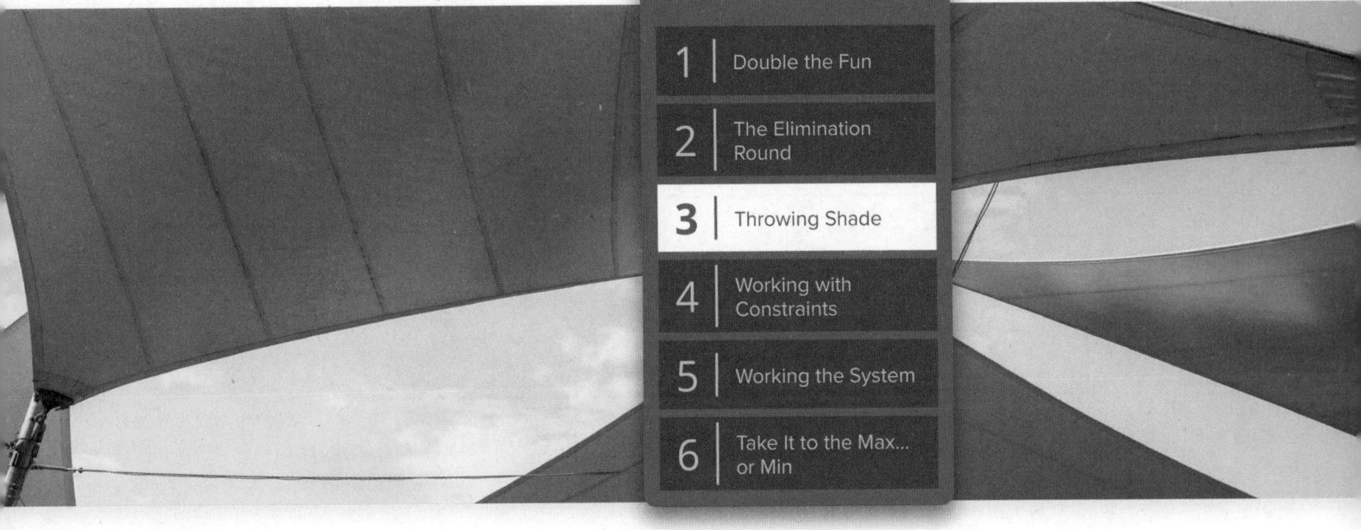

LESSON 3

Throwing Shade

Graphing Inequalities in Two Variables

KEY TERMS

half-plane
boundary line

Learning Goals

- Write an inequality in two variables.
- Graph an inequality in two variables on a coordinate plane.
- Determine whether a solid or dashed boundary line is used to graph an inequality on a coordinate plane.
- Interpret the solutions of inequalities mathematically and in the context of real-world problems.

REVIEW (1–2 minutes)

> Determine whether each point is a solution to $y > x$, $y < x$, or $y = x$.

1. (8, −2)
2. (0, 7)
3. (−1, −1)
4. (−4, −3)
5. (9, 9)
6. (−3, −10)

You have graphed linear inequalities in one variable.

What does the graph of a linear inequality in two variables look like? How does it compare to the graph of a linear equation?

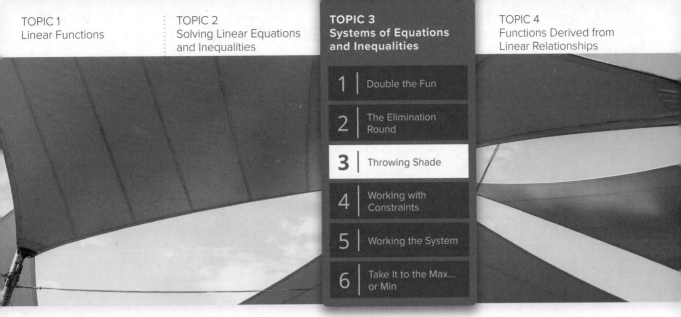

Making a Statement

> Consider each solution statement.

$x = 2$	$x < 2$	$x \leq 2$
	$x > 2$	$x \geq 2$

1. Compare the solution statements. **What does each one mean?**

2. Choose a solution statement and write a scenario to represent it. Then, modify the scenario so the resulting interpretation is one of the other four solution statements.

Linear Inequalities in Two Variables

HABITS OF MIND
- Model with mathematics.
- Use appropriate tools strategically.

Coach Purvis is analyzing the scoring patterns of players on his basketball team. Bena is averaging 20 points per game from scoring on two-point and three-point shots.

1 Consider the situation.

(a) If she scores 6 two-point shots and 2 three-point shots, will Bena meet her points-per-game average?

(b) If she scores 7 two-point shots and 2 three-point shots, will Bena meet her points-per-game average?

(c) If she scores 7 two-point shots and 4 three-point shots, will Bena meet her points-per-game average?

2 Write an equation to represent the number of two-point shots and the number of three-point shots that total 20 points.

3 Graph the equation you wrote on the coordinate plane. **Think about how you should label the graph.**

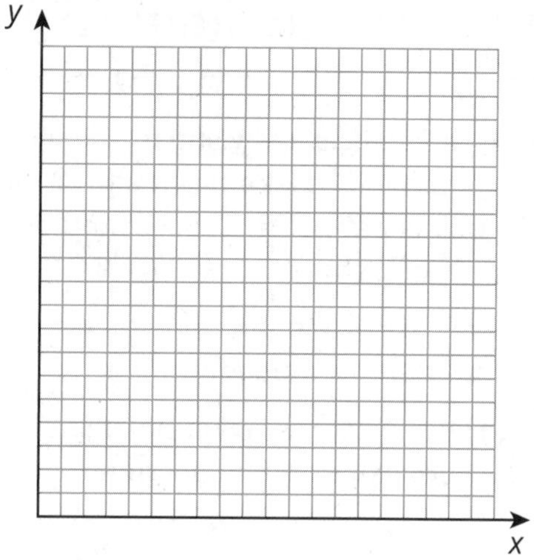

Coach Purvis believes that Danvers High School can win the district playoffs if Bena scores at least 20 points per game.

4 Consider the situation.

ⓐ How can you rewrite the equation you wrote in Question 2 to represent that Bena must score at least 20 points per game?

ⓑ Write an inequality in two variables that represents this problem situation.

REMEMBER...
An inequality is a statement formed by placing an inequality symbol (≥, ≤) between two expressions.

5 Complete the table of values. Then, add the ordered pairs in the table to the graph in Question 3. If the number of total points scored does not meet or exceed Bena's points-per-game average, use an X to plot the point. If the number of total points scored meets or exceeds Bena's points-per-game average, use a dot to plot the point.

Number of Two-Point Shots Scored	Number of Three-Point Shots Scored	Number of Total Points Scored
4	1	
6	1	
7	1	
8	2	
6	4	
9	5	

6 What do you notice about your graph?

7 What can you interpret about the solutions of the inequality from the graph?

8 Choose a different ordered pair located above the line and a different ordered pair that is located below the graph. How do these points confirm your interpretation of the situation? **Explain your reasoning.**

9 Shade the side of the graph that contains the combinations of shots that are greater than or equal to Bena's points-per-game average.

10 How do the solutions of the linear equation $2x + 3y = 20$ differ from the solutions of the linear inequality $2x + 3y \geq 20$?

11 Does the ordered pair (6.5, 5.5) make sense as a solution in the context of this problem situation? **Explain why or why not.**

Like linear equations, linear inequalities take different forms. Each of the linear inequalities in two variables shown represent a different relationship between the variables.

$ax + by < c$ $\qquad$ $ax + by > c$

$ax + by \leq c$ $\qquad$ $ax + by \geq c$

Determining the Graphs of Linear Inequalities

HABITS OF MIND
- Look for and make use of structure.
- Look for and express regularity in repeated reasoning.

The graph of a linear inequality in two variables is a **half-plane**.

A **boundary line**, determined by the inequality, divides the plane into two half-planes and the inequality symbol indicates which half-plane contains all the solutions. You represent these solutions by shading the appropriate half-plane.

TAKE NOTE...
If the inequality symbol is ≤ or ≥, the boundary line is a solid line, because all points on the line are part of the solution set.
If the symbol is < or > the boundary line is a dashed line, because no point on that line is a solution.

> Consider the linear inequality $y > 4x - 6$. The equation $y = 4x - 6$ determines the boundary line that divides the plane.

1. Should you represent the boundary line in this graph as a solid line or a dashed line? **Explain your reasoning.**

2. Graph the boundary line of the inequality on the coordinate plane.

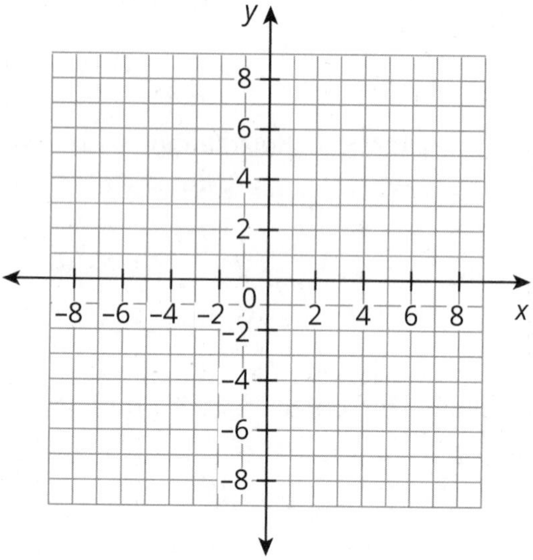

After you graph the solid or a dashed boundary line of the inequality, you need to decide which half-plane to shade. To make your decision, consider the point (0, 0).

- When (0, 0) is a solution, shade the half-plane that contains (0, 0) since it contains the solutions.
- When (0, 0) is not a solution, shade the half-plane that does not contain (0, 0) since it contains the solutions.

3 Decide which half-plane to shade.

(a) Is (0, 0) a solution? **Explain your reasoning.**

THINK ABOUT...
It's a good idea to check points in both half-planes to verify your solution.

(b) Shade the correct half-plane on the coordinate plane.

4 Match each graph to one of the inequalities given. In part (d), graph the inequality that was not graphed in parts (a) through (c).

$y \geq \frac{1}{2}x - 3$ $\qquad$ $y \leq \frac{1}{2}x - 3$ $\qquad$ $y > \frac{1}{2}x - 3$ $\qquad$ $y < \frac{1}{2}x - 3$

(a)

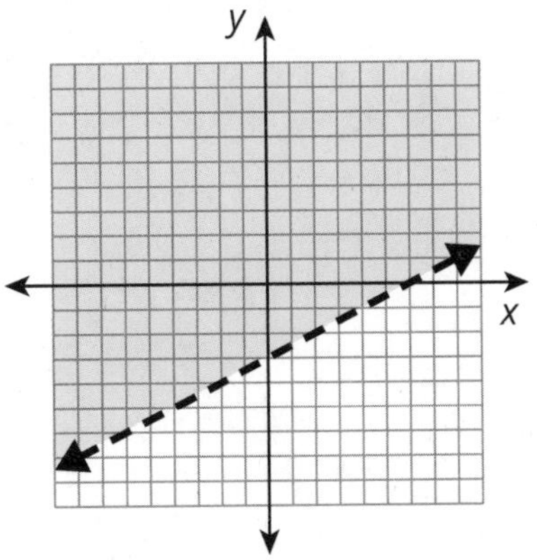

(b)

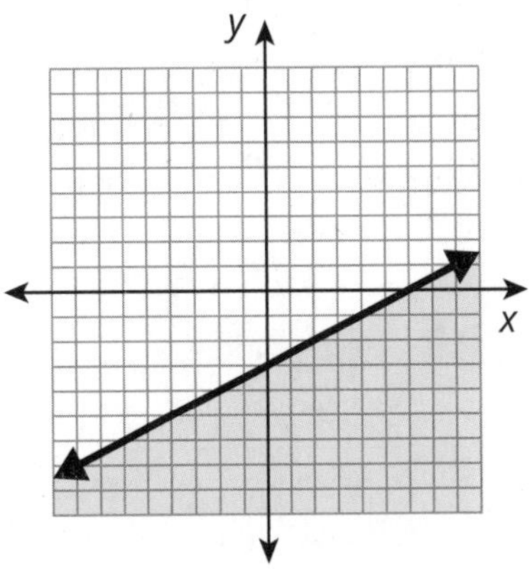

(c)

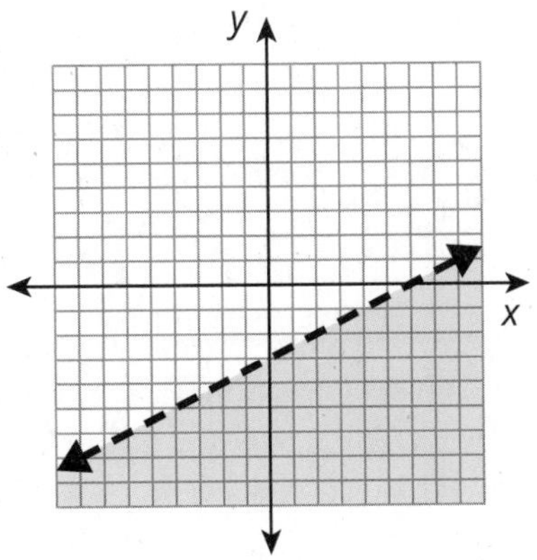

(d)

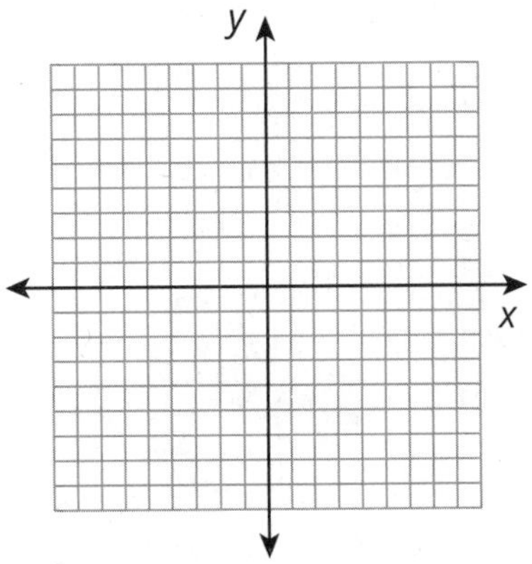

THINK ABOUT...
Consider the inequality symbol and which half-plane you will shade before you test any points.

5 Graph each linear inequality.

ⓐ $y > x + 3$

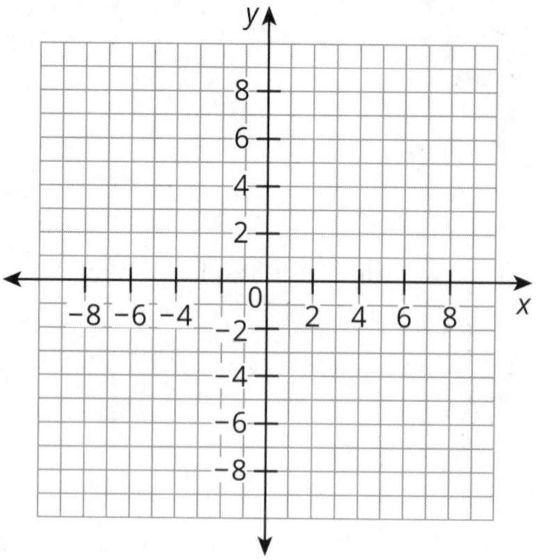

ⓑ $y \leq -\frac{1}{3}x + 4$

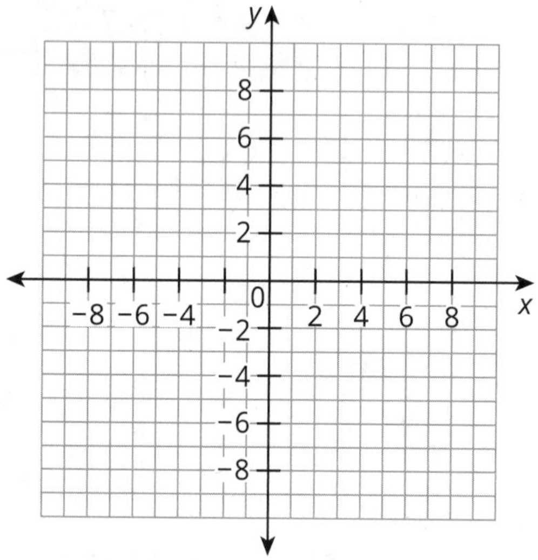

ⓒ $2x - y < 4$

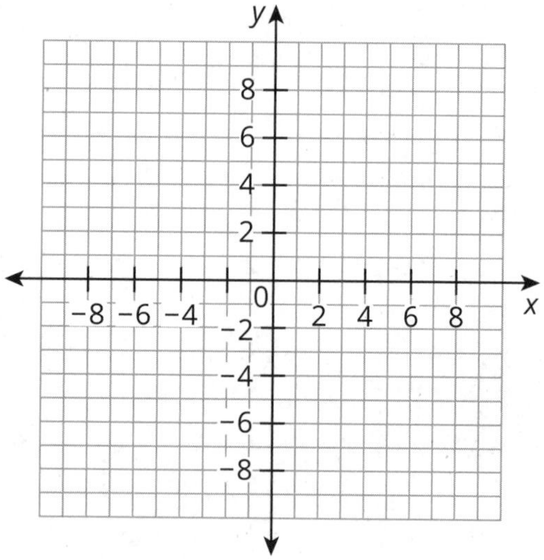

Previously you have written a linear equation given various representations, including two points, one point and the slope, a table of values, or a graph. You can use a similar approach when writing a linear inequality.

WORKED EXAMPLE

Write a linear equality for the graph.

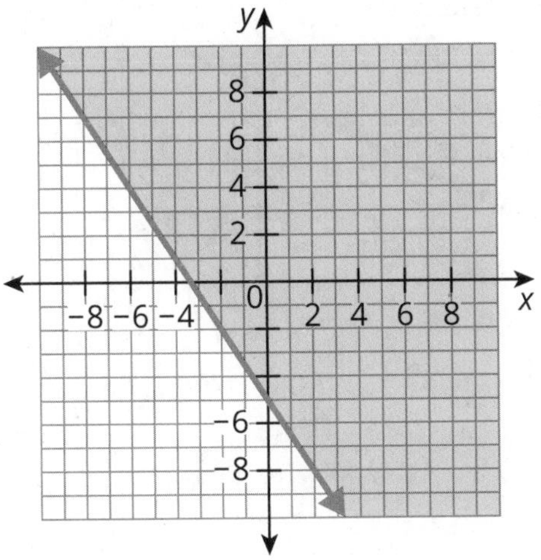

You can use what you have previously learned about the graphs of linear equations to determine that the equation $y = -\frac{3}{2}x - 5$ represents the boundary line. Now you must decide which inequality symbol should replace the equals sign in the equation.

Since the graph shows a solid boundary line and the half-plane above the line is shaded, use the symbol ≥.

$y \geq -\frac{3}{2}x - 5$

Test a point in the solution set to check the linear inequality.

Test the point (0, 0):

$0 \overset{?}{\geq} -\frac{3}{2}(0) - 5$

$0 \geq -5$ ✓

REMEMBER...

You can use the point (0, 0) as a test point unless the boundary line passes through (0, 0).

6 Write a linear inequality for each graph.

ⓐ

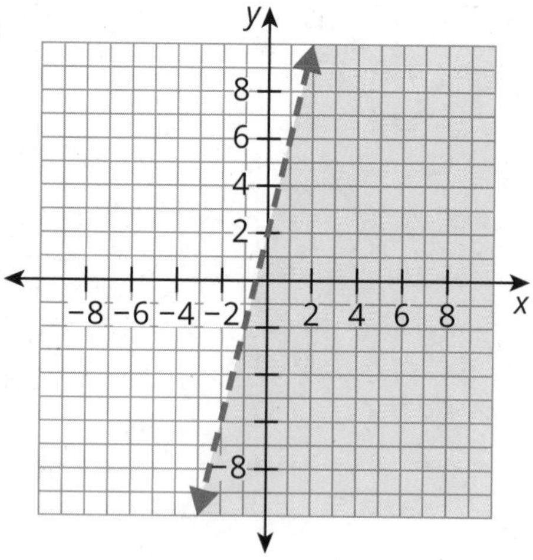

ⓑ

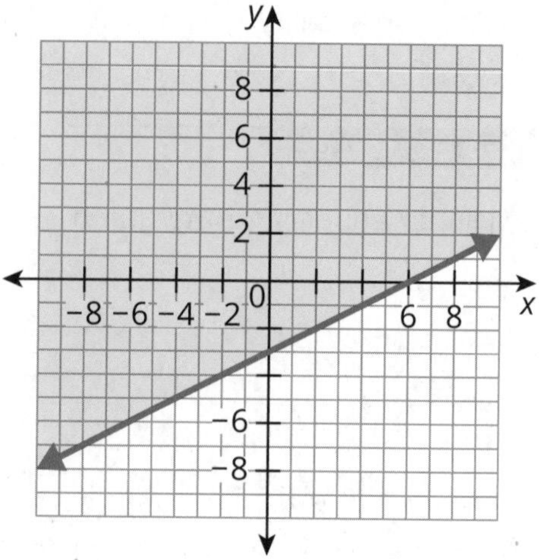

ⓒ

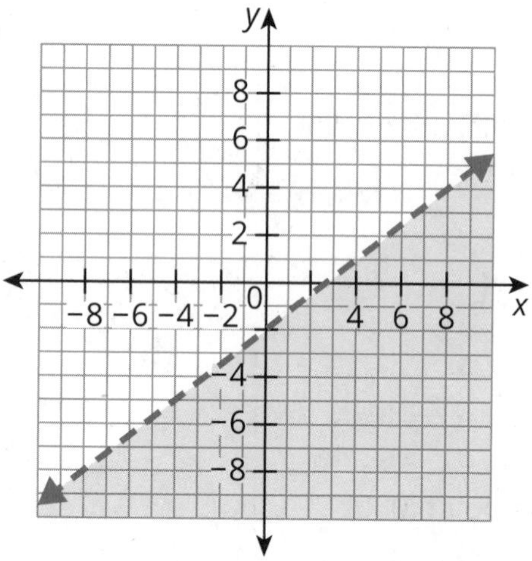

Interpreting the Graph of a Linear Inequality

Let's use an inequality and its graph to answer questions about a real-world situation.

HABITS OF MIND

- Reason abstractly and quantitatively.
- Construct viable arguments and critique the reasoning of others.

César has relatives living in both the United States and Mexico. He is given a prepaid phone card worth $50 for his birthday. The table of values shows combinations of minutes for calls within the United States, *x*, and calls to Mexico, *y*, that expend his $50 prepaid phone card.

1. Write an inequality modeling the number of minutes César can use for calls within the United States and for calls to Mexico.

Length of Calls within United States (minutes)	Length of Calls to Mexico (minutes)
0	100
50	80
140	44
200	20
240	4

2. Graph your inequality on the given coordinate grid. **Be sure to label your axes.**

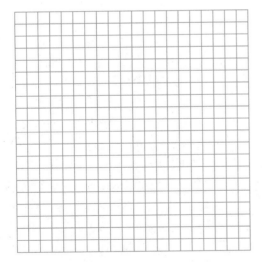

3 If César speaks with his aunt in Guadalajara, Mexico, for 70 minutes using his phone card, how long can he speak with his cousin in New York using the same card?

4 Can César call his uncle in San Antonio for 100 minutes and also call his grandmother in Juárez, Mexico, for 80 minutes using his phone card? **Explain your reasoning.**

5 Can César call his brother in Mexico City, Mexico, for 55 minutes and also call his sister in Denver, for 90 minutes using his phone card? **Explain your reasoning.**

6 Interpret the meaning of each.

(a) Points on the line

(b) Points above the line

(c) Points below the line

There's a Fine Line

> Consider the graph of the linear equation $x + y = 12$.

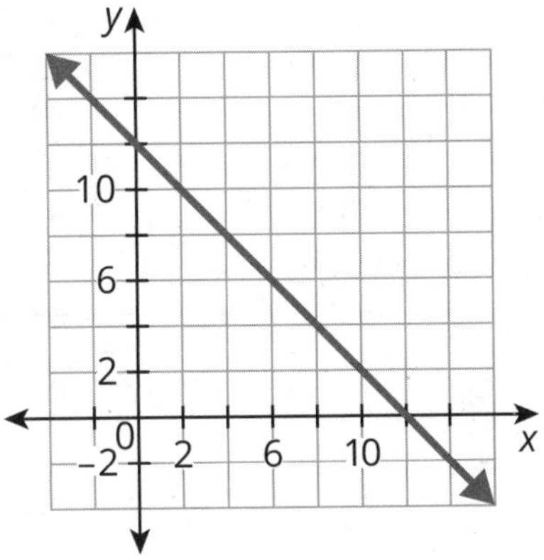

1 Describe how to graph $x + y < 12$ and choose a point to test this region.

2 Describe how to graph $x + y \leq 12$ and choose a point to test this region.

3 Describe how to graph $x + y > 12$ and choose a point to test this region.

4 Complete the table.

Equation or Inequality	Description of the Solution Set
$x + y = 0$	
$x + y \geq 0$	
$x + y \leq 0$	
$x + y > 0$	
$x + y < 0$	

LESSON 3 ASSIGNMENT

> Use a separate piece of paper for your Journal entry.

JOURNAL

Describe a half-plane in your own words.

REMEMBER

The graph of a linear inequality in two variables is the half-plane that contains all the solutions. When the inequality symbol is ≥ or ≤, the graph shows a solid boundary line because the line is part of the solution set. When the symbol is > or <, the boundary line is a dashed line because no point on the line is a solution.

PRACTICE

1 Jeremy is working two jobs to save money for his college education. He makes $8 per hour working for his uncle at Pizza Pie bussing tables and $10 per hour tutoring peers after school in math. His goal is to make $160 per week.

(a) If Jeremy works 8 hours at Pizza Pie and tutors 11 hours during the week, does he reach his goal?

(b) Write an expression to represent the total amount of money Jeremy makes in a week from working both jobs. Let x represent the number of hours he works at Pizza Pie and y represent the number of hours he tutors.

(c) After researching the costs of colleges, Jeremy decides he needs to make more than $160 each week. Write an inequality in two variables to represent the amount of money Jeremy needs to make.

(d) Graph the inequality from part (c).

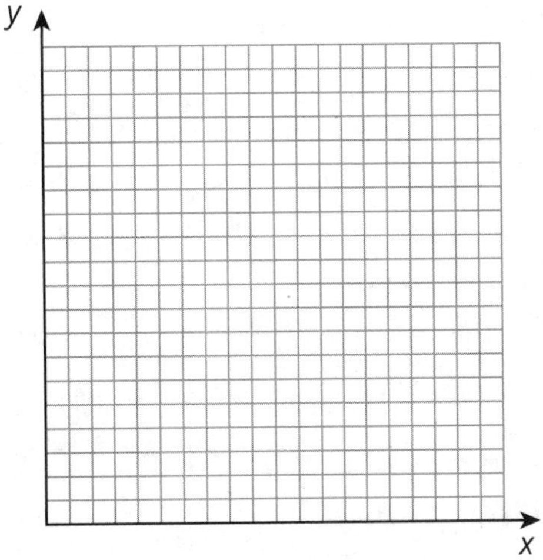

(e) Is the point (0, 0) in the shaded region of the graph? Explain why or why not.

(f) According to the graph, if Jeremy works 5 hours at Pizza Pie and tutors for 10 hours, will he make more than $160? Explain why or why not.

Go to LiveHint.com for help on the PRACTICE questions.

(g) Due to days off from school, Jeremy will only be tutoring for 6 hours this week. Use the graph to determine the least amount of full hours he must work at Pizza Pie to still reach his goal. Then show that your result satisfies the inequality.

2 Graph each inequality on a coordinate plane.

(a) $x + 3y > 9$

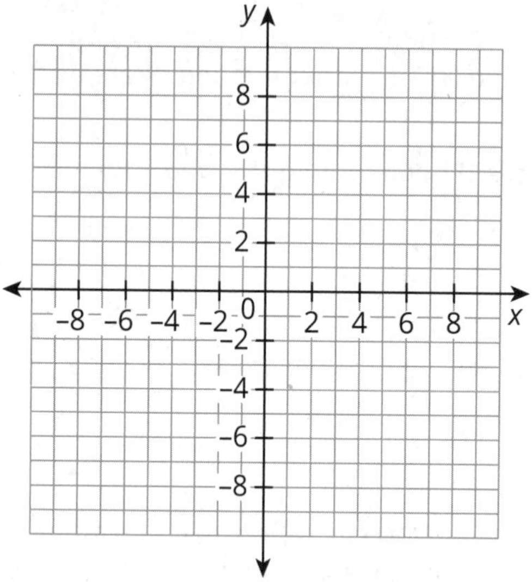

(b) $2x - 6y \leq 15$

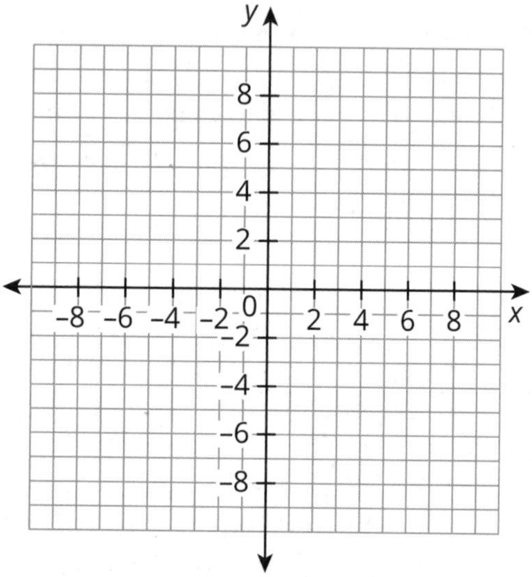

(c) $2x + y < 6$

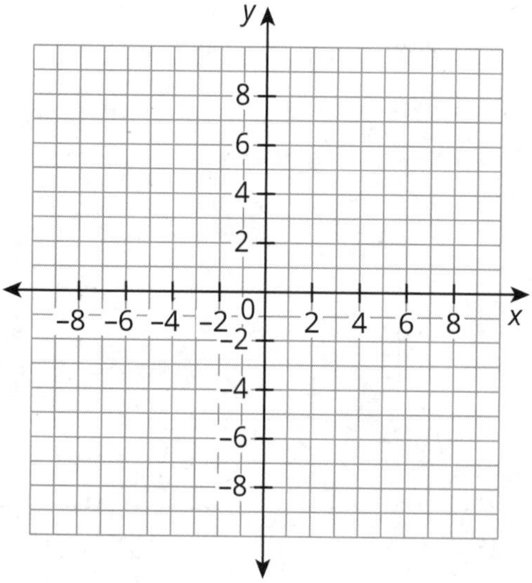

(d) $3x - y \geq 1$

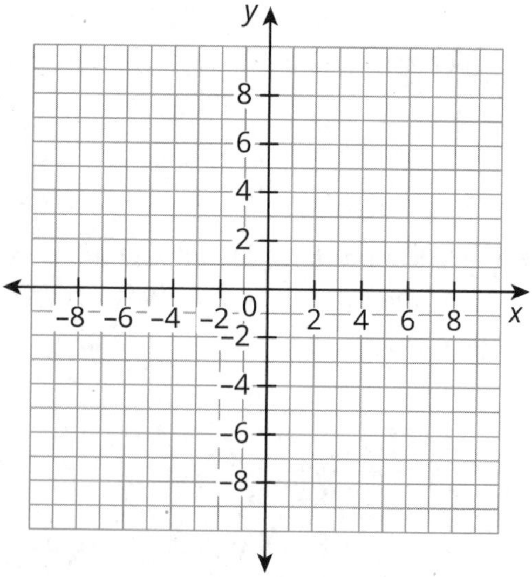

STRETCH Optional

> Use what you know about absolute value functions to graph the inequality $y > 2|x - 3| - 5$.

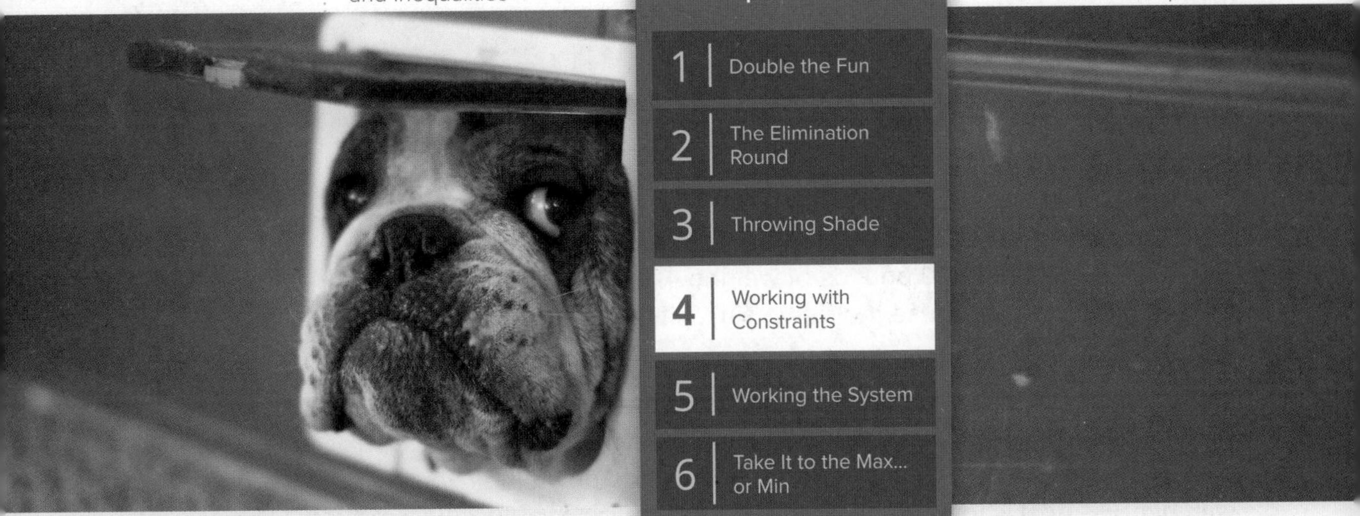

LESSON 4

Working with Constraints

Systems of Linear Inequalities

KEY TERMS

constraints

solution of a system of linear inequalities

Learning Goals

- Represent constraints in a problem situation with systems of inequalities.
- Write and graph systems of linear inequalities.
- Graph the solutions to a system of linear inequalities in two variables as the intersection of the corresponding half-planes.
- Verify solutions to systems of linear inequalities algebraically.

REVIEW (1–2 minutes)

> Determine an ordered pair (x, y) that satisfies each inequality.

1. $x + y < 18$

2. $x - y > -7$

3. $2x + 3y \leq -5$

4. $-5x - 2y \geq 10$

You have graphed a linear inequality in two variables and interpreted the solutions.

What does the graph of a system of linear inequalities look like, and how can you describe the solution set?

A River Runs Through It

Chase is an experienced whitewater rafter who guides groups of adults and children out on the water for amazing adventures. The raft he uses can hold 800 pounds of weight. Any weight greater than 800 pounds can cause the raft to sink, hit more rocks, and maneuver more slowly.

Chase estimates the weight of each adult as approximately 200 pounds and the weight of each child as approximately 100 pounds. Chase charges adults $75 and children $50 to ride down the river with him. His goal is to earn at least $150 each rafting trip.

THINK ABOUT...
Does Chase count himself when determining the weight and the cost?

1. Write an inequality to represent the most weight Chase can carry in terms of rafters. **Define your variables.**

2. Write an inequality to represent the minimum amount of money Chase wants to collect for each rafting trip.

3. Write a system of linear inequalities to represent the maximum weight of the raft and the minimum amount of money Chase wants to earn per trip.

MATHia CONNECTION
- Systems of Linear Inequalities

Determining Solutions to Systems of Linear Inequalities

HABITS OF MIND
- Model with mathematics.
- Use appropriate tools strategically.

In a system of linear inequalities, the inequalities are known as **constraints** because the values of the expressions are "constrained" to lie within a certain region on the graph.

1 Let's consider two trips that Chase guides. Determine whether each combination of rafters is a solution of the system of linear inequalities. Then describe the meaning of the solution in terms of this problem situation.

(a) First Trip: Chase guides 2 adults and 2 children.

(b) Second Trip: Chase guides 5 adults.

2 Graph the system of linear inequalities.

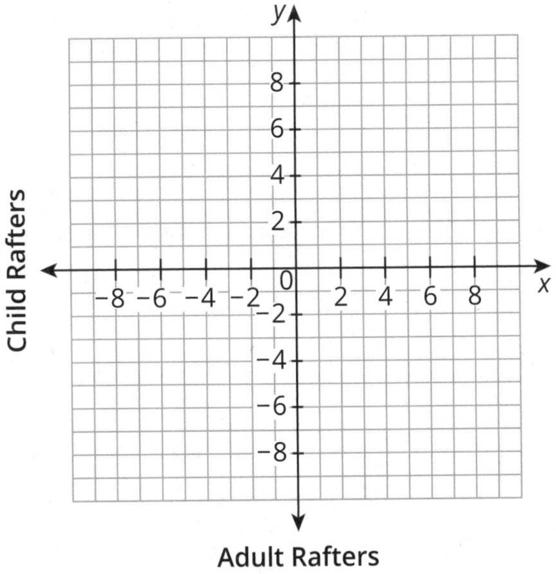

TAKE NOTE...
Shade the half-plane of each inequality differently. You can use colored pencils or simply vertical and horizontal lines.

The **solution of a system of linear inequalities** is the intersection of the solutions to each inequality. Every point in the intersection region satisfies all inequalities in the system.

3 Analyze your graph.

(a) Describe the possible number of solutions for a system of linear inequalities.

(b) Is the intersection point a solution to this system of inequalities? **Why or why not?**

(c) Identify three different solutions of the system of linear inequalities you graphed. **What do the solutions represent in terms of the problem situation?**

(d) Determine one combination of adults and children that is not a solution for this system of linear inequalities. **Explain your reasoning.**

ACTIVITY 2

MATHia CONNECTION

- Interpreting Solutions to Systems of Inequalities

Analyzing Graphs of Systems of Linear Inequalities

> Determine the solution set of the given system of linear inequalities.

$$\begin{cases} x + y > 1 \\ -x + y \leq 3 \end{cases}$$

HABITS OF MIND

- Reason abstractly and quantitatively.
- Construct viable arguments and critique the reasoning of others.

THINK ABOUT...

Notice the inequality symbols. How does this affect your graph?

1 Graph the system of linear inequalities.

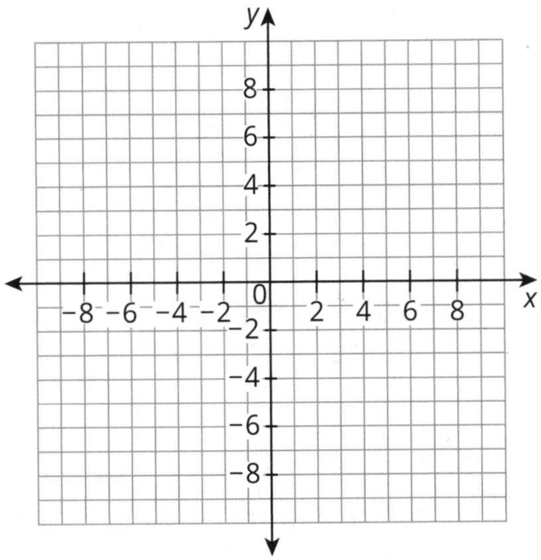

2 Choose a point in each shaded region of the graph. Determine whether each point is a solution of the system. Then describe how the shaded region represents the solution.

Point	$x + y > 1$	$-x + y \leq 3$	Description of Location
(−8, 2)	$-8 + 2 > 1$ $-6 > 1$ ×	$-(-8) + 2 \leq 3$ $10 \leq 3$ ×	The point is not a solution to either inequality.

3 Alan makes the statement about the intersection point of a system of inequalities. **Explain why Alan's statement is incorrect.**

Alan

The intersection point is always a solution to a system of inequalities because that is where the two lines meet.

4 Solve each system of linear inequalities by graphing the solution set. Then identify two points that are solutions of the system.

(a) $\begin{cases} y > 5x + 3 \\ y < 5x - 3 \end{cases}$

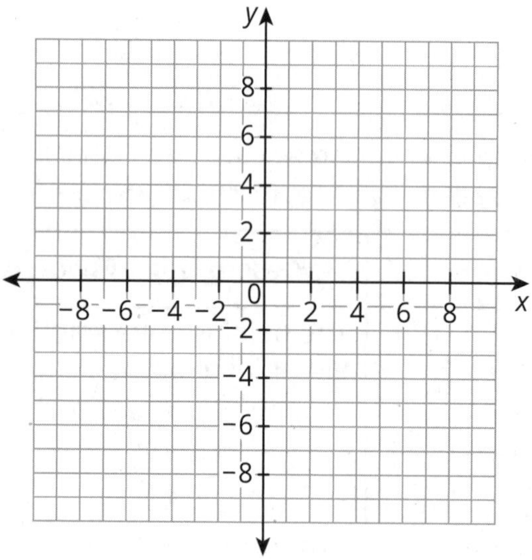

(b) $\begin{cases} x \geq -5 \\ x > 1 \end{cases}$

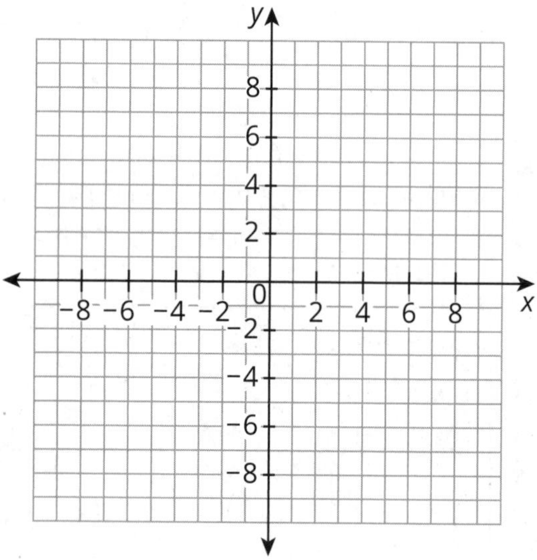

Applying Systems of Linear Inequalities

HABITS OF MIND
- Model with mathematics.
- Use appropriate tools strategically.

Let's use a system of inequalities to model a real-world situation.

> Consider the information on a sign on the wall of a fitness room.

Exercise	Calories Burned per Minute
Treadmill — light effort	7.6
Treadmill — vigorous effort	12.4
Stair Stepper — light effort	6.9
Stair Stepper — vigorous effort	10.4
Stationary Bike — light effort	5.5
Stationary Bike — vigorous effort	11.1

Jackson decides to use the stair stepper. He has at most 45 minutes to exercise, and he wants to burn at least 400 calories.

1 Write a system of linear inequalities to represent Jackson's workout. **Define your variables.**

2 Graph the system of inequalities from Question 1 on the coordinate plane. **Be sure to label your axes.**

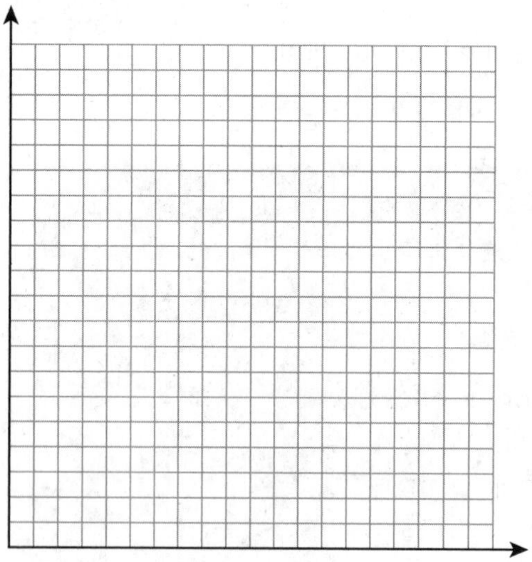

THINK ABOUT...
Use technology to graph your inequalities and check your answer.

3 Analyze your graph.

(a) Identify two different solutions of the system of inequalities.

(b) Interpret your solutions in terms of Jackson's workout.

(c) Algebraically prove that your solutions satisfy the system of linear inequalities.

Identifying Systems of Linear Inequalities

HABITS OF MIND
- Look for and make use of structure.
- Look for and express regularity in repeated reasoning.

> Consider the four systems shown.

System A

$$\begin{cases} y < \frac{3}{5}x + 3 \\ y > -\frac{3}{5}x + 3 \end{cases}$$

System B

$$\begin{cases} y > \frac{3}{5}x + 3 \\ y > -\frac{3}{5}x + 3 \end{cases}$$

System C

$$\begin{cases} y > \frac{3}{5}x + 3 \\ y < -\frac{3}{5}x + 3 \end{cases}$$

System D

$$\begin{cases} y < \frac{3}{5}x + 3 \\ y < -\frac{3}{5}x + 3 \end{cases}$$

1 Match a graph and possible solution to each given system of linear inequalities. Complete the blank graph and partial solution set to make 4 complete sets.

Graph A

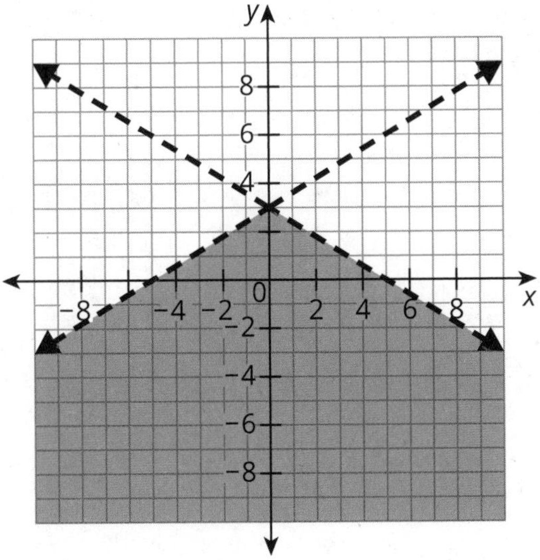

Graph B

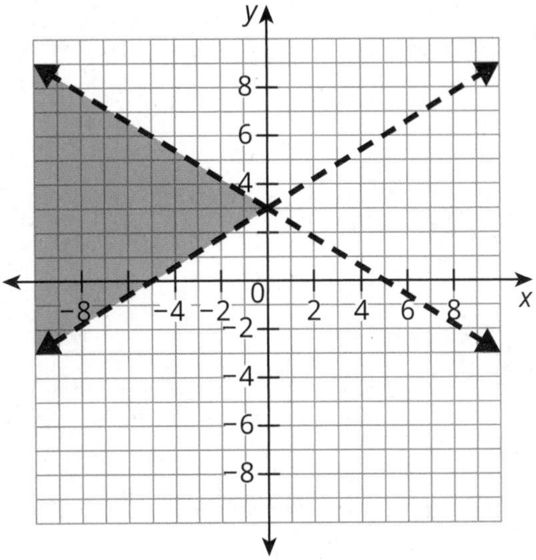

Graph C

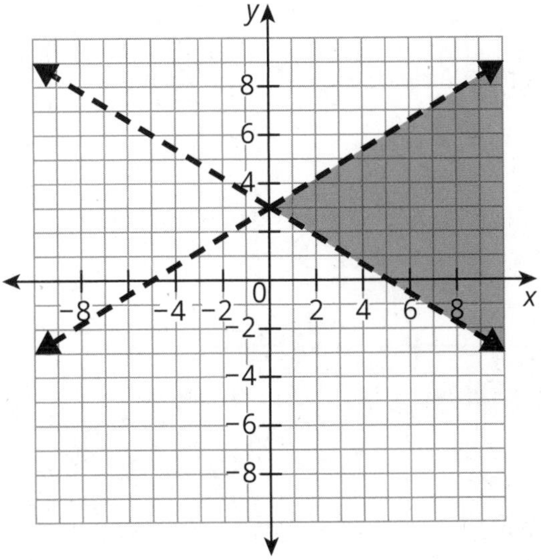

Graph D

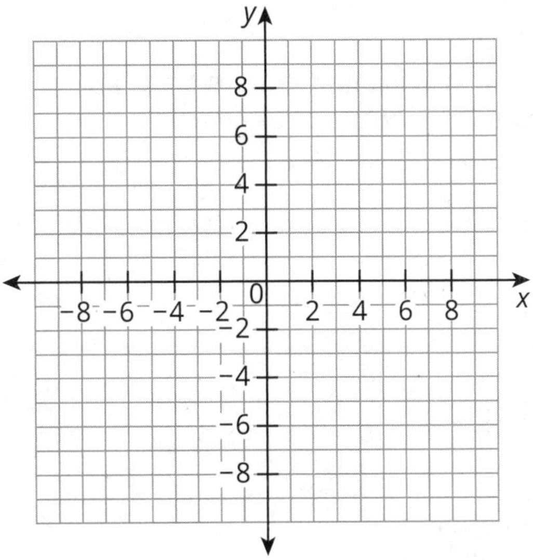

Possible Solutions A
(0, −6) and (4, −4)

Possible Solutions B
(0, 7.5) and (−4, 10)

Possible Solutions C
(−6, 4) and (−10, 8)

Possible Solutions D
________ and ________

TOPIC 3

Get to Know the Region

Any of the four regions on a coordinate plane can represent the solution set to a system of inequalities.

1 Consider each system of linear inequalities and decide which region represents the solution set. **Explain your reasoning.**

- A region above both lines.
- A region below both lines.
- A region between the lines.
- No solution.

(a) $\begin{cases} y < 8 + 2x \\ 3 + 2x > y \end{cases}$

(b) $\begin{cases} 5 + x < y \\ y > 7 + x \end{cases}$

(c) $\begin{cases} y > 12 - 3x \\ 10 - 3x > y \end{cases}$

(d) $\begin{cases} 6 - x < y \\ y < 9 - x \end{cases}$

2 How is the solution to a system of linear inequalities the same as or different from the solution to a system of linear equations?

LESSON 4 ASSIGNMENT

> Use a separate piece of paper for your Journal entry.

JOURNAL

Describe how you know which region, if any, represents the solution to a system of linear inequalities.

REMEMBER

The solution of a system of linear inequalities is the intersection of the solutions to each inequality. Every point in the intersection region satisfies all inequalities in the system.

PRACTICE

1. Samuel is remodeling his basement. One part of the planning involves the flooring. He knows that he would like both carpet and hardwood but isn't sure how much of each he will use. The most amount of flooring area he can cover is 2000 square feet. The carpet is \$4.50 per square foot, and the hardwood is \$8.25 per square foot. Both prices include labor costs. Samuel has budgeted \$10,000 for the flooring.

   (a) Write a system of inequalities to represent the maximum amount of flooring needed and the maximum amount of money Samuel wants to spend.

   (b) One idea Samuel has is to make two rooms—one having 400 square feet of carpeting and the other having 1200 square feet of hardwood. Determine whether this amount of carpeting and hardwood are solutions to the system of inequalities. Explain your reasoning in terms of the problem situation.

   (c) Graph this system of inequalities.

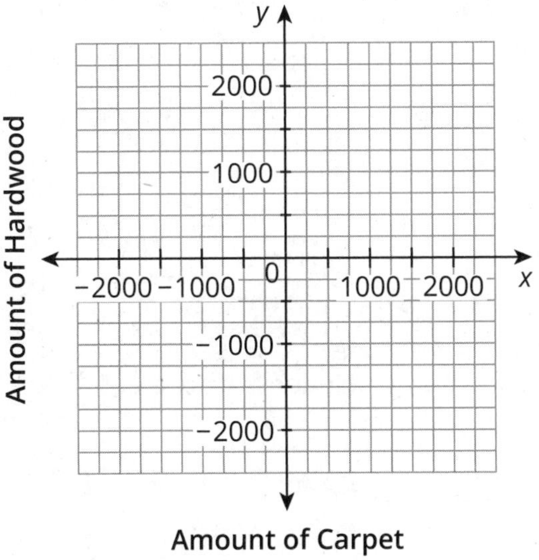

Go to LiveHint.com for help on the PRACTICE questions.

ⓓ Determine the intersection point of the two lines. Is this a solution to this system of inequalities in terms of the problem situation?

ⓔ Identify two different solutions to the system of inequalities. Explain what the solutions represent in terms of the problem situation.

2 Solve each system of linear inequalities by graphing the solution set.

ⓐ $\begin{cases} -x + 3y \leq -6 \\ -5x + 3y \geq 6 \end{cases}$

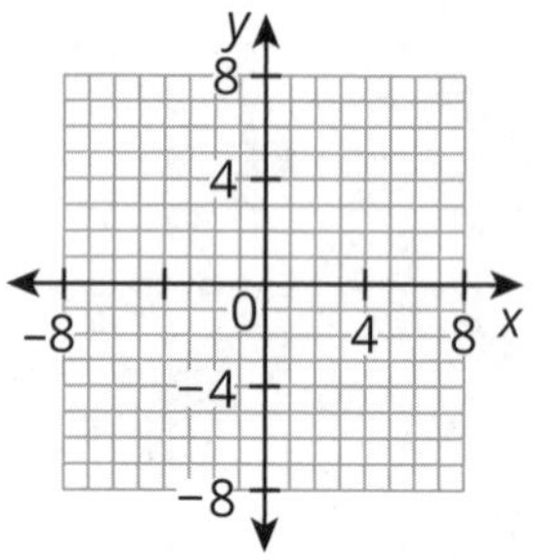

ⓑ $\begin{cases} -x + 2y < 6 \\ 3x + 2y \leq 2 \end{cases}$

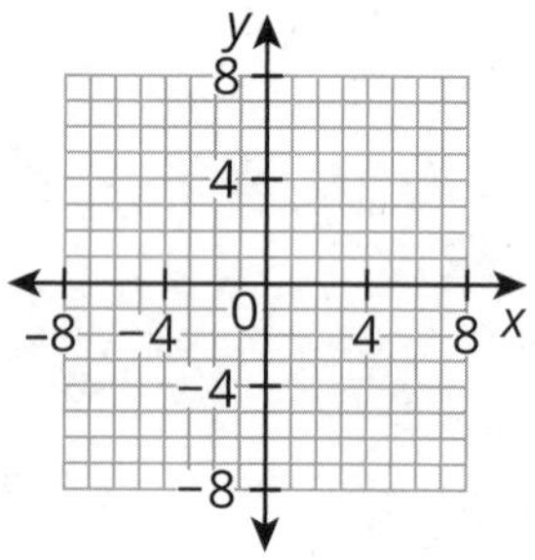

ⓒ $\begin{cases} -x + 3y \leq 18 \\ x \leq 3 \end{cases}$

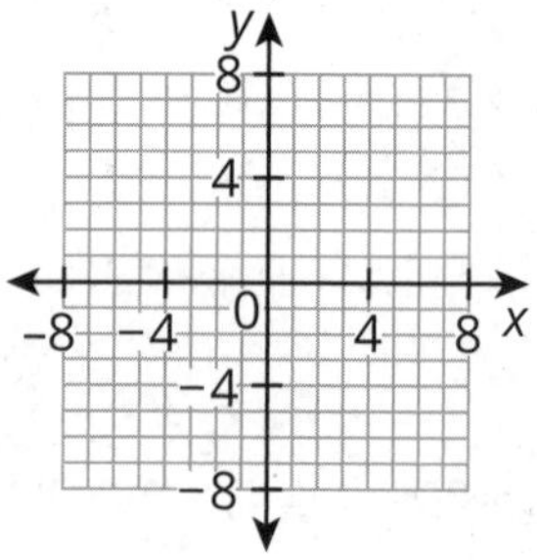

STRETCH Optional

1 Is it possible to create a system of inequalities that has no solutions? If so, create one and explain how the graph would show no solutions. If not, explain why.

2 Is it possible to create a system of two inequalities that has only one solution? If so, create one. If not, explain why.

3 Is it possible to create a system of three inequalities that has only one solution? If so, sketch a graph to show the solution. If not, explain why.

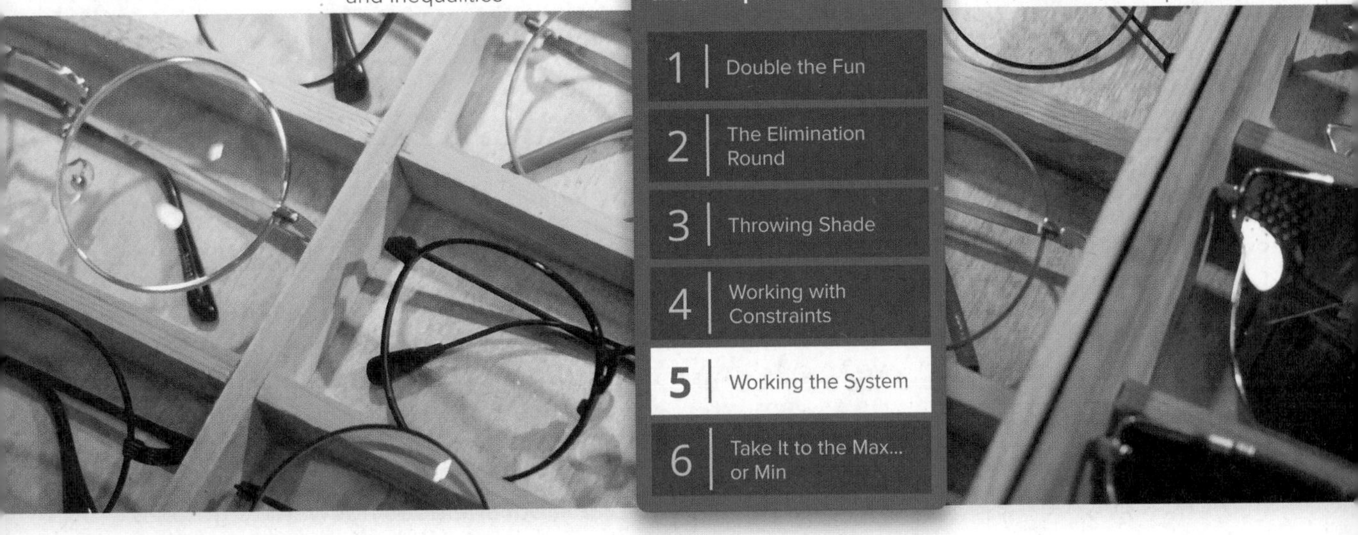

LESSON 5

Working the System

Solving Systems of Equations and Inequalities

Learning Goals

- Use various methods of solving systems of linear equations to determine the better buy or the better job offer.
- Solve systems of linear inequalities with more than two inequalities.
- Graph the solutions to a system of linear inequalities in two variables as the intersection of the corresponding half-planes.

REVIEW (1–2 minutes)

> Determine whether the point (1, 7) is a solution to each system.

1. $\begin{cases} 4x - y = -3 \\ -2x + y = 5 \end{cases}$

2. $\begin{cases} x + y > 4 \\ 4x - y < -4 \end{cases}$

3. $\begin{cases} y = -3.5x - 2 \\ y = 4.5x - 10 \end{cases}$

4. $\begin{cases} -2x + y < 8 \\ x - y > -8 \end{cases}$

You have solved systems of linear equations by graphing, using substitution, and using linear combinations. You have also graphed systems of linear inequalities to determine possible solutions.

How can you use these various methods to reason about real-world problems?

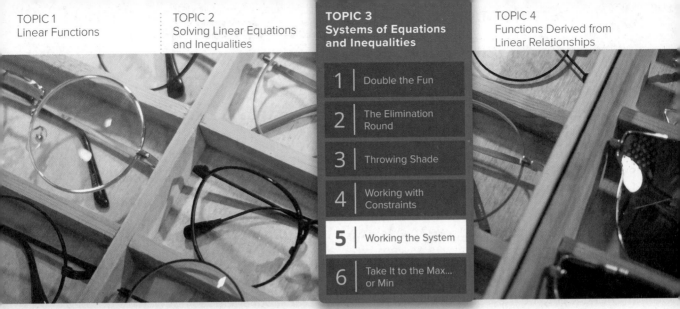

Systems for Summer Savings

A neighborhood pool club offers two membership plans.

- Plan A includes a seasonal sign-up fee of $100 and charges $2 each time you use the pool.
- Plan B has no sign-up fee but charges $6 each time you use the pool.

Susan chooses Plan A. She has a budget of $200 to spend on pool fees during the months of July and August.

Susan wants to be sure she uses the pool enough times so that the plan she chooses works out to be the better deal between the two plans, but she does not want to go over her budget.

1. Use a system of linear equations and a system of linear inequalities to make a recommendation to Susan as to how often she should use the pool in July and August.

Determining the Better Deal

You can analyze the solution to a system of linear equations that model two real-world options.

HABITS OF MIND
- Reason abstractly and quantitatively.
- Construct viable arguments and critique the reasoning of others.

The Bici Bicycle Company is planning to make a low price ultra-light bicycle. They are considering two plans for building this bicycle.

- The first plan includes a cost of $125,000 to design and build a prototype bicycle. The combined materials and labor costs for each bike made under the first plan will be $225.
- The second plan includes a cost of $100,000 to design and build the prototype. The combined materials and labor costs for each bike made under the second plan will be $275.

1. You recently got a job at Bici Bicycle Company as a financial analyst. Analyze the costs for each proposed bicycle prototype and determine which plan Bici should follow. **Provide evidence for your proposal.**

Solving a System of Linear Inequalities with Four Constraints

HABITS OF MIND

- Model with mathematics.
- Use appropriate tools strategically.

Previously, you solved a system containing two linear inequalities. However, systems can consist of more than two linear inequalities.

Miguel's eye doctor informed him that he needs glasses. Miguel sees an advertisement for a sale on all eyeglass frames in the window of the local vision store.

Save **60% to 75%** On All Frames

1. Use the advertisement to write two inequalities that represent the regular price of eyeglass frames. Let r represent the regular price of the frames.

2. Use the same advertisement to write two inequalities that represent the reduced price of the eyeglass frames. Let s represent the sales price of the frames in terms of r.

REMEMBER...
When an item is 20% off the regular price, you can think of that item costing 80% of the regular price.

3. Explain why the system of linear inequalities that Heather wrote for the problem situation is incorrect.

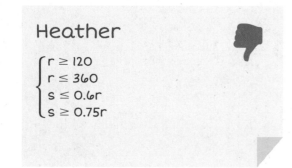

Heather

$$\begin{cases} r \geq 120 \\ r \leq 360 \\ s \leq 0.6r \\ s \geq 0.75r \end{cases}$$

4 Graph each inequality on the grid.

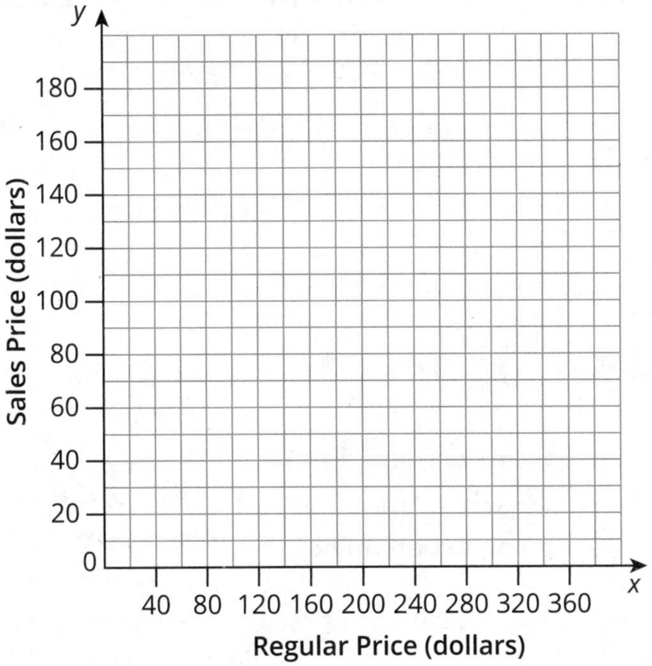

5 Shade the portion of the graph that satisfies the system of linear inequalities. What shape does the solution region resemble?

6 About how much would Miguel expect to spend if he purchases eyeglass frames that are regularly priced at $320?

7 Miguel is definitely going to purchase eyeglass frames that are on sale. What is the least amount of money Miguel can expect to spend? What is the greatest amount he can expect to spend?

8 Miguel decides on eyeglass frames that are regularly priced at $240.

(a) Can Miguel expect to save more or less than $140 off the purchase price of these frames? **Use your graph to determine an approximate answer.**

ASK YOURSELF...
The graph shows you the sale price of the eyeglasses, but how can you determine how much he will save?

(b) Use algebra to determine the greatest amount of money Miguel can save by purchasing eyeglass frames that are regularly priced at $240.

Determining the Better Job Offer

HABITS OF MIND
- Reason abstractly and quantitatively.
- Construct viable arguments and critique the reasoning of others.

Sometimes you may need to use a linear inequality along with a system of linear equations to compare two real-world options.

Jose interviewed for two different sales positions at competing companies.

- Reliable Robotics has offered Jose a salary of $31,200 per year, plus a 9% commission on his total sales.
- Robot Renegades will offer him $26,000 per year, plus a 15% commission on his total sales.

Jose isn't sure which offer to accept. He's great at making a sale, but he's just not sure which job will be better in terms of his pay. He is confident that he can make at least $2000 worth of sales each week.

1. Write an email to Jose with your recommendation of which job offers better compensation. **Provide evidence in your response.**

Which Cab Is More Fab?

The Red Cab Company charges $3.50 upon entry and an additional $1.25 per mile driven. The Yellow Cab Company charges $5 upon entry and an additional $1.15 per mile driven.

1 Emma needs to take a cab to the airport. Which company should she use when she wants to minimize the cost? Use any method to solve.

LESSON 5 ASSIGNMENT

> Use a separate piece of paper for your Journal entry.

JOURNAL

You have used three methods to solve systems: graphing, substitution, and linear combinations. Describe the characteristics you would look for when determining which method to use.

REMEMBER

The solution set to a system of inequalities with more than two constraints is the region where all the graphs overlap.

PRACTICE

The Brunstown Ballet Company needs to rent a venue for their production of the Nutcracker. There are a number of arenas they are considering. The arenas have seating capacities that range from 800 to 1876 seats The management of the company knows the ticket sales may not be good this year but their goal is to sell between 65% and 90% of the available seats. Whichever arena they choose, one hundred seats must be set aside for the company's donors.

1. Write a system of inequalities that represents the problem situation. Define your variables.

2. Graph each inequality on the coordinate plane.

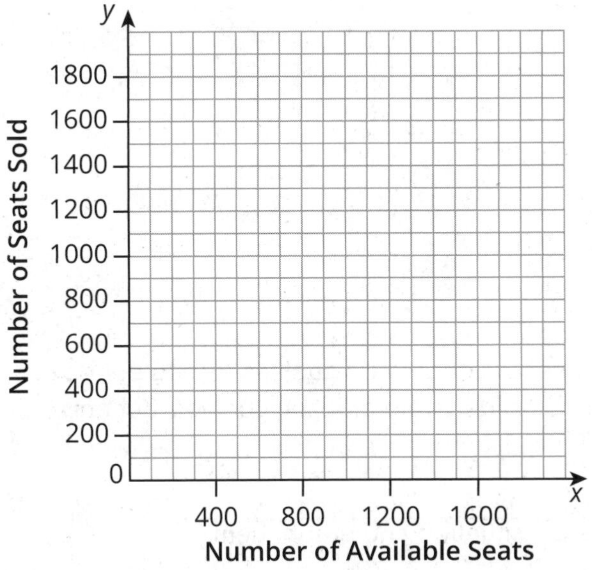

3. One of the arenas they are considering has 1200 available seats. Determine the minimum and maximum number of seats they would need to sell in order for management to reach their goal.

Go to LiveHint.com for help on the PRACTICE questions.

4. If the company sold 900 seats, what is the range of seating capacities for the arenas they may have rented?

5. If they rented an arena that had a 1300-seat capacity and sold 800 tickets, would management reach their goal? **Explain your reasoning.**

STRETCH Optional

Isla sells baked goods from her home kitchen. She offers decorated cookies for $15 per dozen and cupcakes for $13 per dozen. It takes her an hour to decorate a dozen cookies, but only 20 minutes to decorate a dozen cupcakes. She would like to make at least $300 per week and not put in more than 20 hours of work per week.

1. Create a system of linear inequalities that fits the situation and graph them.
2. Isla just discovered that she is running out of cake mix for the cupcakes and royal icing for the cookies. She can make a maximum of 40 dozen cupcakes and 12 dozen cookies. What are the new inequalities you need to add to your problem? Add them to your graph.
3. What is the maximum amount of baked goods that she could make? How much will she earn? How long will it take her?
4. What is the least amount of time she could work and still earn $300? What baked goods would she make?

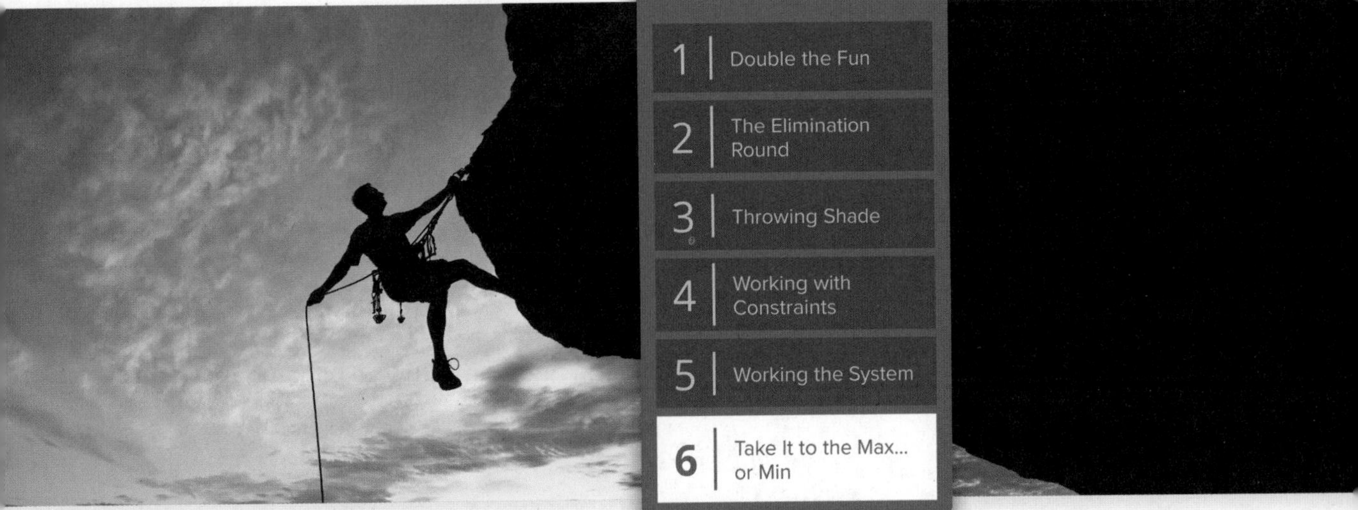

LESSON 6

Take It to the Max...or Min

Linear Programming

KEY TERM

linear programming

- Write systems of inequalities with more than two inequalities.
- Determine constraints from a problem situation.
- Graph systems of linear inequalities and determine the solution set.
- Identify the maximum and minimum values of a linear expression.

REVIEW (1–2 minutes)

> Evaluate each function.

1. $f(x) = 3x + 8$ for $x = -2$

2. $f(a) = -\frac{1}{2}a + 5$ for $a = 12$

3. $f(p) = 4p - 10$ for $p = 1.5$

4. $f(w) = 36 - 2.5w$ for $w = -8$

You have graphed a system of linear inequalities with more than two constraints and determined the region of the solution set.

How can you use this region to determine maximums or minimums in a real-world problem?

A New Notation

Tiara has four math tests to take this semester. It takes her 2 minutes to complete a multiple-choice question, m, and it takes her 5 minutes to complete a short-answer question, s.

You can write an equation for this function using function notation with two variables.

$$f(m, s) = 2m + 5s$$

Given a value for each variable in the function, you can determine the output.

1. Use the function $f(m, s)$ to determine how long it takes Tiara to complete each test.

   a. Test 1

      $f(15, 5)$

   b. Test 2

      $f(10, 8)$

   c. Test 3

      $f(25, 0)$

   d. Test 4

      $f(0, 13)$

Introduction to Linear Programming

HABITS OF MIND
- Model with mathematics.
- Use appropriate tools strategically.

Linear programming is a branch of mathematics that determines the maximum and minimum value of linear expressions on a region produced by a system of linear inequalities. Let's look at how linear programming relates to systems of equations.

A company, TVs4U, makes and sells two different television models: the HD Big View and the MegaTeleBox.

- The HD Big View takes 2 person-hours to make, and the MegaTeleBox takes 3 person-hours to make.
- TVs4U has 24 employees, each working 8 hours a day, which is equivalent to 192 person-hours per day.
- TVs4U's total manufacturing capacity is 72 televisions per day.
- TVs4U cannot make a negative number of televisions.

1. Define variables to represent the number of each model television produced.

2. Identify the constraints as a system of linear inequalities.

ASK YOURSELF...
How do you represent the fact that TVs4U cannot make a negative number of televisions?

3. Graph the system of inequalities on the coordinate plane. Shade the region that represents the solution set.

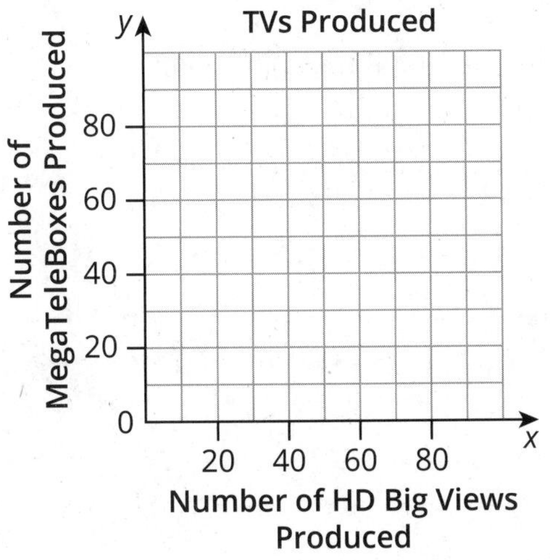

Many companies and businesses are interested in determining when they are maximizing or minimizing their profit or costs. The maximum and minimum values of a system of inequalities occur at a vertex of the shaded region that represents the solution set of the system.

4 Label the vertices of the shaded region that represents the solution set of the system.

To determine the maximum and minimum values, you must substitute the coordinates of each vertex of the solution set into a given function.

WORKED EXAMPLE

Let's say TVs4U profits $175 for each HD Big View it sells and profits $205 for each MegaTeleBox it sells. They want to determine how many of each television they should make and sell to maximize their profits.

Write the function for the given problem situation.

$P(b, m) = 175b + 205m$

Insert the coordinates of each intersection point of the system.

$P(\mathbf{0}, \mathbf{0}) = 175(\mathbf{0}) + 205(\mathbf{0}) = 0$

$P(\mathbf{0}, \mathbf{64}) = 175(\mathbf{0}) + 205(\mathbf{64}) = 13{,}120$

$P(\mathbf{24}, \mathbf{48}) = 175(\mathbf{24}) + 205(\mathbf{48}) = 14{,}040$

$P(\mathbf{72}, \mathbf{0}) = 175(\mathbf{72}) + 205(\mathbf{0}) = 12{,}600$

The maximum profit is represented by the number of televisions made and sold that results in the greatest value.

5 How many of each television should TVs4U produce to earn the maximum profit? **Explain your reasoning.**

TVs4U is trying to determine the price of each model of television.

6 For each set of profits, determine how many of each model they should make to maximize the profit. Then determine the maximum profit. Assume they sell all the televisions they make.

(a) The profit on the HD Big View is $250, and the profit on the MegaTeleBox is $300.

(b) The profit on the HD Big View is $250, and the profit on the MegaTeleBox is $375.

7 TVs4U's boss, Mr. Corazon, sends out a memo with his ideas on maximizing the company's profit. Examine Mr. Corazon's idea and explain why it is incorrect.

Mr. Corazon

Obviously, we will make the most money by only making and selling the television model that gives us the most profit. Therefore, we should focus on producing and selling 72 MegaTeleBoxes each day for a profit of $375 a piece.

Maximizing Profit

Let's use linear programming to analyze maximize values in another situation.

HABITS OF MIND
- Model with mathematics.
- Use appropriate tools strategically.

The cell phone company, Speed of Sound (SOS), produces two types of cell phones. The SOS Smartcall has advanced download speeds and capability, which the SOS Basic does not.

- The assembly lines can produce at most a total of 180 cell phones each day, and the company always has at least 40 of each type of cell phone produced and ready for shipping.
- One SOS Smartcall requires 3 person-hours and $75 worth of materials to produce.
- One SOS Basic requires 4 person-hours and $60 worth of materials to produce.
- The company has 640 person-hours of labor available daily.
- The company has budgeted $12,900 for the cost of materials each day.

1 Define your variables and identify the constraints as a system of linear inequalities.

2 Graph the solution set for the system of linear inequalities on the coordinate plane. Label all intersection points of the boundary lines.

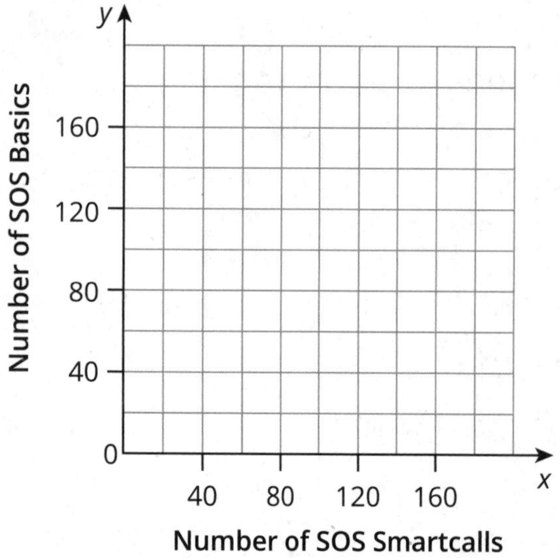

3 The profit from the Smartcall is $30 and the profit from the Basic is $35.

(a) Write a function to represent the total profit.

(b) Paige states that this problem is unrealistic because no one would ever sell a really good cell phone for only $30. Is Paige's statement correct? **Why or why not?**

4 How many of each type of cell phone should the company produce and sell to maximize its profit? Determine the maximum profit.

5 A competitor has reduced the price of its advanced capability cell phone. To compete, SOS will have to decrease its profit on the Smartcall to $25. How will this affect the number and type of cell phones SOS needs to produce and sell to maximize its profit?

Minimizing Cost

A building developer is planning a new housing development. He plans to build two types of houses: townhouses and single-family homes.

- The plot of land has room for the developer to build 100 houses.
- It takes the workers 2 months to build a townhouse and 3 months to build a single-family home.
- The developer wants this development complete in 20 years.
- It costs the developer $300,000 to build each townhouse and $450,000 to build each single-family home.

1 How many of each type of house should he build if he wants to minimize his costs while still completing the development? **Explain your reasoning.**

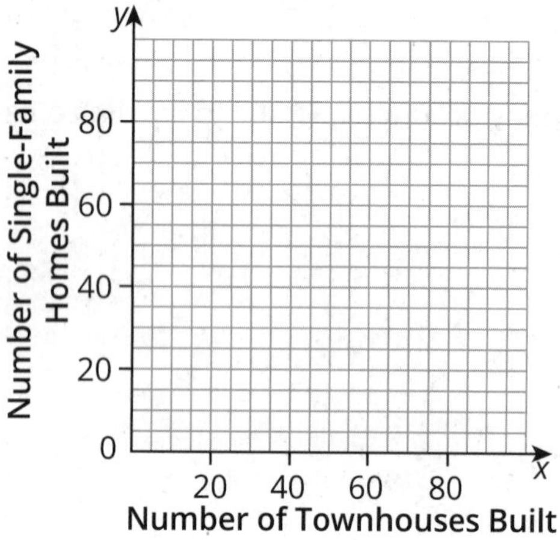

REMEMBER...
When comparing or calculating, you must use the same units of measure.

LESSON 6 ASSIGNMENT

> Use a separate piece of paper for your Journal entry.

JOURNAL

Describe linear programming in your own words.

REMEMBER

You can use the vertices of the solution region determined by a system of linear inequalities to determine maximum and minimum values of linear expressions.

PRACTICE

The Smartway Rental Car Company has $180,000 to invest in the purchase of at most 16 cars of two different types, compact and full-size.

	Purchase Price	Rental Fee	Maintenance Cost
Compact Car	$9000	$30	$8
Full-Size Car	$15,000	$48	$10

1 Due to demand, Smartway needs to purchase at least 5 compact cars.

(a) Identify the constraints as a system of linear inequalities. Define your variables.

(b) Graph the solution set for the system of linear inequalities. Label all points of the intersection of the boundary lines.

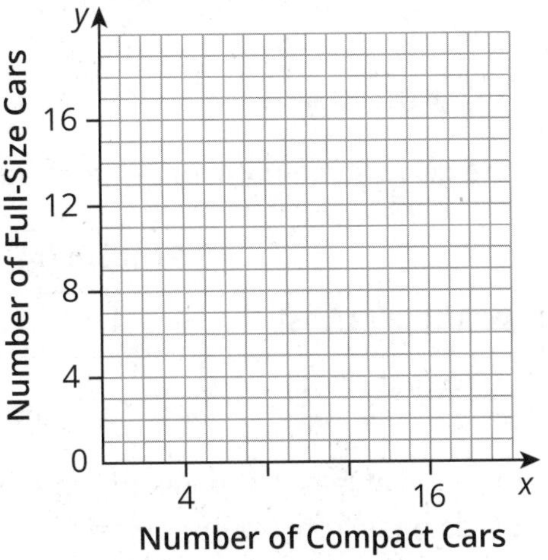

(c) Smartway Rental Car's income comes from renting out their cars. How many of each type of car should they purchase if they want to maximize their income? What is the maximum income?

Go to LiveHint.com for help on the PRACTICE questions.

(d) To keep up with their competitors, Smartway must purchase at least 3 full-size cars and at least 5 compact cars.
Identify the constraints as a system of linear inequalities. Define your variables.

(e) Graph the solution set for this system of linear inequalities. Label all points of the intersection of the boundary lines.

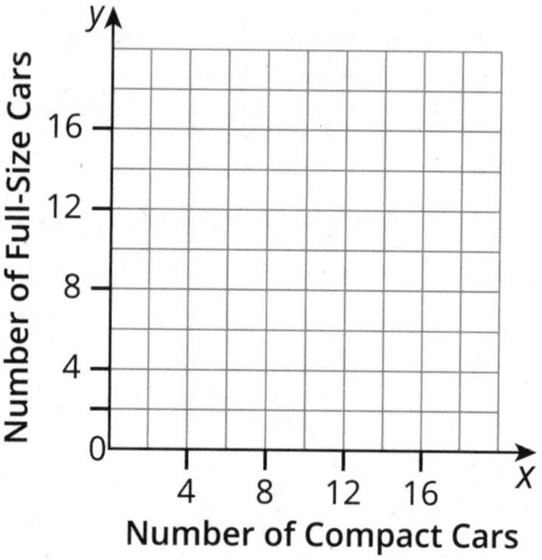

(f) How many of each type of car should Smartway Rental purchase to minimize their maintenance fees?

STRETCH Optional

The table gives some nutritional information for granola and yogurt.

	Protein (g)	Fiber (g)	Potassium (mg)	Calories
Granola (2 Tbsp)	1.5	2	0	70
Yogurt (3 oz)	3	1.5	260	75

Reagan wants at least 10 grams of protein, 9 grams of fiber, 300 milligrams of potassium, and 250 calories from her breakfast.

1. Create a system of inequalities.
2. Graph your system.
3. Determine the intersection points of your boundary lines.
4. What is the cheapest Reagan can eat breakfast that meets her requirements if granola is \$0.34 per serving and yogurt is \$0.50 per serving? (Use only full serving sizes, always round the serving up.)

MIXED PRACTICE

> This Mixed Practice worksheet includes two sections: Spaced Review and End-of-Topic Review. **Use a separate piece of paper to show your work.**

Spaced Review

> Practice concepts from previous topics.

1 Each pair of graphs has been grouped together. Use characteristics of the graphs to explain why they were likely grouped together.

ⓐ **Graph A**

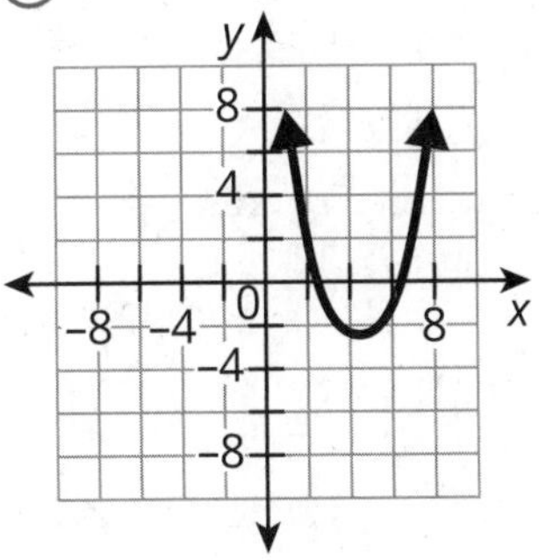

Graph B

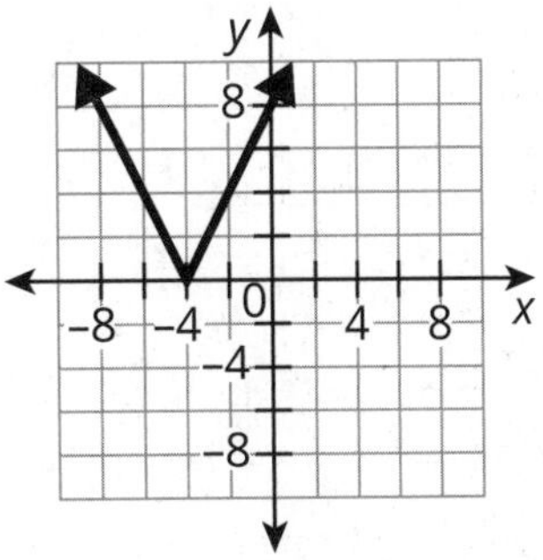

ⓑ **Graph A**

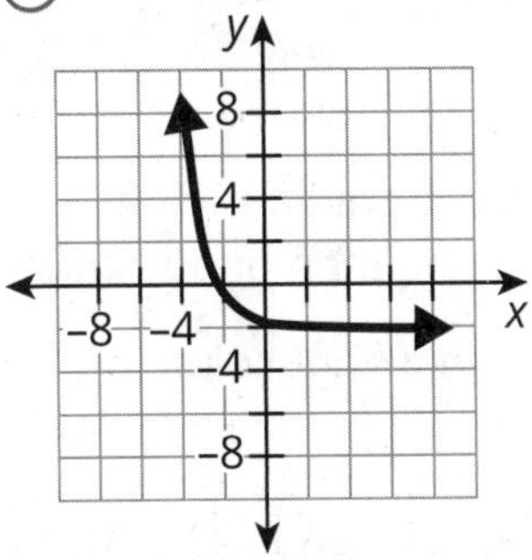

Graph B

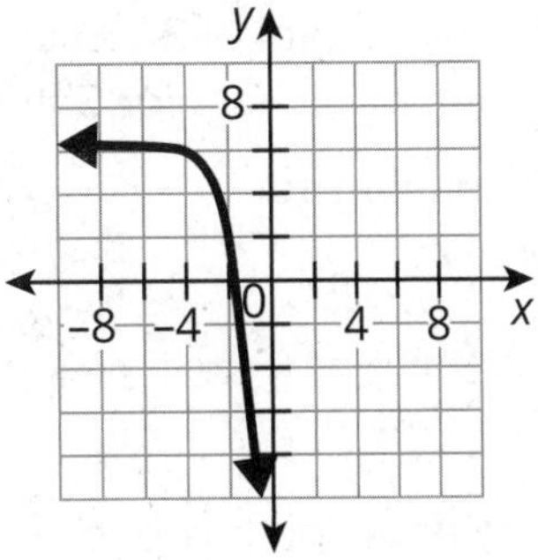

2 Nelson grows tomatoes and sells them at a nearby farmer's roadside stand. He sells them for \$2.50 each. The farmer charges him \$15 a day to use the stand. Write a linear function in factored form and general form that represents the amount of money, M, Nelson will make from selling x tomatoes.

3 Consider the equation $\frac{2}{5}x - 2y = 14$. Write the equation in general form and identify the slope and y-intercept.

4 Solve each linear inequality.

ⓐ $-2(x + 1) + 4 < 8$

ⓑ $20 - 2x < -2(x + 2) + 4x$

5 The graph represents a linear relationship between x and y.

ⓐ Describe whether the graph is increasing or decreasing. Justify your reasoning.

ⓑ Identify the x- and y-intercept.

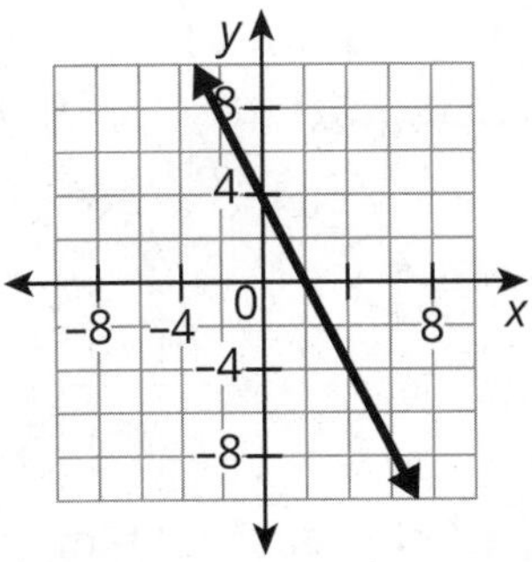

End-of-Topic Review

AVAILABLE ONLINE
1. A **Topic Summary** reviews the main concepts for the topic.
2. A video of the **Worked Example** is provided.

> Practice concepts you learned in **Systems of Equations and Inequalities**.

6 Graph $3x + y \le 7$.

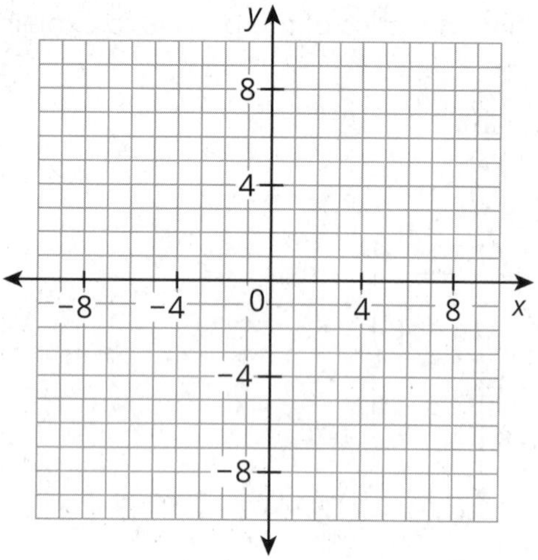

7 Write a linear inequality for the graph.

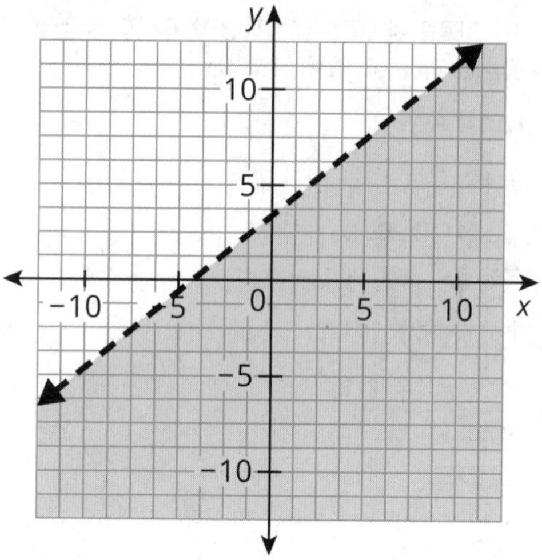

8 The drama department sold a total of 360 tickets to their Friday and Saturday night shows. They sold three times as many tickets for Saturday's show than for Friday's show.

ⓐ Write a system of equations to represent this scenario.

ⓑ How many tickets were sold for Friday? Saturday? Is there more than one solution?

ⓒ Graph the system of equations on a coordinate plane. Label the axes.

ⓓ Justify algebraically that your solution is correct.

9 Determine whether each equation has one solution, no solution, or infinite solutions.

ⓐ $24x - 22 = -3(1 - 8x)$

ⓑ $-3(4a + 3) + 2(12a + 2) = 43$

ⓒ $4(x + 1) = 6x + 4 - 2x$

10 Graph the system of inequalities. Then identify two points that are solutions of the system.

$$\begin{cases} y \ge 5x - 3 \\ y < -3x + 5 \end{cases}$$

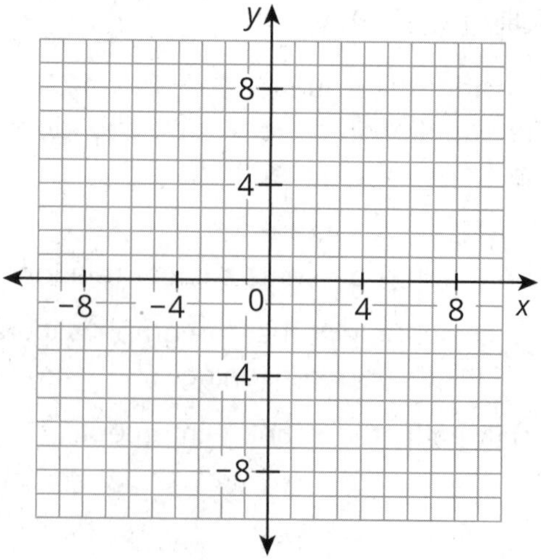

11 Solve each system using linear combinations.

ⓐ $\begin{cases} 8x - 6y = -20 \\ -16x + 7y = 30 \end{cases}$

ⓑ $\begin{cases} x + 3 = -7y + 3 \\ 2x - 8y = 22 \end{cases}$

LESSON 1

Putting the V in Absolute Value

Defining Absolute Value Functions and Transformations

KEY TERMS

absolute value
reflection
line of reflection
argument of a function

Learning Goals

- Experiment with transformations of absolute value functions using technology.
- Graph absolute value functions and transformations of absolute value functions.
- Determine the effect of replacing the basic absolute value function $f(x) = |x|$ with $f(x) + D$, $Af(x)$, and $f(x - C)$ for different values of A, C, and D.
- Distinguish between function transformations that occur outside the function and inside the argument of the function.

REVIEW (1–2 minutes)

Consider the graph of $f(x) = x$. Then graph each transformation.

1. $g(x) = f(x) + 5$
2. $h(x) = 2 \cdot f(x) - 3$
3. $j(x) = \frac{1}{2} \cdot f(x) - 1$

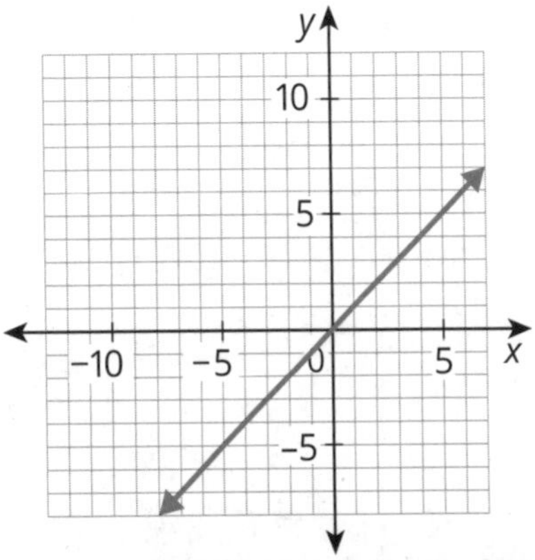

You know how to transform linear functions.

How can you define absolute value functions and show transformations of this function type?

Distance Is Always Positive

The **absolute value** of a number is its distance from zero on the number line.

1 Follow your teacher's instructions to model each absolute value expression on the *x*-axis of the classroom coordinate plane. Rewrite each expression without the absolute value symbol.

ⓐ $|-2|$

ⓑ $|2|$

ⓒ $|1 - 2|$

ⓓ $|-3 - (-5)|$

ⓔ $|-2 \cdot 3|$

ⓕ $|0 \cdot 4|$

ⓖ $\left|\frac{12}{-3}\right|$

ⓗ $|8 \div (-4)|$

TAKE NOTE...

Vertical bars around a value indicate absolute value. You read $|-4|$ as "the absolute value of -4."

2 Write your observations about the absolute value expressions you and your classmates modeled on the number line.

3 Provide counterexamples to show why Sonja's statement is incorrect.

> Sonja
>
> Absolute values are always positive.
> So, $|a| = -a$ is not possible.

ACTIVITY 1

MATHia CONNECTION

- Building Absolute Value Functions

Graphs of Absolute Value Functions

HABITS OF MIND

- Model with mathematics.
- Use appropriate tools strategically.

In the beginning of this course, you compared and contrasted various graphs to identify function families. You learned that there exists the family of linear absolute value functions of the form
$f(x) = a|x + b| + c$, where a, b, and c are real numbers, and a is not equal to 0.

In this activity you will build a graph of an absolute value function.

> Follow your teacher's instructions to model the function $f(x) = x$ on the classroom coordinate plane with your classmates.

1 Record the coordinates of the plotted points for $f(x) = x$ in the table.

x	y	
	$f(x) = x$	$f(x) = \lvert x \rvert$
−9		
−6		
−4		
−1		
0		
3		
5		
8		

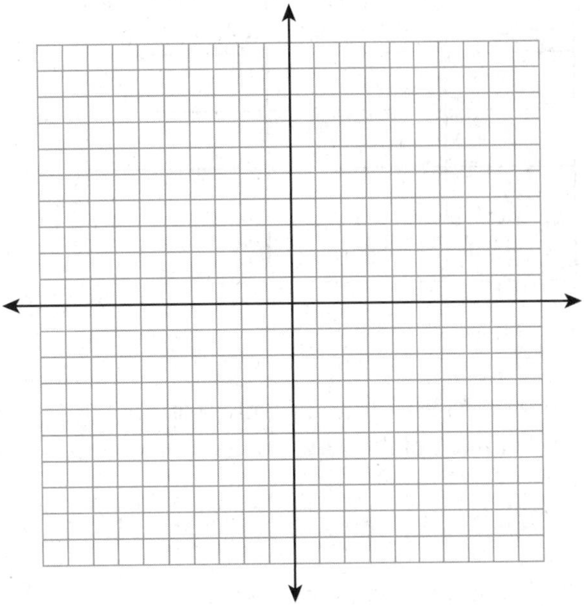

2 Change all the plotted points to model the function $f(x) = |x|$. In the table, record the coordinates of the new points for $f(x) = |x|$.

3 Describe how the points move from the graph of $f(x) = x$ to the graph of $f(x) = |x|$.

4 Graph the function $f(x) = |x|$. **Describe the characteristics of the function that you notice.**

THINK ABOUT...
What are the domain and range?

TOPIC 4

> Next, consider the function $f(x) = -x$. Model this function on the classroom coordinate plane with your classmates.

5 Record the coordinates of the plotted points for $f(x) = -x$ in the table.

x	y	
	$f(x) = -x$	$f(x) = \lvert -x \rvert$
−9		
−6		
−4		
−1		
0		
3		
5		
8		

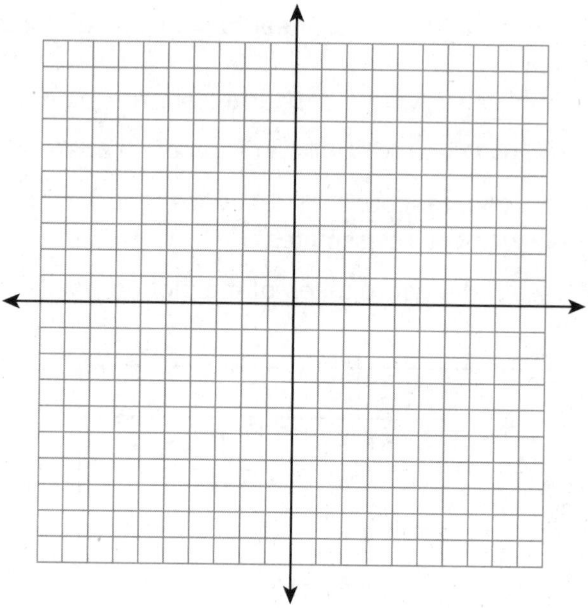

6 Change all the plotted points to model the function $f(x) = \lvert -x \rvert$. In the table, record the coordinates of the new points for $f(x) = \lvert -x \rvert$.

7 Describe how the points move from the graph of $f(x) = -x$ to the graph of $f(x) = \lvert -x \rvert$.

8 Graph the function $f(x) = \lvert -x \rvert$. **Compare this function with the function $f(x) = \lvert x \rvert$.**

REMEMBER...
Use a straightedge to be precise when you graph.

ACTIVITY 2

MATHia CONNECTION
- Vertically Dilating Absolute Value Functions
- Vertically Translating Absolute Value Functions
- Horizontally Translating Absolute Value Functions

Transformations Inside and Outside the Function

HABITS OF MIND
- Model with mathematics.
- Use appropriate tools strategically.

Just as with other functions, you can perform transformations on absolute value functions.

> Consider the three absolute value functions.

$g(x) = |x|$ $c(x) = |x| + 3$ $d(x) = |x| - 3$

1 Use technology to graph each function. Then, sketch and label the graph of each function.

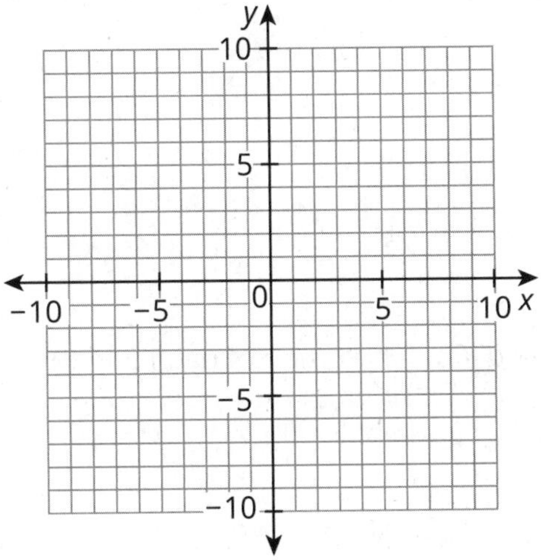

2 Write the functions $c(x)$ and $d(x)$ in terms of the basic function $g(x)$. Then describe the transformations of each function.

3 Describe the similarities and differences between the three graphs. How do these similarities and differences relate to the equations of the functions $g(x)$, $c(x)$, and $d(x)$?

TOPIC 4

Recall that a function $t(x)$ of the form $t(x) = f(x) + D$ is a vertical translation of the function $f(x)$. The value $|D|$ describes the number of units to translate the original graph up or down.

4 Describe each graph in relation to the basic function $g(x) = |x|$. Then use coordinate notation to represent the vertical translation.

(a) $f(x) = g(x) + D$ when $D > 0$

(b) $f(x) = g(x) + D$ when $D < 0$

(c) Each point (x, y) on the graph of $g(x)$ becomes the point ________ on $f(x)$.

> Consider these absolute value functions.

$g(x) = \|x\|$	$k(x) = \frac{1}{2}\|x\|$
$j(x) = 2\|x\|$	$p(x) = -\|x\|$

5 Use technology to graph each function. Then, sketch and label the graph of each function.

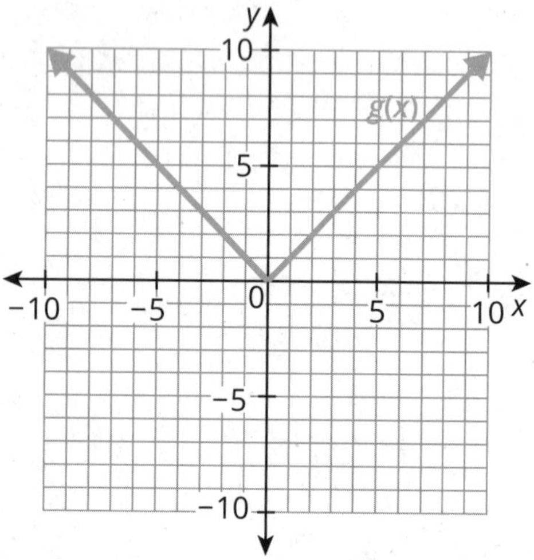

6 Write the functions $j(x)$, $k(x)$, and $p(x)$ in terms of the basic function $g(x)$. Then describe the transformations of each function.

Recall that a function $t(x)$ of the form $t(x) = A \cdot f(x)$ is a vertical dilation of the function $f(x)$. The A-value describes the vertical dilation of the graph of the original function.

7 Describe each graph in relation to the basic function $g(x) = |x|$. Then use coordinate notation to represent the vertical dilation.

(a) $f(x) = A \cdot g(x)$ when $A > 1$

(b) $f(x) = A \cdot g(x)$ when $A < 0$

(c) $f(x) = A \cdot g(x)$ when $0 < A < 1$

(d) Each point (x, y) on the graph of $g(x)$ becomes the point ________ on $f(x)$.

REMEMBER...

A **reflection** of a graph is the mirror image of the graph about a line of reflection.

A **line of reflection** is the line that the graph is reflected across.

A horizontal line of reflection affects the y-coordinates.

You know that changing the A-value of a function to its opposite reflects the function across a horizontal line. But the *line of reflection* for the function might be different depending on how you write the transformation and the order in which you apply the transformations.

8 Josh and Vicki each sketched a graph of the function $b(x) = -|x| - 3$ using different strategies. Write the step-by-step reasoning used by each student.

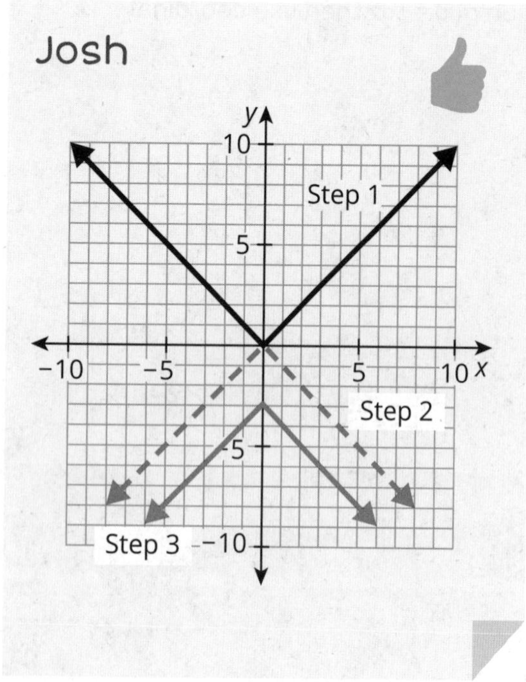

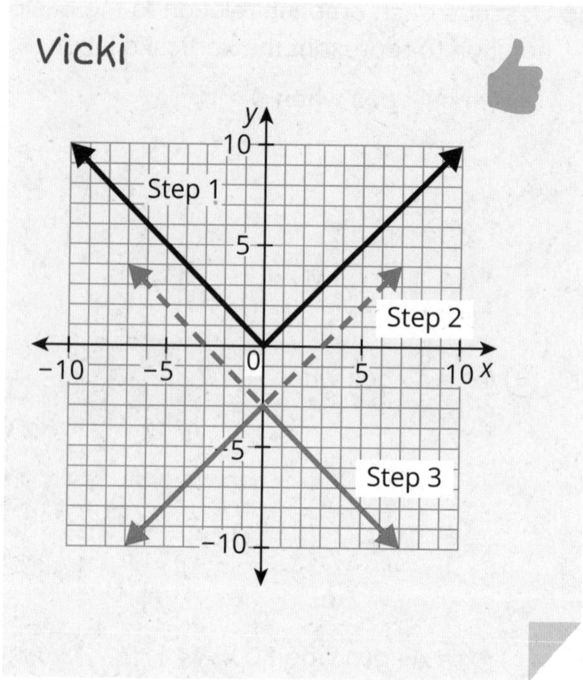

STEP 1:

STEP 2:

STEP 3:

STEP 1:

STEP 2:

STEP 3:

9 Explain how changing the order of the transformations affects the line of reflection.

> Given the function $f(x) = |x|$, use the coordinate plane to answer Questions 10 through 14.

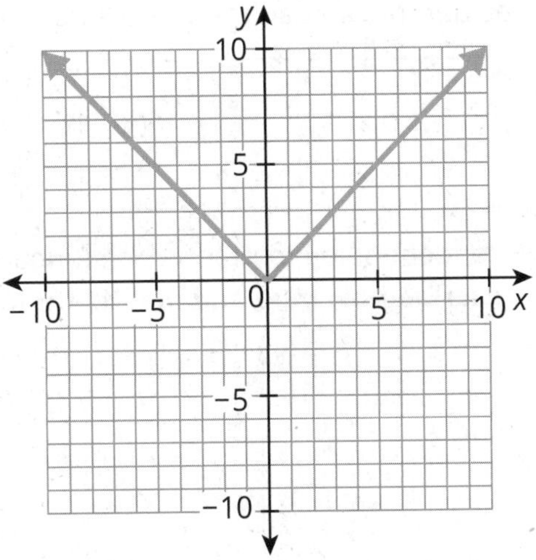

10 Consider the function $a(x) = 2f(x) + 1$.

(a) Use coordinate notation to describe how each point (x, y) on the graph of $f(x)$ becomes a point on the graph of $a(x)$.

(b) Graph and label $a(x)$ on the coordinate plane.

11 Consider the function $b(x) = -2f(x) + 1$.

(a) Use coordinate notation to describe how each point (x, y) on the graph of $f(x)$ becomes a point on the graph of $b(x)$.

(b) Graph and label $b(x)$ on the same coordinate plane.

12 Describe the graph of $b(x)$ in terms of $a(x)$.

13 Consider the function $-a(x)$.

(a) Use coordinate notation to describe how each point (x, y) on the graph of $a(x)$ becomes a point on the graph of $-a(x)$.

(b) Graph and label $-a(x)$ on the same coordinate plane.

14 Describe the graph of $-a(x)$ in terms of $a(x)$.

TOPIC 4

> Consider these absolute value functions.

$g(x) = |x|$ $m(x) = |x - 2|$ $n(x) = |x + 2|$

15 Use technology to graph each function. Then, sketch and label the graph of each function. **Describe how $m(x)$ and $n(x)$ relate to $g(x)$.**

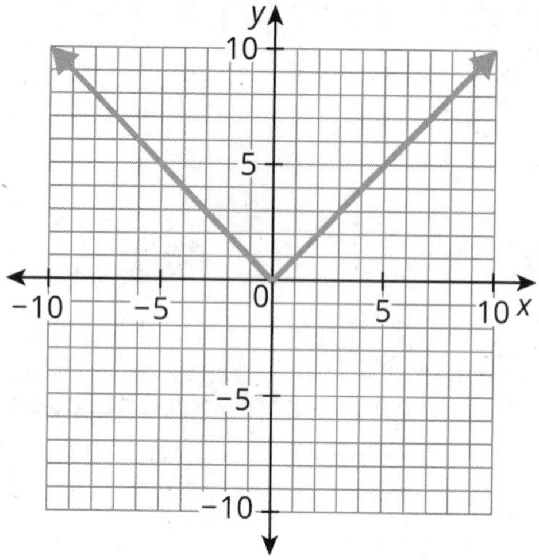

A function $t(x)$ of the form $t(x) = f(x - C)$ is a horizontal translation of the function $f(x)$. The value $|C|$ describes the number of units the graph of $f(x)$ is translated right or left. When $C > 0$, the graph is translated to the right. When $C < 0$, the graph is translated to the left.

REMEMBER...
The expression $x + C$ is the same as $x - (-C)$.

16 Write the functions $m(x)$ and $n(x)$ in terms of the basic function $g(x)$. **Describe how changing the C-value in the functions $m(x)$ and $n(x)$ horizontally translated the function $g(x)$.**

17 Use coordinate notation to show how each point (x, y) on the graph of $g(x)$ becomes a point on a graph that has been horizontally translated.

Combining Transformations of Absolute Value Functions

HABITS OF MIND
- Model with mathematics.
- Use appropriate tools strategically.

When a function is transformed by changing the *A*- or *D*-values or both, these changes occur outside the function. These values affect the output to a function, *y*.

When the *C*-value is changed, this changes the *argument of the function.* A change to the argument of a function happens inside the function. These values affect the input to a function, *x*.

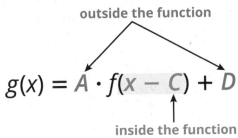

outside the function

$$g(x) = A \cdot f(x - C) + D$$

inside the function

TAKE NOTE...

The **argument of a function** is the expression inside the parentheses. For $y = f(x - C)$ the expression $x - C$ is the argument of the function.

1. Use coordinate notation to describe how each point (x, y) on the graph of $f(x)$ becomes a point on the graph of $g(x)$.

The ordered pair $(x, |x|)$ describes any point on the graph of the basic absolute value function $f(x) = |x|$. For a transformation of the function, you can write any point on the graph of the new function as $(x + C, A|x + C| + D)$.

2. Given the basic absolute value function $f(x) = |x|$, consider each transformation. Describe how the transformations affected $f(x)$. Then use coordinate notation to describe how each point (x, y) on the graph of $f(x)$ becomes a point on the graph of the transformed function. Finally, sketch a graph of each new function.

   a. $m(x) = 2f(x - 1)$

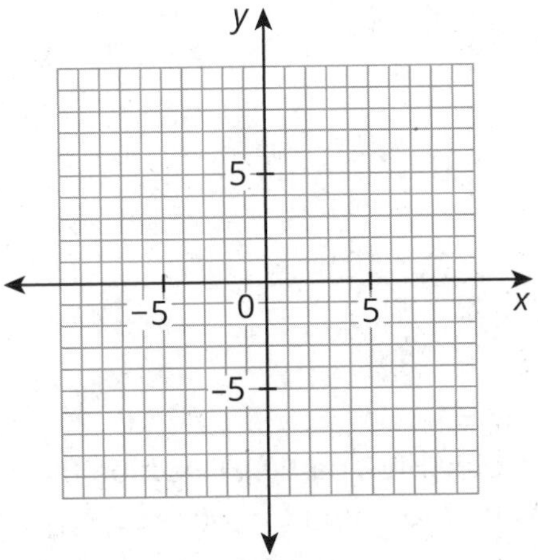

(b) $r(x) = \frac{1}{2}f(x + 2) - 2$

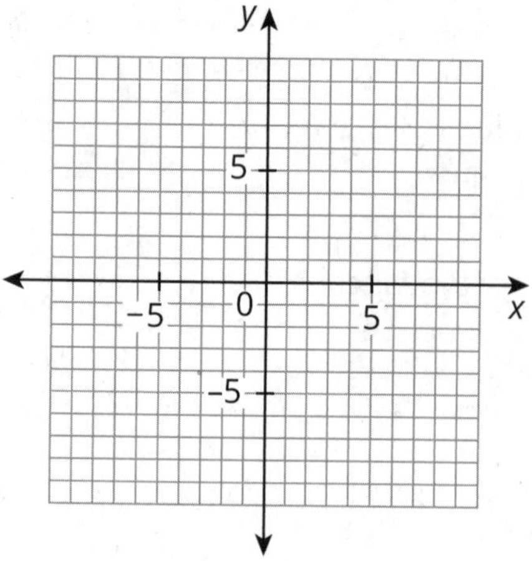

(c) $w(x) = 2f(x + 3) + 1$

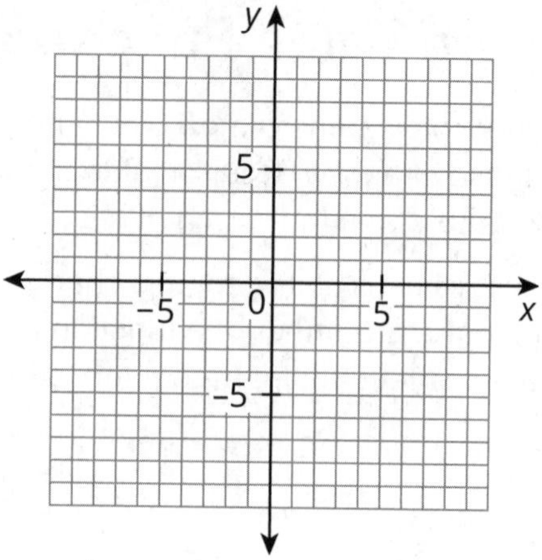

(d) $v(x) = -2f(x + 3) + 1$

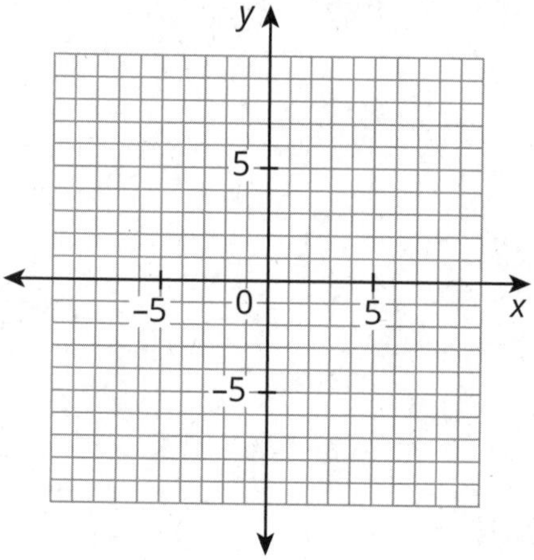

3 Graph $-w(x)$ on the same coordinate plane as $w(x)$ in Question 2 part (c). Describe the similarities and differences between the graph of $v(x)$ and the graph of $-w(x)$.

Writing Equations in Transformation Form

HABITS OF MIND
- Model with mathematics.
- Use appropriate tools strategically.

> Consider the function, $f(x) = |x|$.

1 Write the function in transformation function form in terms of the transformations described, then write an equivalent equation.

Transformation	Transformation Function Form	Equation
Reflection across the *x*-axis		
Horizontal translation of 2 units to the left and a vertical translation of 3 units up		
Vertical stretch of 2 units and a reflection across the line $y = 0$		
Vertical dilation of 2 units and a reflection across the line $y = 3$		
Horizontal translation of 3 units to the right, a vertical translation down 2 units, and a vertical dilation of $\frac{1}{2}$		
Vertical compression by a factor of 4		
Vertical stretch by a factor of 4		

A, C, and D

> Consider the function $f(x) = A|x - C| + D$ graphed with varying values for A, C, and D.

Graph A

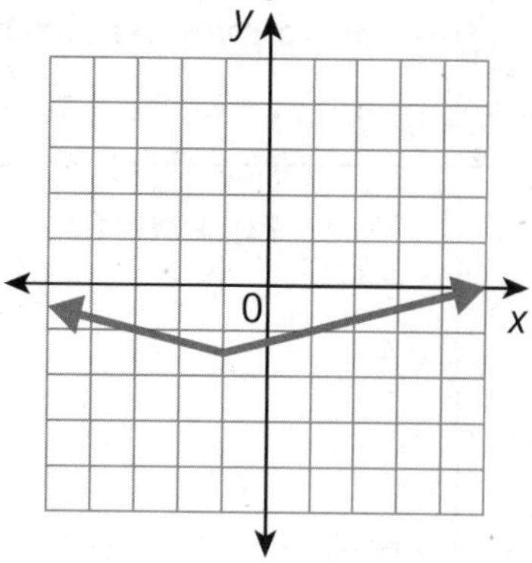

Graph B

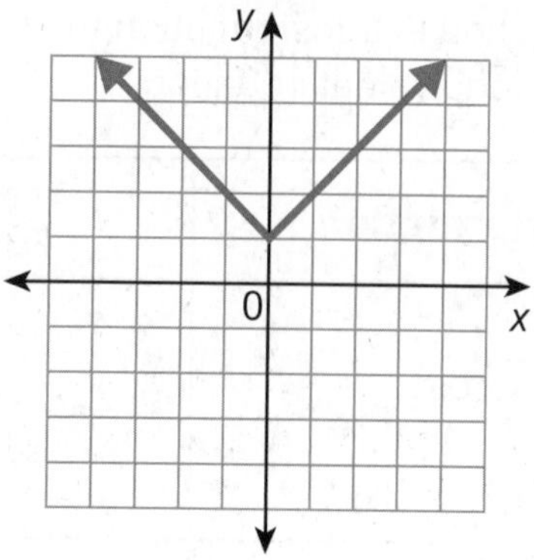

Graph C

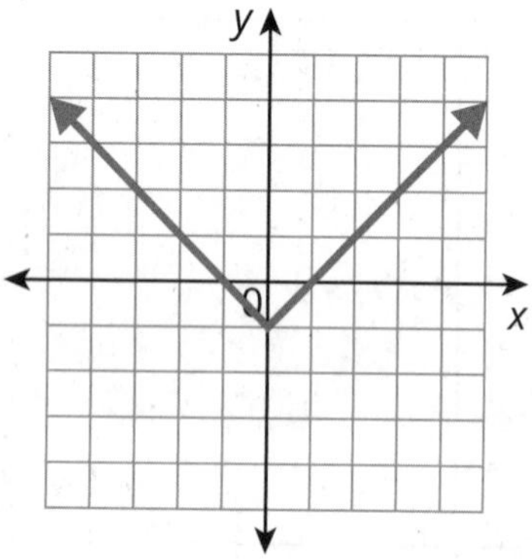

Graph D

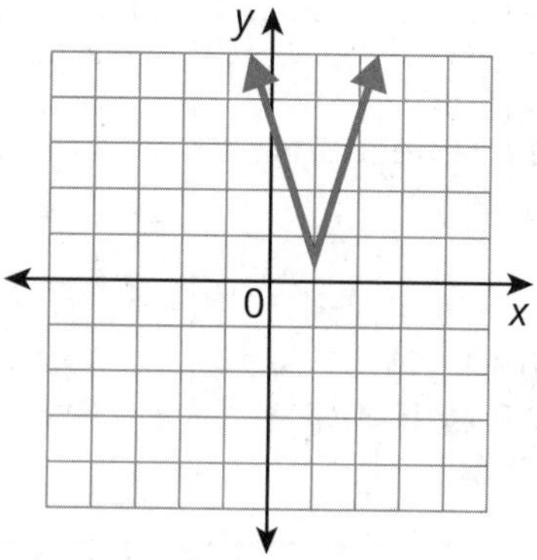

1 Match the given values of A, C, and D with the graph of the function with corresponding values. **Explain your reasoning.**

(a) $A = 1$, $C = 0$, and $D > 0$

(b) $A = 1$, $C = 0$, and $D < 0$

(c) $A > 1$, $C > 0$, and $D > 0$

(d) $0 < A < 1$, $C < 0$, and $D < 0$

TALK THE TALK

2 Complete the table by describing the graph of each function as a transformation of the basic function $f(x) = |x|$. Write the ordered pair that describes any point on the graph of the transformed function.

Function Form	Equation Information	Description of Transformation	Ordered Pair of Transformed Function
$f(x) = \|x\| + D$	$D < 0$		
	$D > 0$		
$f(x) = A\|x\|$	$A < 0$		
	$0 < A < 1$		
	$A > 1$		
$f(x) = \|x - C\|$	$C < 0$		
	$C > 0$		

3 Determine whether each statement is true or false. If the statement is false, rewrite the statement as true.

(a) In the transformation function form $g(x) = Af(x - C) + D$, the A-value vertically stretches or compresses $f(x)$, the C-value translates $f(x)$ horizontally, and the D-value translates the function $f(x)$ vertically.

(b) Key characteristics of the basic absolute value function include a domain and range of real numbers.

(c) The domain of absolute value functions is not affected by translations or dilations.

(d) Vertical translations do not affect the range of absolute value functions.

(e) Horizontal translations do not affect the range of absolute value functions.

(f) Vertical dilations do not affect the range of absolute value functions.

LESSON 1 ASSIGNMENT

JOURNAL

Given a basic function $y = f(x)$ and a function written in transformation form $g(x) = A \cdot f(x - C) + D$, describe how the transformations that are inside a function affect a graph differently than those on the outside of the function.

REMEMBER

The basic absolute value function is $f(x) = |x|$.

The transformed function $y = f(x) + D$ shows a vertical translation of the function.

The transformed function $y = Af(x)$ shows a vertical dilation of the function when $A > 0$ and when $A < 0$ it shows a vertical dilation and reflection across the x-axis.

The transformed function $y = f(x - C)$ shows a horizontal translation of the function.

PRACTICE

> Given the basic function $f(x) = |x|$, consider each transformation. Describe how the transformations affected $f(x)$. Then use coordinate notation to describe how each point (x, y) on the graph of $f(x)$ becomes a point on the graph of the transformed function. Finally, sketch a graph of each new function.

1. $g(x) = \frac{1}{3}f(x) - 2$

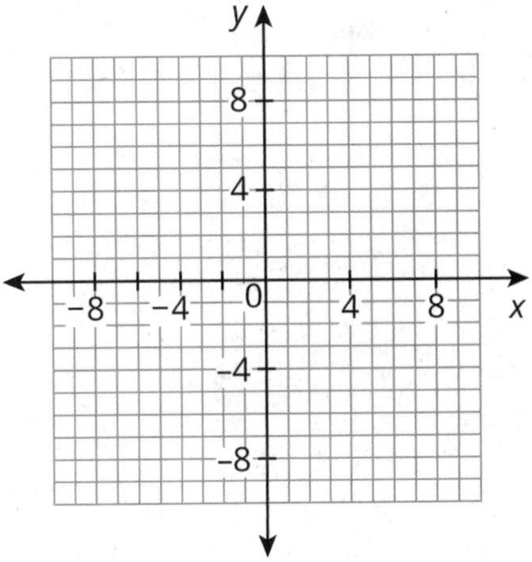

2. $j(x) = 2f(x + 1) + 4$

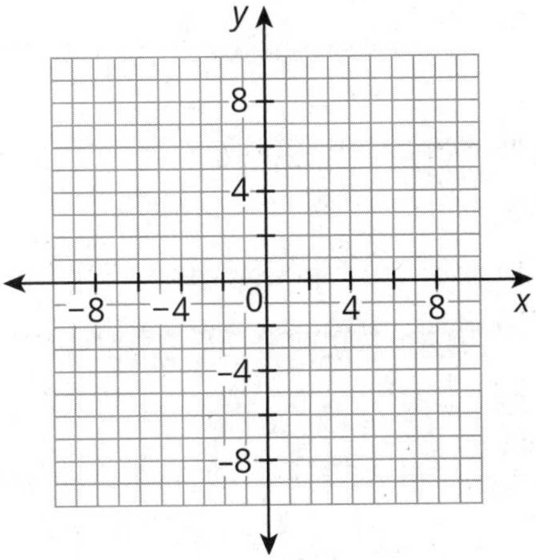

3. $m(x) = -\frac{1}{2}f(x - 3) - 1$

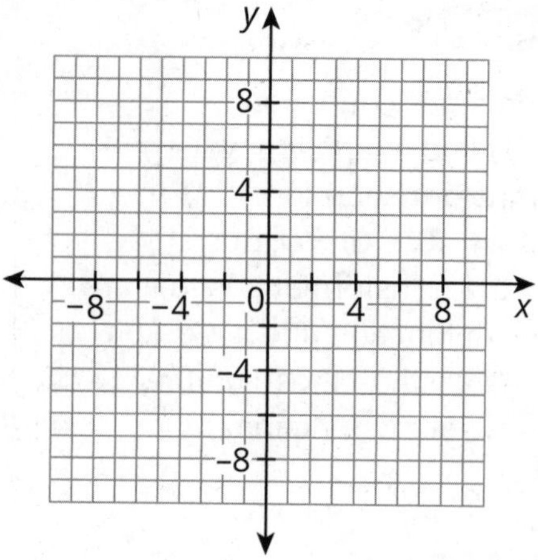

4. $p(x) = -f(x + 4) + 3$

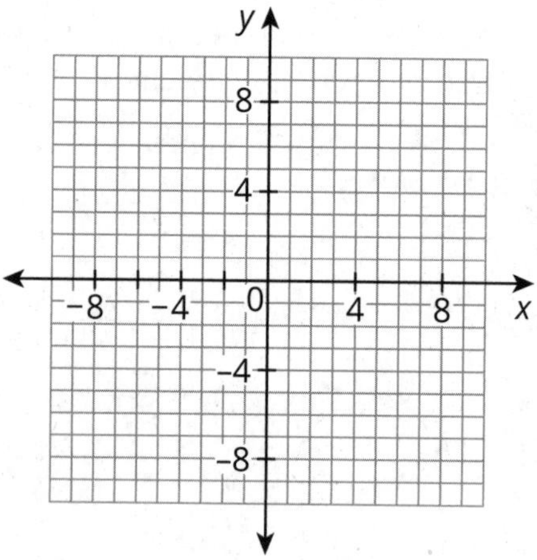

STRETCH Optional

> Consider the function $g(x)$ which is a transformation of $f(x) = |x|$.

1. Write the function $g(x)$ in terms of $f(x)$.

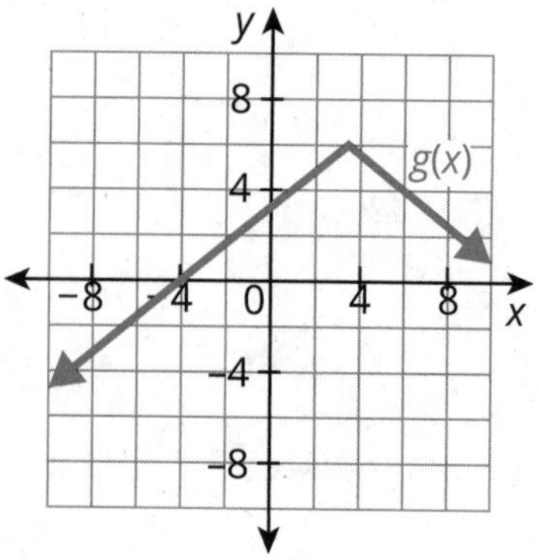

LESSON 2

Play Ball!

Absolute Value Equations and Inequalities

Learning Goals

- Understand and solve absolute value equations.
- Solve and graph linear absolute value inequalities on number lines.
- Graph absolute value functions and use the graph to determine solutions.

KEY TERMS

linear absolute value equation

linear absolute value inequality

equivalent compound inequality

REVIEW (1–2 minutes)

> Evaluate each expression.

1. $|9 + (-4)|$

2. $|-1 - 5|$

3. $|4(-6)|$

4. $|0 \div (-2)|$

You know what the graphs of absolute value functions look like.

How can you use what you know to solve absolute value equations and inequalities?

Opposites Attract? Absolutely!

You can solve many absolute value equations using inspection.

1 Graph the solution set of each equation on the number line given.

ⓐ $|x| = 5$

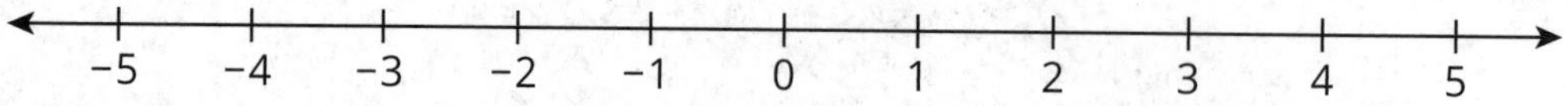

ⓑ $|x| = 2$

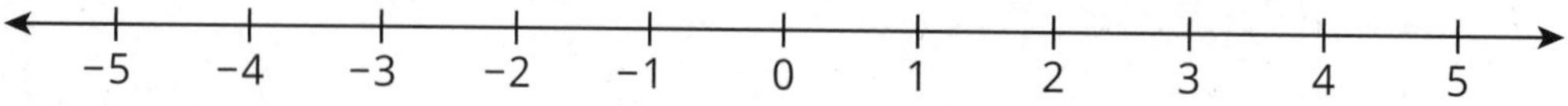

ⓒ $|x| = -3$

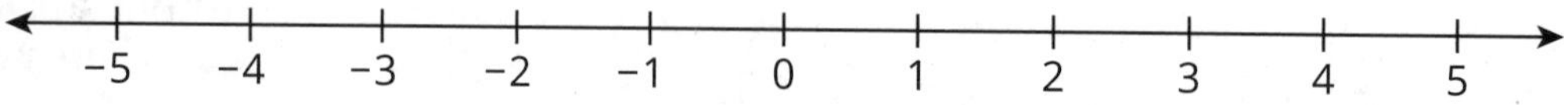

ⓓ $|x| = 0$

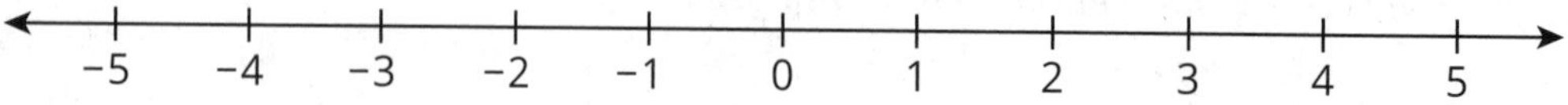

2 Write the absolute value equation for each solution set graphed.

ⓐ

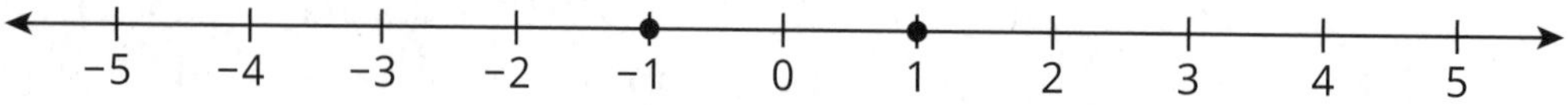

ⓑ

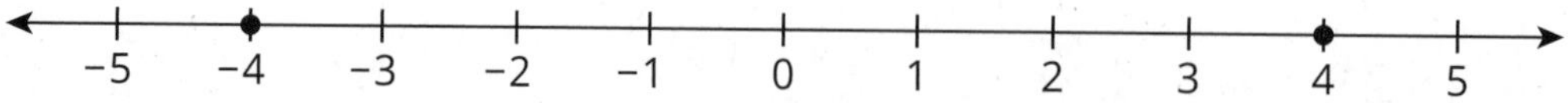

MATHia CONNECTION

- Reasoning About Absolute Value Functions
- Graphing Simple Absolute Value Equations Using Number Lines

Creating an Absolute Value Function from a Situation

HABITS OF MIND

- Reason abstractly and quantitatively.
- Construct viable arguments and critique the reasoning of others.

You can model a situation using an absolute value function.

The official rules of baseball state that all baseballs used during professional games must be within a specified range of weights. The baseball manufacturer sets the target weight of the balls at 145.045 grams on its machines.

1 Sketch a graph that models the relationship between a manufactured baseball's weight, x, and its distance from the target weight, y. **Explain how you constructed your sketch.** Then write an absolute value equation to represent the situation and the graph.

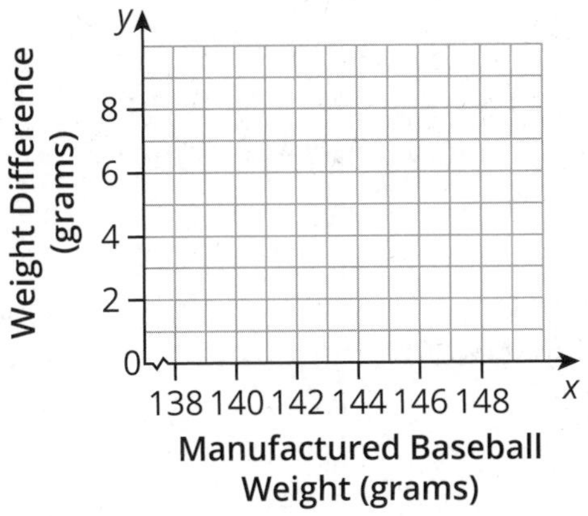

2 The specified weight allows for a difference of 3.295 grams in the actual weight of a ball and the target weight. The weight must be within a distance of 3.295 grams from the target weight, $y = 3.295$.

(a) Graph the equation $y = 3.295$ on the coordinate plane in Question 1.

ASK YOURSELF...
How is the function transformed from the basic function $f(x) = |x|$?

(b) What two equations can you write, without absolute values, to show the least acceptable weight and the greatest acceptable weight of a baseball?

(c) Use the graph to write the solutions to the equations you wrote in part (b).

TOPIC 4

MATHia CONNECTION
- Introduction to Absolute Value Equations
- Solving Absolute Value Equations

Solving Absolute Value Equations

HABITS OF MIND
- Look for and make use of structure.
- Look for and express regularity in repeated reasoning.

You can represent the two equations you wrote using the **linear absolute value equation** $|w - 145.045| = 3.295$. To solve any absolute value equation, recall the definition of absolute value.

WORKED EXAMPLE

Consider this linear absolute value equation.

$$|a| = 6$$

There are two points that are 6 units away from zero on the number line: one to the right of zero, and one to the left of zero.

$+(a) = 6$ or $-(a) = 6$

$a = 6$ or $a = -6$

Now consider the case where $a = x - 1$.

$$|x - 1| = 6$$

If you know that you can write $|a| = 6$ as two separate equations, you can rewrite any absolute value equation.

$+(a) = 6$ or $-(a) = 6$

$+(x - 1) = 6$ or $-(x - 1) = 6$

1. How do you know the expressions $+(a)$ and $-(a)$ represent opposite distances?

2. Martina and Bob continued to solve the linear absolute value equation $|x - 1| = 6$ in different ways. Compare their strategies and then determine the solutions to the equation.

Martina

$(x - 1) = 6$ or $(x - 1) = -6$

Bob

$x - 1 = 6$ or $-x + 1 = 6$

3 Solve each linear absolute value equation. **Show your work.**

ⓐ $|x + 7| = 3$

ⓑ $|x - 9| = 12$

ⓒ $|3x + 7| = -8$

ⓓ $|2x + 3| = 0$

THINK ABOUT...
Before you solve each equation, think about the number of solutions each equation may have. You may be able to save yourself some work—and time!

4 Artie, Donald, Cho, and Steve each solved the equation $|x| - 4 = 5$.

Artie

$|x| - 4 = 5$

$(x) - 4 = 5$ $\quad$ $-(x) - 4 = 5$

$(x) = 9$ $\quad$ $-x = 9$

$x = -9$

Donald

$|x| - 4 = 5$

$|x| = 9$

$(x) = 9$ $\quad$ $-(x) = 9$

$x = -9$

Cho

$|x| - 4 = 5$

$(x) - 4 = 5$ $\quad$ $-[(x) - 4] = 5$

$x - 4 = 5$ $\quad$ $-x + 4 = 5$

$x = 9$ $\quad$ $-x = 1$

$x = -1$

Steve

$|x| - 4 = 5$

$(x) - 4 = 5$ $\quad$ $-(x) - 4 = -5$

$x = 9$ $\quad$ $-x - 4 = -5$

$-x = -1$

$= 1$

ⓐ Explain how Cho and Steve incorrectly rewrote the absolute value equation as two separate equations.

ⓑ Explain the difference in the strategies that Artie and Donald used.

TOPIC 4

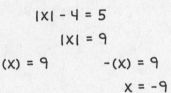

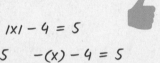

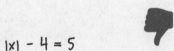

5 Solve each linear absolute value equation.

(a) $|x| + 16 = 32$

THINK ABOUT...
Consider isolating the absolute value part of the equation before you rewrite it as two equations.

(b) $23 = |x - 8| + 6$

(c) $3|x - 2| = 12$

(d) $35 = 5|x + 6| - 10$

Absolute Value Inequalities

HABITS OF MIND
- Model with mathematics.
- Use appropriate tools strategically.

You determined the linear absolute value equation $|w - 145.045| = 3.295$ to identify the most and least a baseball could weigh and still be within the specifications.

The manufacturer wants to determine all of the acceptable weights that the baseball could be and still fit within the specifications.

You can write a **linear absolute value inequality** to represent this problem situation.

1. Write a linear absolute value inequality to represent all baseball weights that are within the specifications.

2. Use the graph to determine whether the weight of each given baseball is acceptable. Substitute each value in the inequality to verify your answer.

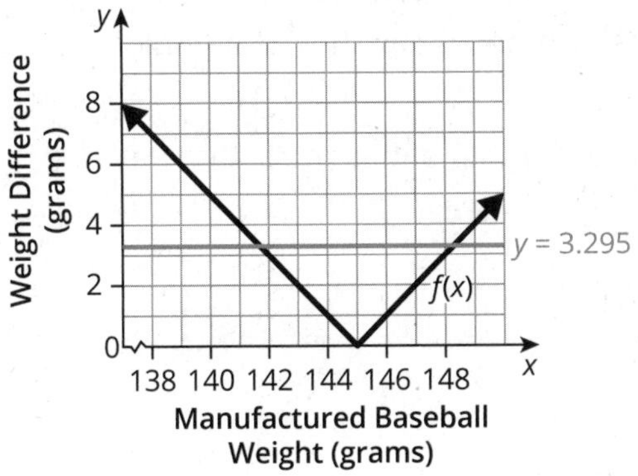

(a) 147 grams

(b) 140.8 grams

(c) 148.34 grams

(d) 141.75 grams

3 Use the graph on the coordinate plane to graph the inequality on the number line showing all the acceptable weights. **Explain the process you used.**

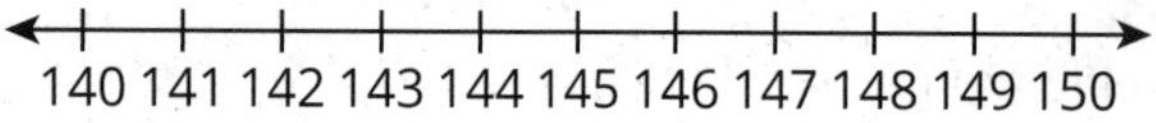

4 Complete the inequality to describe all the acceptable weights, where w is the baseball's weight.

________ $\leq w \leq$ ________

5 Raymond has the job of disposing of all baseballs that are not within the acceptable weight limits.

ⓐ Write an absolute value inequality to represent the weights of baseballs that Raymond can dispose of.

ⓑ Graph the inequality on the number line. **Explain the process you used.**

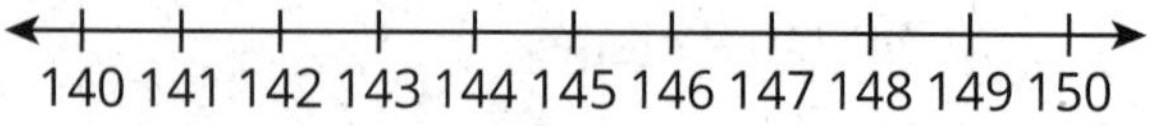

Solving Problems with Absolute Value Functions

HABITS OF MIND
- Attend to precision.

For Little League baseballs, the manufacturer sets the target diameter at 7.47 centimeters. The specified diameter allows for a difference of 1.27 centimeters. You can model this situation using the function $f(d) = |x - 7.47|$.

1 Consider the situation.

(a) Sketch the graph of $f(d)$ on the coordinate plane.

(b) Use your graph to estimate the diameters of all the Little League baseballs that fit within the specifications. **Explain how you determined your answer.**

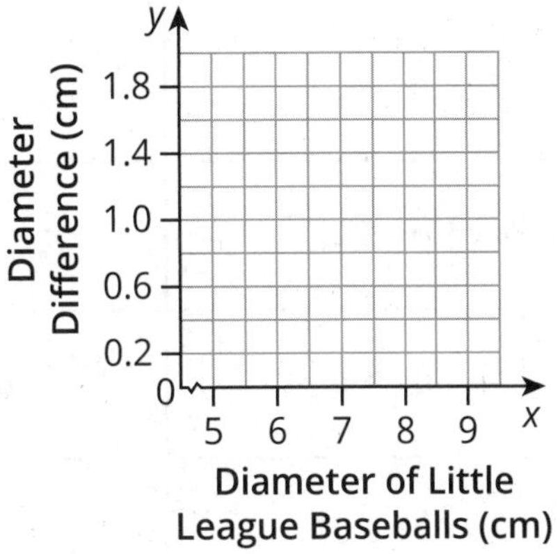

(c) Algebraically determine the diameters of all the baseballs that fit within the specification. Write your answer as an inequality.

The manufacturer knows that the closer the diameter of the baseball is to the target, the more likely it is to be sold. The manufacturer decides to keep only the baseballs that are less than 0.75 centimeter from the target diameter.

2 Consider the situation.

(a) Algebraically determine which baseballs do not fall within the new specified limits and will not be kept. Write your answer as an inequality.

(b) How can you use your graph to determine whether you are correct?

Absolute Value and Compound Inequalities

HABITS OF MIND
- Look for and make use of structure.
- Look for and express regularity in repeated reasoning.

Absolute value inequalities can take four different forms, as shown in the table. To solve a linear absolute value inequality, you can first write it as an **equivalent compound inequality**.

Absolute Value Inequality	Equivalent Compound Inequality
$\lvert ax + b \rvert < c$	$-c < ax + b < c$
$\lvert ax + b \rvert \leq c$	$-c \leq ax + b \leq c$
$\lvert ax + b \rvert > c$	$ax + b < -c$ or $ax + b > c$
$\lvert ax + b \rvert \geq c$	$ax + b \leq -c$ or $ax + b \geq c$

TAKE NOTE...
Notice that the equivalent compound inequalities do not contain absolute values.

1. Solve the linear absolute value inequality by rewriting it as an equivalent compound inequality. Then graph your solution on the number line.

(a) $\lvert x + 3 \rvert < 4$

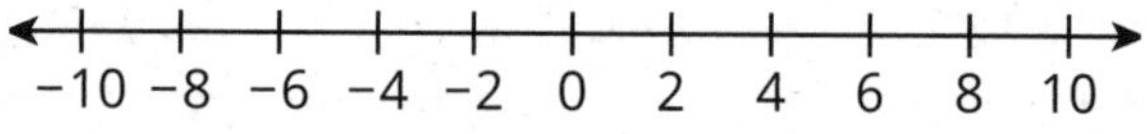

(b) $6 \leq \lvert 2x - 4 \rvert$

REMEMBER...
As a final step, don't forget to check your solution.

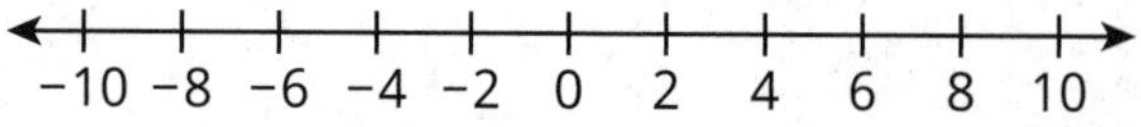

(c) $|-5x + 8| + 2 < 25$

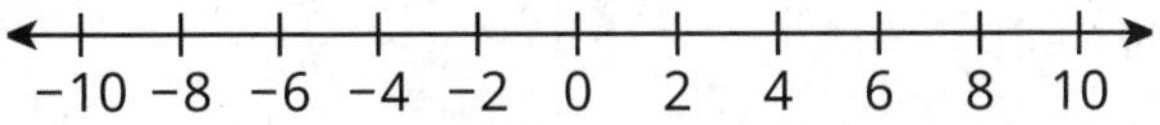

(d) $|x + 5| > -1$

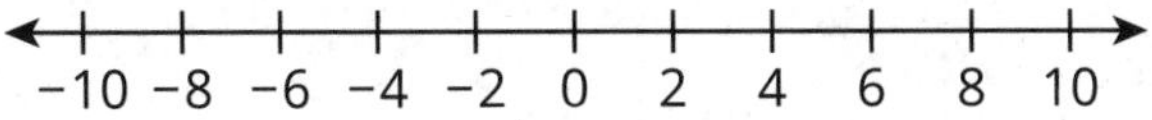

(e) $|x + 5| < -1$

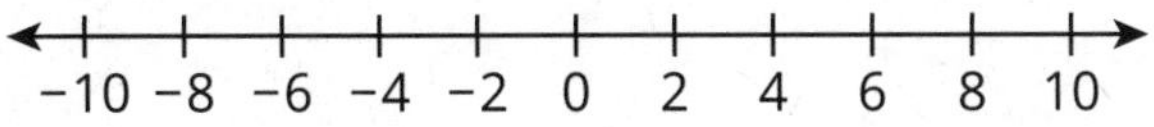

Seeing Double

> Consider the situation from the first activity.

A baseball manufacturer sets the target weight of the baseballs at 145.045 grams. The specified weight allows for a certain distance, y, between the actual weight and the target weight.

1 Suppose this distance between the target weight and the actual weight is cut in half. Describe how this represents a transformation of the original function. Sketch a graph of the new function and write the new equation.

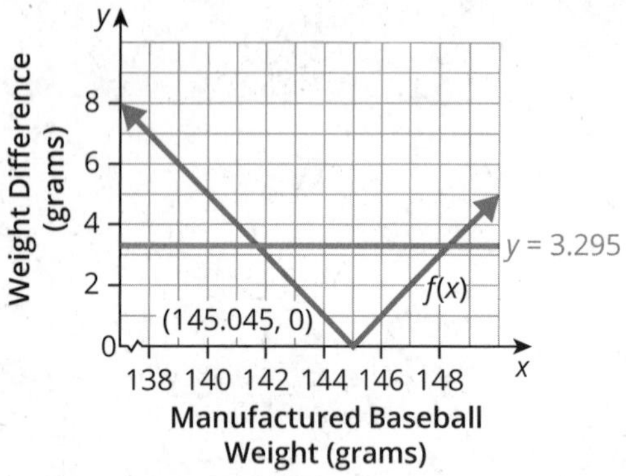

2 Describe why you can rewrite an absolute value equation as two separate equations.

JOURNAL

Describe the similarities and differences between solving a linear absolute value equation and a linear absolute value inequality.

REMEMBER

You can rewrite any absolute value equation as two equations to solve. When $|x| = c$, where c is any real number, then $+(x) = c$ or $-(x) = c$.

Absolute value inequalities can take four different forms. To solve a linear absolute value inequality, you can first write it as an equivalent compound inequality.

Absolute Value Inequality	Equivalent Compound Inequality
$\lvert ax + b\rvert < c$	$-c < ax + b < c$
$\lvert ax + b\rvert \le c$	$-c \le ax + b \le c$
$\lvert ax + b\rvert > c$	$ax + b < -c$ or $ax + b > c$
$\lvert ax + b\rvert \ge c$	$ax + b \le -c$ or $ax + b \ge c$

PRACTICE

1. The Billingsly Cookie Company is trying to come up with a cookie that is low in fat but still has good taste. The company decides on a target fat content of 5 grams per cookie. In order to be labeled low-fat, a difference of 1.8 grams per cookie is acceptable.

   a. Write an expression that represents the difference between the fat in a cookie from the new recipe and the target fat content. Use f to represent the amount of fat in a cookie from the new recipe.

   b. Write an absolute value inequality to represent the restrictions on the difference in the amount of fat.

   c. One of the bakers creates a cookie recipe that has 6.5 grams of fat per cookie. Is this recipe acceptable? Explain your reasoning.

TOPIC 4

Go to LiveHint.com for help on the PRACTICE questions.

(d) Algebraically determine the greatest and least number of grams of fat a cookie can contain and still fall within the required specifications. Write your answer as an inequality.

(e) Sketch the graph of the absolute value inequality from part (b).

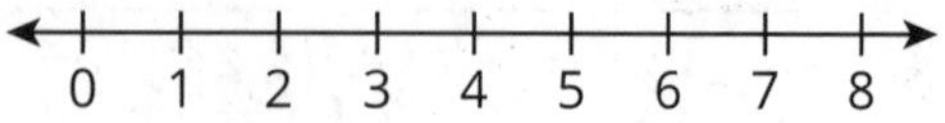

2 Solve each absolute value equation or inequality.

(a) $|x| + 8 = 15$

(b) $|x + 5| = -15$

(c) $|x + 4| \leq 9$

(d) $|3x - 1| > 14$

(e) $|x - 9| > -1$

STRETCH Optional

John, Rasheed, and Jeorge are different ages. Rasheed is six less than twice John's age. Jeorge's age is nine more than half of John's age. The difference between Rasheed and Jeorge's ages is no more than nine years.

1 Write an expression that represents the difference between Rasheed and Jeorge's ages.

2 Write an absolute value inequality to represent the maximum difference in their ages.

3 Determine whether it is possible for John to be twenty years old. Explain your reasoning.

4 Algebraically determine the greatest and least age John can be so that the difference between Rasheed and Jeorge's ages is no more than nine years.

LESSON 3

I Graph in Pieces

Linear Piecewise Functions

KEY TERMS

piecewise function

Learning Goals

- Create graphs of linear piecewise functions.
- Write linear piecewise functions from scenarios, tables, and graphs.
- Interpret or write a scenario for a piecewise graph.
- Use technology to graph and evaluate linear piecewise functions.
- Compare a linear absolute value function to a linear piecewise function.

REVIEW (1–2 minutes)

> Consider the graph.

1. Is the relation a function? Why or why not?

2. Did the bathtub fill or drain faster? How do you know?

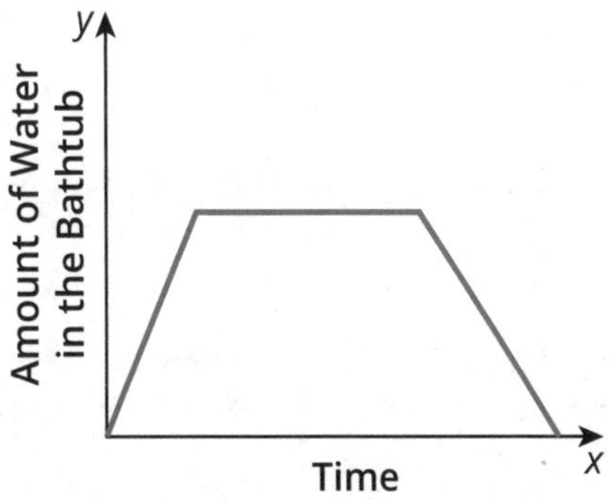

You explored the graphs of absolute value functions.

What other functions involve graphs composed of more than one line or line segment?

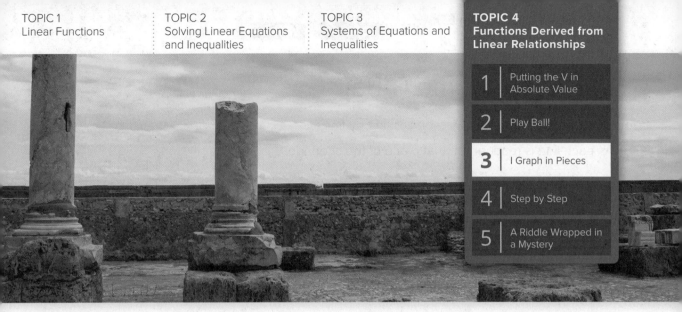

Just Playing Some B-Ball

Your teacher is going to read a scenario line by line.

1. As each line is read, graph that piece of the scenario.

REMEMBER...
Label your axes.

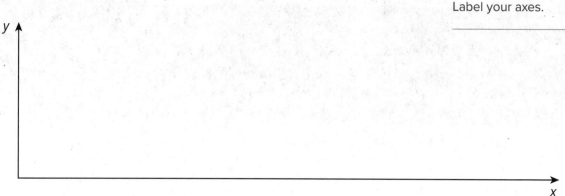

> Reflect on your process and the mathematics by responding to these questions.

2. Will everyone in class have the exact same graph? **Explain your reasoning.**

3. What clues from the scenario did you use to decide how steep to make each line segment?

4. How did you determine the length of each line segment?

5 How many segments does your graph have? **What does this indicate about the scenario?**

6 Does your graph have any horizontal line segments? **If so, what do they represent? If not, explain why not.**

7 Does your graph have any decreasing line segments? **If so, what do they represent? If not, explain why not.**

8 Does your graph have any increasing line segments? **If so, what do they represent? If not, explain why not.**

9 What do the y-intercept and x-intercept represent?

Developing a Piecewise Function from a Scenario

HABITS OF MIND
- Model with mathematics.
- Use appropriate tools strategically.

The relation you graphed in the Getting Started represents a *piecewise function*. A **piecewise function** is a function that you can represent by more than one function, each which corresponds to a part of the domain. Recall that a linear piecewise function is a function that you can represent using linear functions only, each of which corresponds to a part of the domain.

Paulina owns a popular pizza parlor. She noticed a daily trend in her pizza sales. When her shop opens for lunch at 11 A.M., she sells 30 pizzas each hour for the first three hours. Sales dwindle to 10 pizzas per hour for the next 3 hours. Business picks up from 5 P.M. until closing time at 11 P.M., when she sells 40 pizzas each hour for all 6 hours.

THINK ABOUT...
To model this problem, make the assumption that pizza is sold at a constant rate throughout each hour.

1. Represent this problem situation with a table of values and a graph. Don't forget to label your axes.

Time of Day	Number of Hours Since the Pizza Shop Opened	Total Number of Pizzas Sold
11 A.M.	0	0
12 P.M.		
1 P.M.		
2 P.M.		
3 P.M.		
4 P.M.		
5 P.M.		
6 P.M.		
7 P.M.		
8 P.M.		
9 P.M.		
10 P.M.		
11 P.M.		

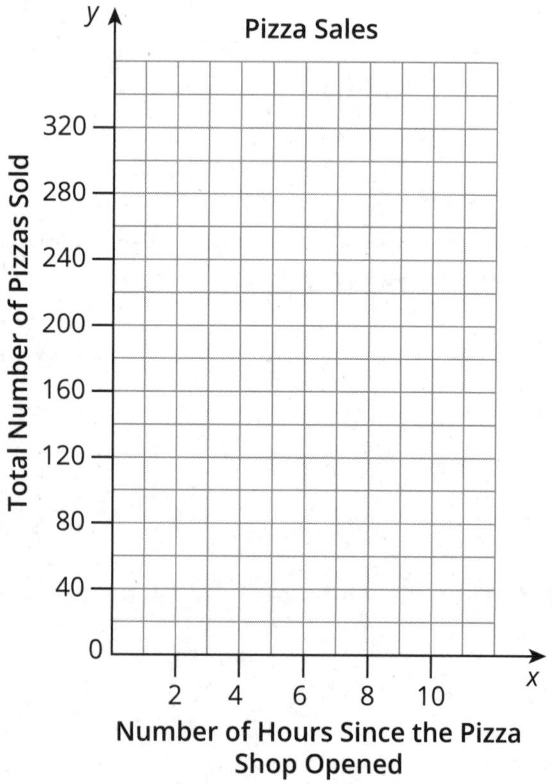

2 Use the graph and table to answer each question.

(a) Identify the domain of this problem situation.

(b) How many pieces make up this function? What is the domain of each piece?

3 Determine the equation that represents each piece of the function for each given time period. **Show your work.**

(a) From 0 to 3 hours

(b) From more than 3 hours to 6 hours

(c) From more than 6 hours to 12 hours

4 To write a piecewise function, you must write the equation followed by its domain for each piece of the function. Complete the function by transferring the information from Question 3 into the proper format. **Define your variables.**

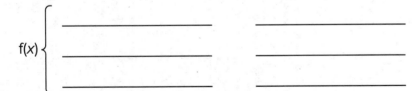

$$f(x)\begin{cases} \_\_\_\_\_\_\_\_\_\_\_\_ & \_\_\_\_\_\_\_\_\_\_\_\_ \\ \_\_\_\_\_\_\_\_\_\_\_\_ & \_\_\_\_\_\_\_\_\_\_\_\_ \\ \_\_\_\_\_\_\_\_\_\_\_\_ & \_\_\_\_\_\_\_\_\_\_\_\_ \end{cases}$$

5 Which piece of the function should you use to determine the y-intercept? **Explain your reasoning.**

6 Use technology to graph your function. Then answer each question and identify the piece of the function you used. **Explain your reasoning.**

(a) At what time of day will the pizza shop sell its 300th pizza?

(b) At what time of day will the pizza shop sell its 150th pizza?

(c) At what time of day will the pizza shop sell its 70th pizza?

MATHia CONNECTION
- Graphing Linear Piecewise Functions
- Interpreting Piecewise Functions

Interpreting the Graph of a Piecewise Function

HABITS OF MIND
- Model with mathematics.
- Use appropriate tools strategically.

Now that you have built a piecewise function, let's analyze and interpret the different pieces of a given piecewise function.

The graph shows the percent of the charge remaining on a cell phone battery over time.

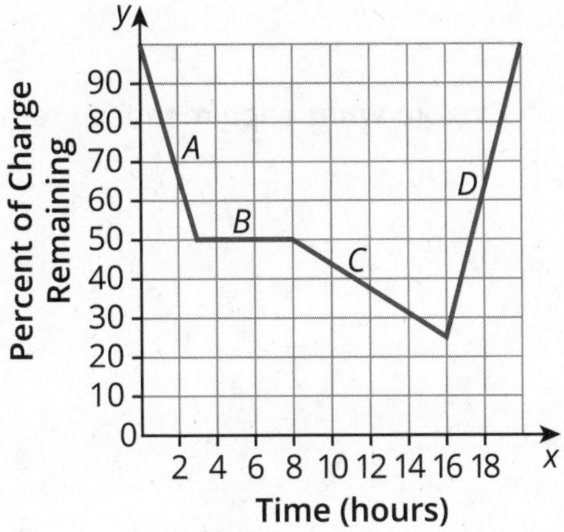

1. Write a possible scenario that models the graph.

2. Explain how you know the graph represents a function in terms of this problem situation.

3 Write a function $f(x)$ to model the graph. **Define your variables.**

4 Determine the slope, x-intercept(s), and y-intercept. **Explain what each means in terms of this problem situation.**

5 Determine which piece(s) of the graph each statement describes.

(a) The cell phone was not in use.

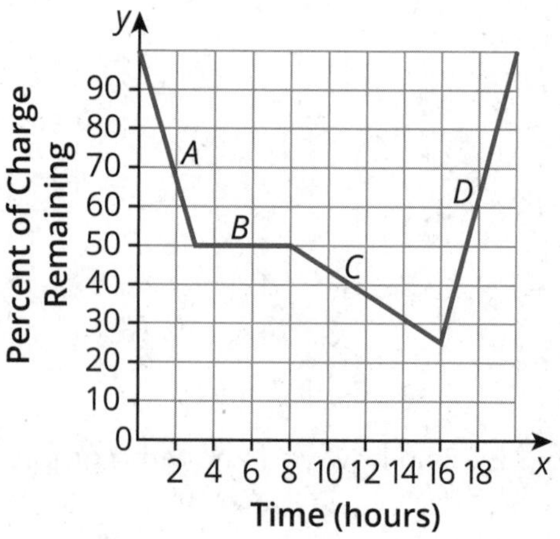

(b) The cell phone battery was recharging.

(c) The cell phone was in use.

(d) The cell phone battery was fully charged.

(e) The cell phone battery was half-charged.

6 Determine whether each statement is true or false. **If it is false, explain why it is false.**

(a) The cell phone battery died after 20 hours.

(b) The cell phone battery lost 25% of its charge during an 8-hour period.

(c) The cell phone was used the most between the 16th and 20th hours.

(d) The cell phone battery was charged twice.

(e) After the first 3 hours, the battery had half the charge it began with.

7 Write a scenario to model your own cell phone use during a typical day. Give your scenario to your partner and have them graph it while you graph your partner's scenario. Then, work together to determine the equation of each piecewise function.

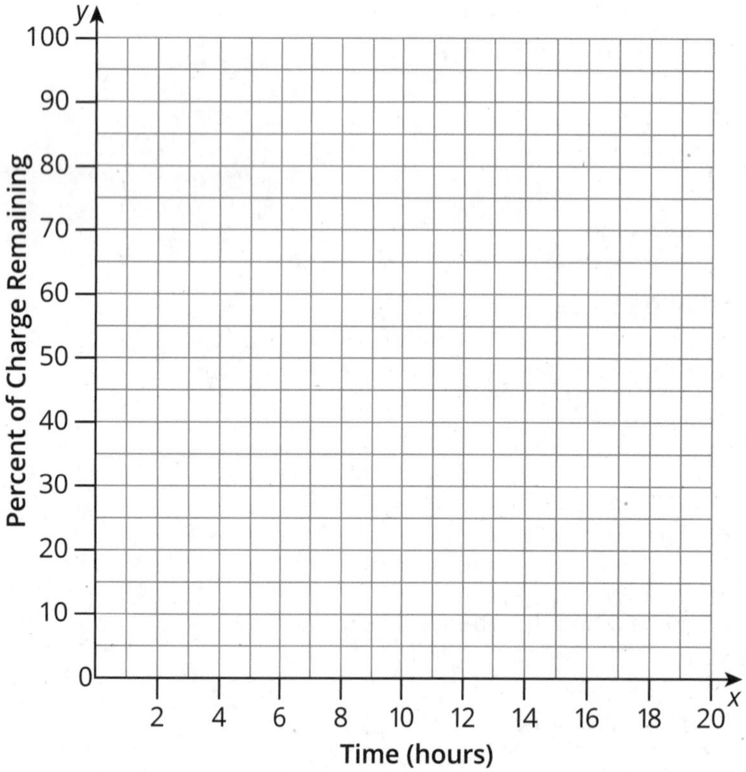

Transformations of Piecewise Functions

HABITS OF MIND
- Reason abstractly and quantitatively.
- Construct viable arguments and critique the reasoning of others.

You can use what you know about transformations to transform any function, including a piecewise function. A transformed function is often written using the prime symbol (′).

For example, you write a transformation of the function $f(x)$ as $f'(x)$.

1 The graph of a function $z(x)$ is shown. Sketch the graphs of $z'(x)$ and $z''(x)$.

(a) $z'(x) = z(x) + 3$

(b) $z''(x) = z(x) - 4$

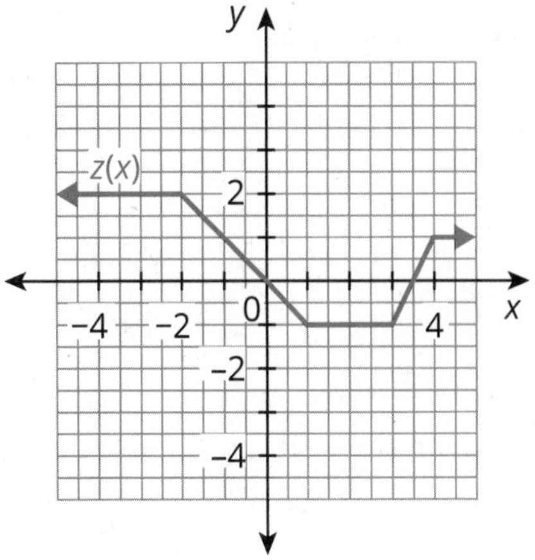

2 The graph of a function $t(x)$ is shown. Sketch the graphs of $t'(x)$ and $t''(x)$.

(a) $t'(x) = t(x + 3)$

(b) $t''(x) = t(x - 1)$

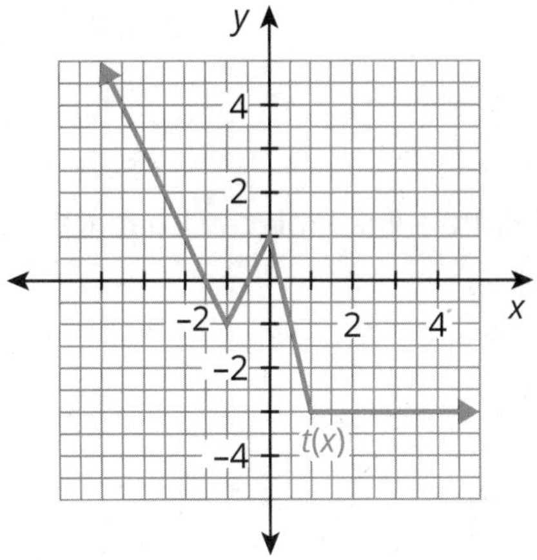

3 The graph of a function $w(x)$ is shown. Sketch the graphs of $w'(x)$ and $w''(x)$.

(a) $w'(x) = -w(x)$

(b) $w''(x) = w(-x)$

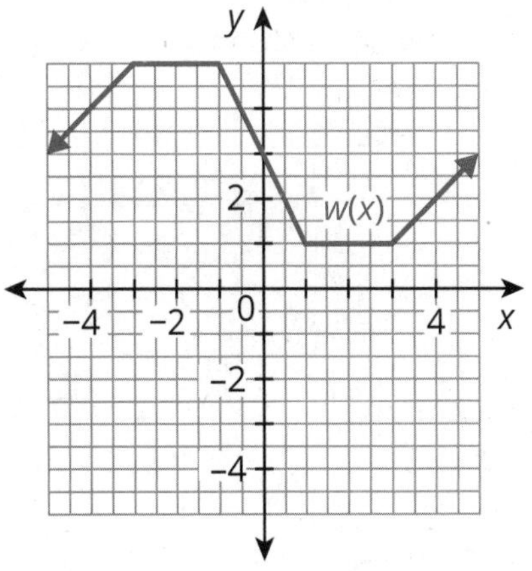

A Special Type of Piecewise Function

HABITS OF MIND
- Model with mathematics.
- Use appropriate tools strategically.

An absolute value function is a special type of linear piecewise function.

> Consider the graph of $f(x) = |x|$.

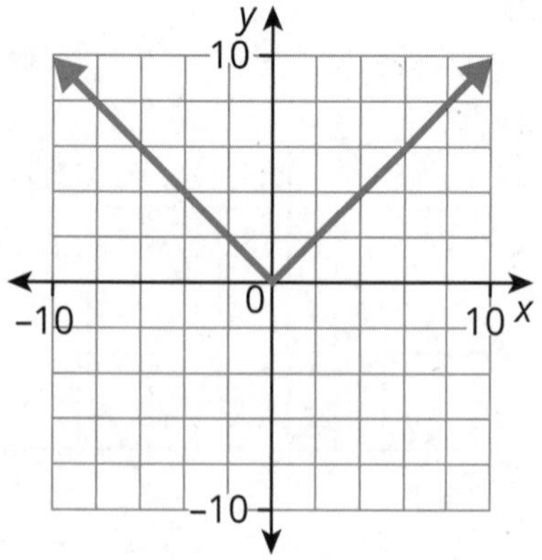

1 Explain how the graph also represents a linear piecewise function.

2 Write a linear piecewise function to represent the graph.

3 How is the symmetry of the absolute value function reflected in the equivalent linear piecewise function?

> Consider this linear piecewise function.

$$g(x) = \begin{cases} x + 50, & -50 \leq x \leq 0 \\ -x + 50, & 0 < x \leq 50 \end{cases}$$

4 Sketch a graph of this function.

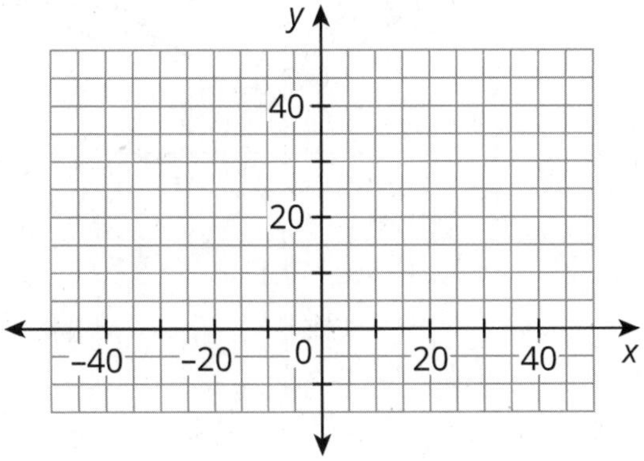

5 Explain how the graph also represents a linear absolute value function.

6 Write $g(x)$ as a linear absolute value function.

Piecing It All Together

> Write a piecewise function to model each absolute value function.

1.

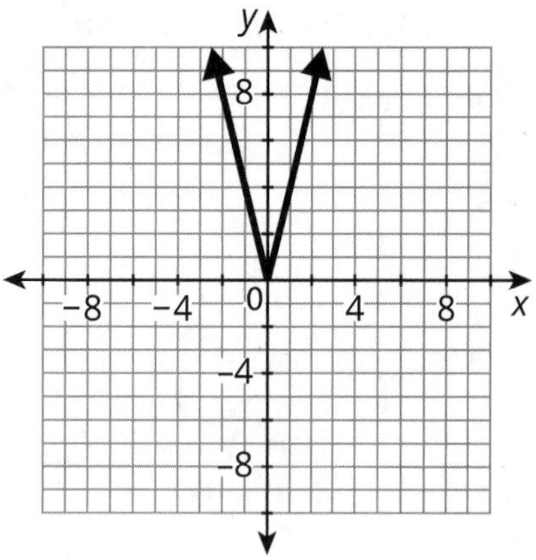

2.

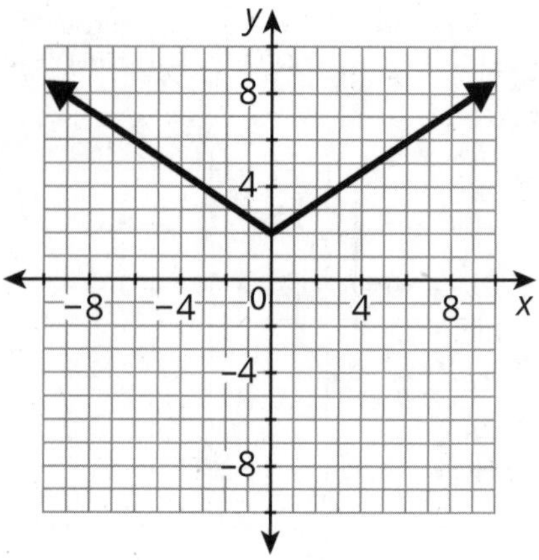

3.

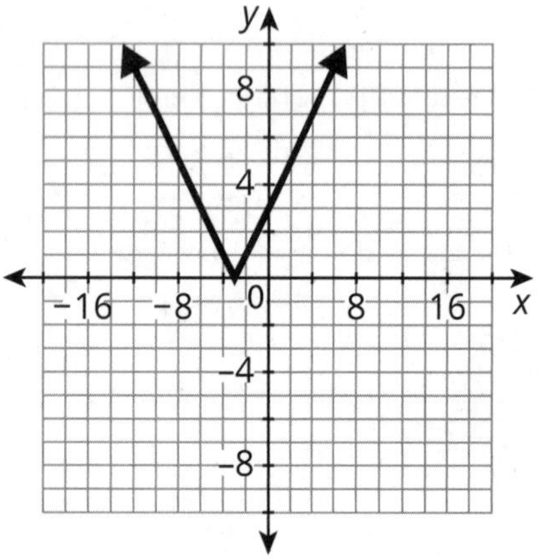

> Use a separate piece of paper for your Journal entry.

JOURNAL

Explain the basic absolute value function using the definition of a linear piecewise function.

REMEMBER

A linear piecewise function is a function that you can represent with linear functions, each of which corresponds to a part of the domain. To write a linear piecewise function, you must write the linear equation and domain for each part of the function.

PRACTICE

1. Jin fills up a 510-gallon pool in the backyard for her children. She fills it with the garden hose at a rate of 17 gallons per minute. After it is filled, she lets it sit for 30 minutes in order to let the water temperature rise. The children then get in and have fun for an hour. The pool loses about $\frac{1}{2}$ gallon of water each minute due to their splashing and playing. At the end of the hour, they tear the pool while getting out, which causes a leak. The pool then begins to lose water at a rate of 2 gallons per minute.

   (a) Complete the table to show the amount of water in the pool after each minute.

   (b) Create a graph to model the problem situation. Include when the pool will be empty.

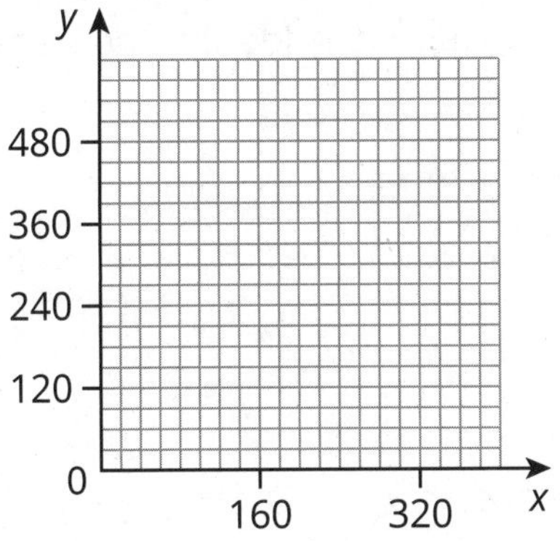

Time (minutes)	Amount of Water (gallons)
0	
5	
20	
30	
45	
60	
80	
100	
120	
150	
200	

Go to LiveHint.com for help on the PRACTICE questions.

(c) Write a piecewise function that models this problem situation. Explain your reasoning for each piece of the function.

(d) Identify the x- and y-intercept. Explain what they mean in terms of the problem situation.

(e) Determine when the pool will have 470 gallons of water in it. Identify the piece(s) of function you used. Explain your reasoning.

STRETCH Optional

> Consider the graphs of the two linear piecewise functions.

1. Describe the similarities and differences in the two graphs.
2. Determine the value of $f(x)$ for each graph when $x = 8$.
3. Determine the value of $f(x)$ for each graph when $x = 18$.
4. Write the piecewise functions for each graph.

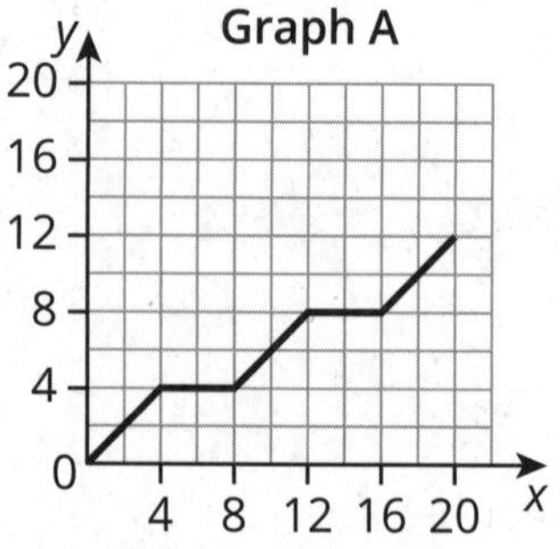

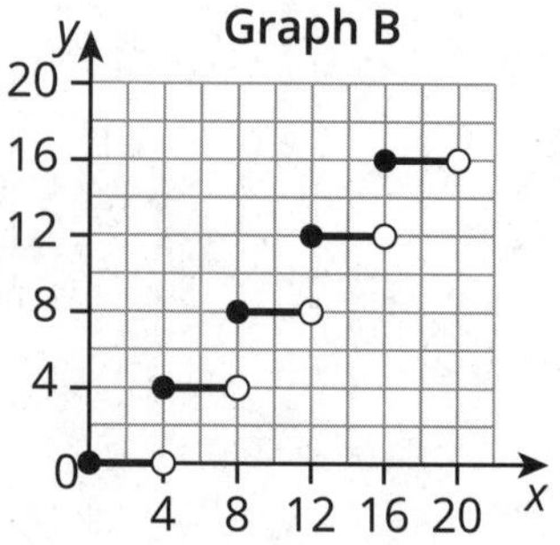

LESSON 4

Step By Step

Step Functions

Learning Goals

- Write and graph step functions from problem situations.
- Interpret the graphs and function notation representing step functions.
- Use technology to graph a step function.

KEY TERMS

discontinuous graph
step function
greatest integer function (floor function)
least integer function (ceiling function)

REVIEW (1–2 minutes)

1 What is the significance of the open and closed endpoints in this graph?

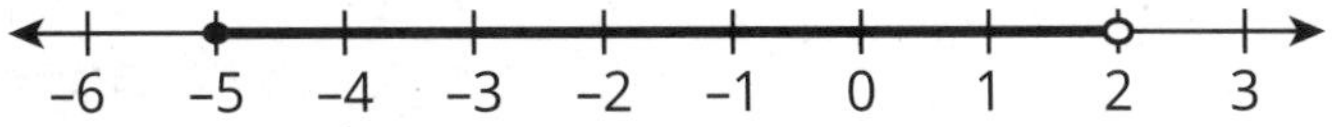

You have seen the absolute value function as an example of a linear piecewise function.

What are other special cases of linear piecewise functions?

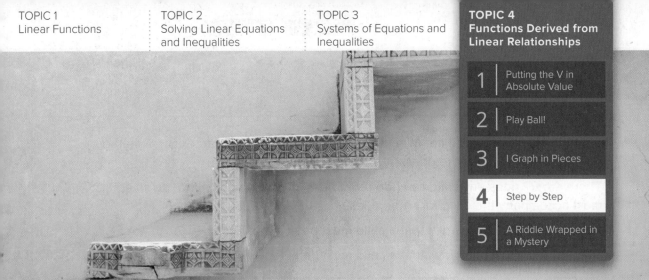

A High-Five for Height

At Adventure Village, there are minimum height requirements to determine whether children can safely enjoy the rides.

- There are 22 rides any child can ride regardless of their height, although an adult must accompany the child for some rides.
- There are 10 additional rides that a child must be at least 36 inches tall to ride.
- There are 12 additional rides that a child must be at least 46 inches tall to ride.

1. Identify the independent and dependent quantities in this scenario.

2. Use the scenario to graph the function. **Label the axes.**

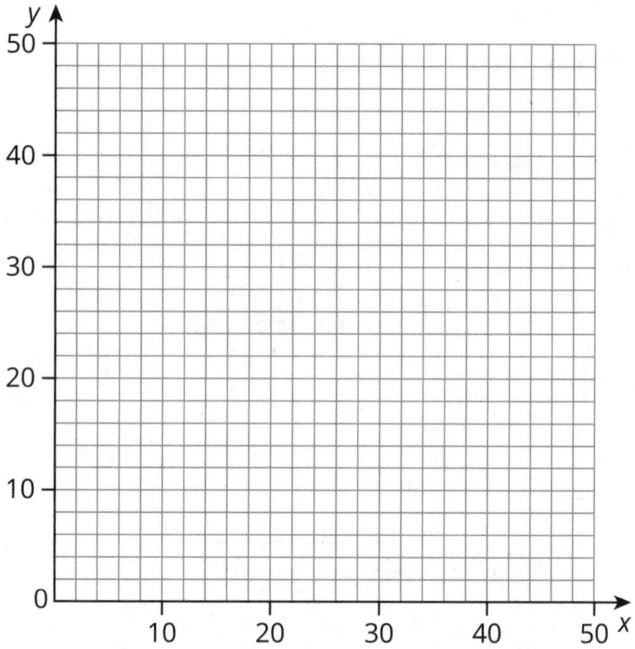

3. Determine the number of rides a child is eligible to ride for each height.

   (a) 36 inches

   (b) $45\frac{15}{16}$ inches

   (c) 46 inches

4. How is this graph similar to the graphs in the previous lesson? How is it different?

Introducing Step Functions

HABITS OF MIND
- Model with mathematics.
- Use appropriate tools strategically.

You have just graphed an unusual function. Let's analyze how functions like this work.

Jason has a fitness tracker, and developed a program where he plans to increase the number of steps he takes until he reaches his goal of 10,000 steps per day. Jason set a daily step goal for each week, Sunday through Saturday. He recorded his plan in the graph shown.

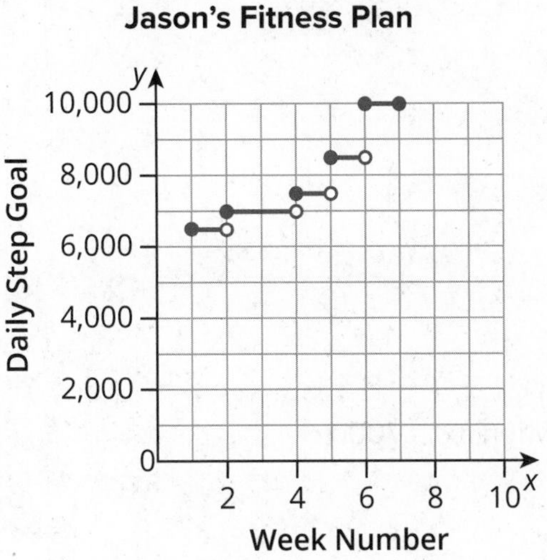

1 Use the graph and scenario to answer each question.

(a) When does Jason plan to reach his goal of 10,000 steps per day?

(b) Why does the graph start at $x = 1$?

(c) On which day(s) is Jason's goal to walk 8000 steps?

(d) Why do you think one piece of the graph has closed circles on both of its ends?

2 Consider the graph at $x = 2$.

(a) What is $f(2)$?

(b) Explain what is happening in the scenario right before $x = 2$.

3 Consider the graph at $f(x) = 7000$.

(a) What is the value of x?

(b) Explain what is happening in the scenario when $f(x) = 7000$.

4 Write a piecewise function to represent this graph and scenario.

This graph and the piecewise graph in the previous activity are neither discrete nor continuous. They are *discontinuous*. A **discontinuous graph** is continuous for some values of the domain with at least one disjoint area between consecutive x-values.

> Consider the examples of discontinuous graphs.

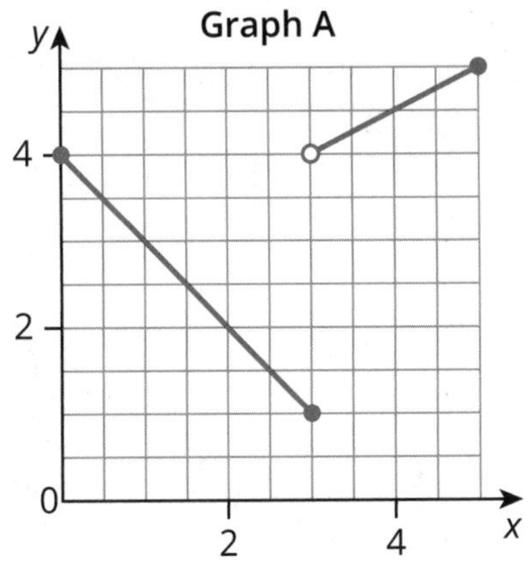

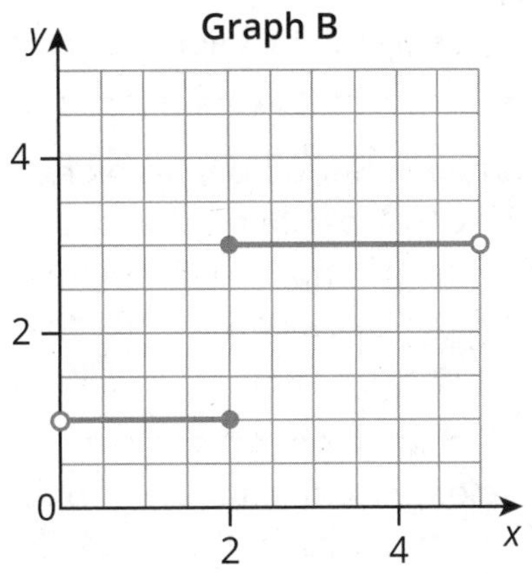

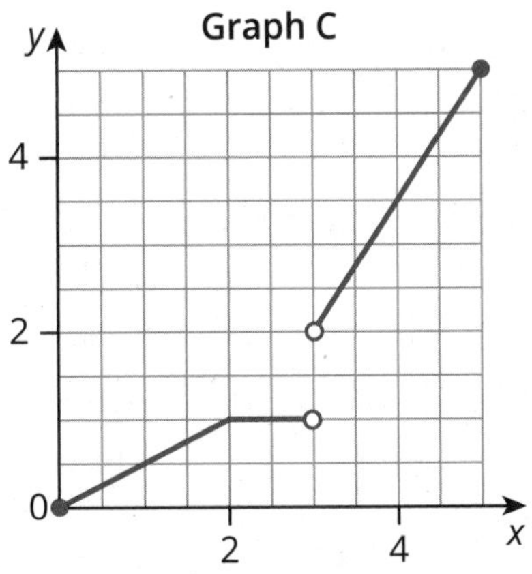

5 Which graph(s) represent functions? **Use the definition of function to justify your response.**

Jason's Fitness Plan graph represents a specific discontinuous function, a *step function*. A **step function** is a piecewise function on a given interval whose pieces are discontinuous constant functions.

6 How do you think step functions got their name?

7 Use technology to graph your piecewise function, *f*(*x*). Can you determine by viewing your graph using technology whether an endpoint is included or not included in the graph?

A Decreasing Step Function

Can you describe a step function as increasing or decreasing?

HABITS OF MIND
- Model with mathematics.
- Use appropriate tools strategically.

Robert borrowed $400 from his older brother to take a weekend trip with his friends. A week after he returns from his trip, he will begin paying his brother $80 per week until he has completely paid off his debt.

1 Define a piecewise function, $f(x)$, for the total amount of Robert's debt based on the number of weeks he pays his brother back. Then create a graph to represent the function.

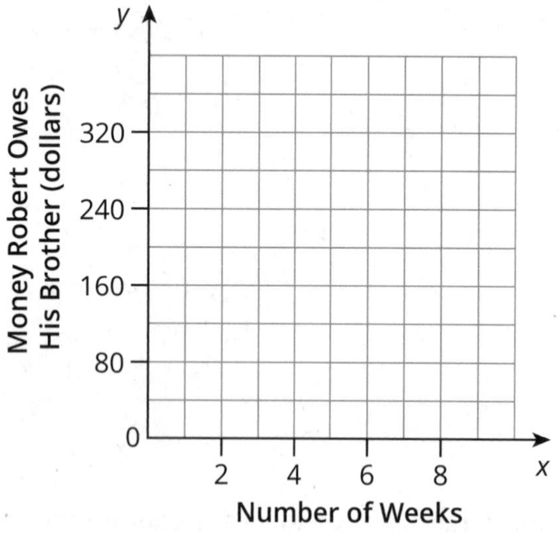

2 How does each representation fit the definition of a step function?

(a) Context

(b) Function

(c) Graph

3 How did you determine where to place the open and closed circles?

Special Linear Piecewise Functions

HABITS OF MIND
- Model with mathematics.
- Use appropriate tools strategically.

The *greatest integer function* is a special linear piecewise function. The **greatest integer function**, also known as a **floor function**, $G(x) = \lfloor x \rfloor$ is the greatest integer less than or equal to x.

1. Evaluate each expression using the greatest integer function.

   a. $\lfloor 2 \rfloor =$ ________
   b. $\lfloor 0.17 \rfloor =$ ________
   c. $\lfloor 2.34 \rfloor =$ ________
   d. $\lfloor -1.2 \rfloor =$ ________
   e. $\lfloor 2.99999 \rfloor =$ ________
   f. $\lfloor -0.2 \rfloor =$ ________

2. Graph $G(x) = \lfloor x \rfloor$.

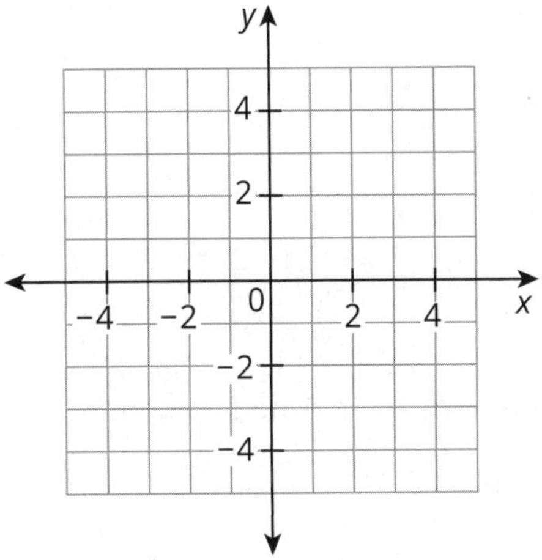

THINK ABOUT...
Consider that the function $G(x)$ is equal to 0 when $0 \le x < 1$. How can you graph this step? How can you graph the steps greater or less than this?

3. Why do you think the greatest integer function is also referred to as the floor function?

The *least integer function* is another special linear piecewise function. The **least integer function** $L(x) = \lceil x \rceil$, also known as the **ceiling function**, is the least integer greater than or equal to x.

4 Evaluate each expression using the least integer function.

TAKE NOTE...
Do you notice the difference in the symbol for a least integer function?

ⓐ $\lceil 2 \rceil$ = ________

ⓑ $\lceil 0.17 \rceil$ = ________

ⓒ $\lceil 2.34 \rceil$ = ________

ⓓ $\lceil -1.2 \rceil$ = ________

ⓔ $\lceil 2.99999 \rceil$ = ________

ⓕ $\lceil -0.2 \rceil$ = ________

5 Graph $L(x) = \lceil x \rceil$.

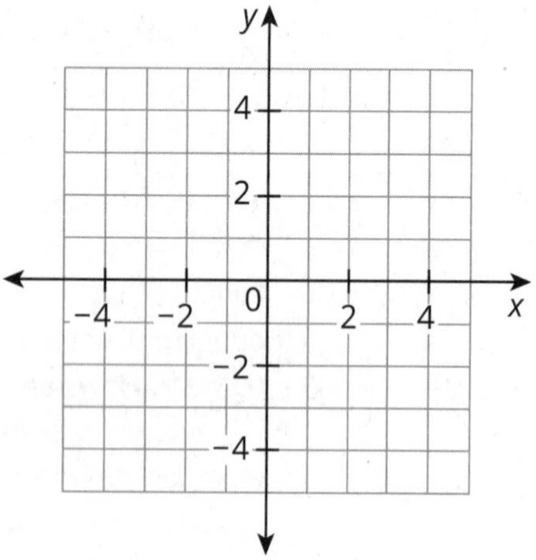

6 Why do you think the least integer function is also referred to as the ceiling function?

7 Compare the graphs you created for the greatest integer function and the least integer function. **What do you notice?**

8 Use technology to graph $G(x) = \lfloor x \rfloor$ and $L(x) = \lceil x \rceil$. Compare the graphs and equations for the greatest integer function and the least integer function. **What do you notice?**

9 While technology provides a reasonable representation of the graph, why might it not be the best representation to use?

10 Determine whether each scenario identifies the greatest integer function, least integer function, or neither.

(a) Mark is parking his car in a garage that charges by the hour. When he parks there for 3.2 hours, he is charged for 4 hours. When he parks there for 3.9 hours, he is charged for 4 hours.

(b) Tamara gets reward points for every dollar she spends at the mall. When she spent $34.25, she received 34 reward points. When she spent $15.95, she received 15 reward points.

(c) Julie's teacher records only whole number values in her gradebook. When Julie earned 88.3 points, the teacher recorded 88 points. When Julie earned 92.5 points, the teacher recorded 93 points.

(d) The yogurt shop charges by the weight of the yogurt sundae you create. Everly is charged as if her 4.2-ounce sundae weighs 5 ounces, and Greyson is charged as if his 5.7-ounce sundae weighs 6 ounces.

Wrapping It Up and Sending It Off

> Consider these postal rates for first class mail.

- A letter weighing up to one ounce will cost $0.55 to mail.
- A letter weighing more than one ounce and up to two ounces will cost $0.75 to mail.
- A letter weighing more than two ounces and up to three ounces will cost $0.95 to mail.

1. Write a function, $f(x)$, to describe this situation.

2. Which graph best represents this situation? **Explain your reasoning.**

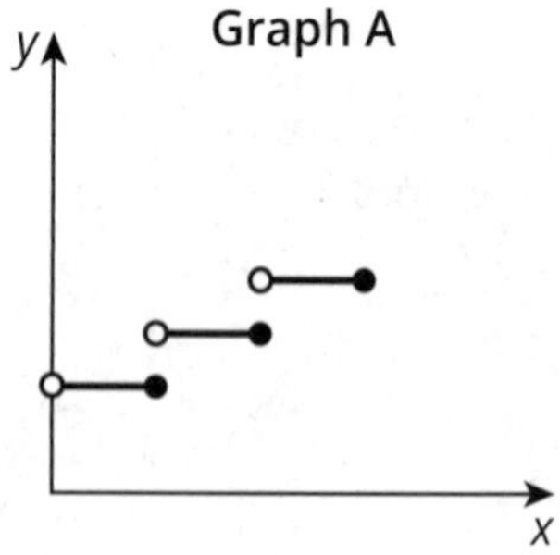

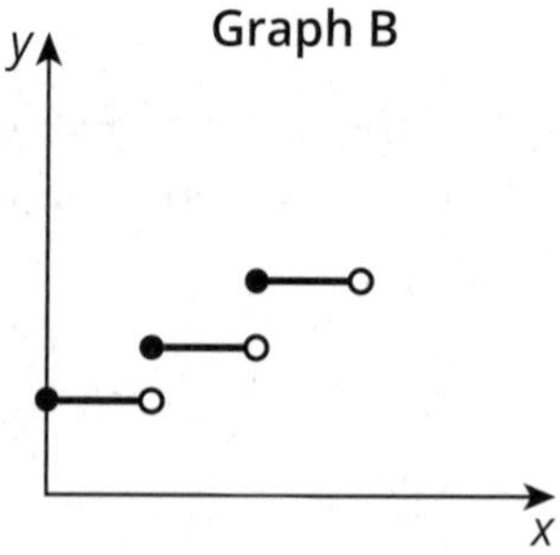

3. Complete each statement using *always*, *sometimes*, or *never*.

   a. Step functions are ______________ piecewise functions.

   b. Piecewise functions are ________________ step functions.

   c. The graphs of step functions are ______________ discontinuous.

   d. The graphs of piecewise functions are ________________ discontinuous.

> Use a separate piece of paper for your Journal entry.

JOURNAL

Any part of a linear piecewise function is written in the form $ax + b$. Describe the possible a- and b-values that define a step function.

REMEMBER

A discontinuous graph is continuous for some values of the domain with at least one disjoint area between consecutive x-values. A step function is a piecewise function on a given interval whose pieces are discontinuous constant functions.

PRACTICE

1 A department store offers store credit but has the listed rules.

- For a bill less than $15 the entire amount is due.
- For a bill of at least $15 but less than $50, the minimum due is $15.
- For a bill of at least $50 but less than $100, the minimum due is $20.
- For a bill of $100 or more, a minimum of 25% of the bill is due.

(a) Write a piecewise function, $f(x)$, for the minimum amount due for the amount of the bill, x. Then, graph the function. Be sure to label the axes.

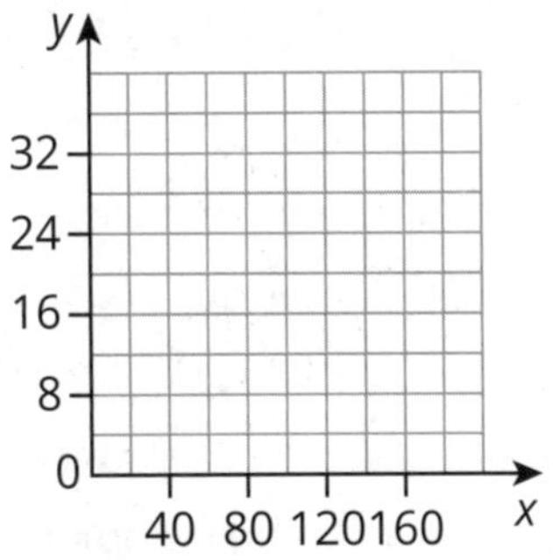

(b) Is your piecewise function a step function? Why or why not?

(c) Describe the rate of change when $0 \le x < 15$. What does it mean in terms of this problem situation?

(d) A customer comes in the store to pay the minimum amount on his bill of $100. The customer thinks he owes $20, but the cashier tells him he owes $25. Who is correct? Explain your reasoning.

Go to LiveHint.com for help on the PRACTICE questions.

2 A department store has an online site that customers can order from. The shipping rates are calculated as listed.

- A package that weighs no more than 10 pounds costs $5.
- A package that weighs more than 10 pounds but no more than 20 pounds costs $10.
- A package that weighs more than 20 pounds but no more than 30 pounds costs $15.
- A package that weighs more than 30 pounds but no more than 40 pounds costs $20.
- A package that weighs more than 40 pounds but no more than 50 pounds costs $25.

(a) Write a piecewise function, $f(x)$, for the shipping cost for the weight of the package, x. Then, graph the function. Be sure to label the axes.

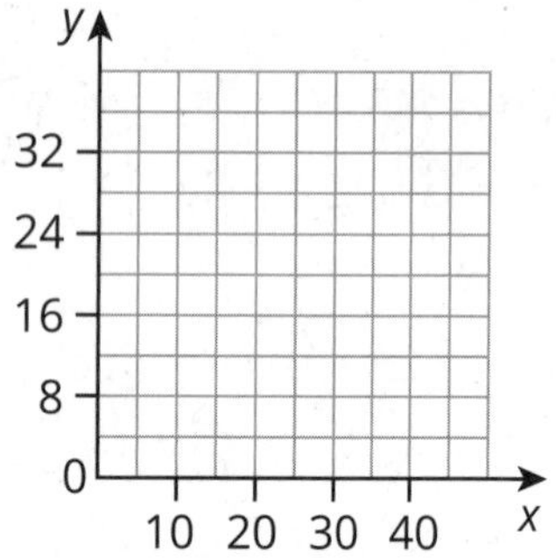

(b) Is this piecewise function a step function? Why or why not?

(c) Rewrite the step function as a greatest integer function. How do the shipping costs change for a 10-pound package?

STRETCH Optional

After the first statistics test of the year, a professor asked her students to write down the number of hours they studied for the test. A student created the graph to show the relationship between the grade earned and the number of hours studied.

1 Describe why this graph does not represent a piecewise function.

2 Write the situation as a piecewise function.

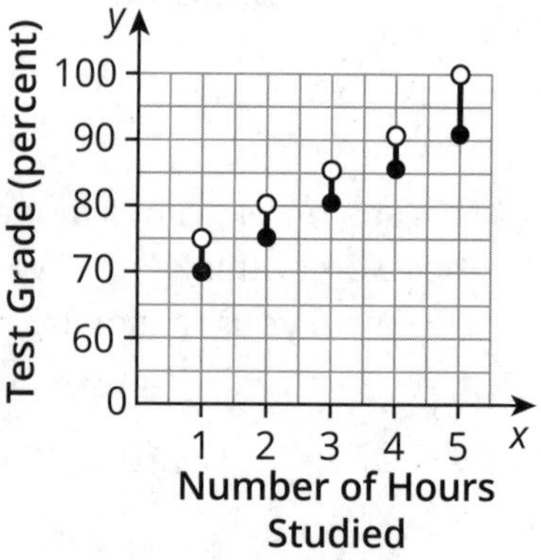

LESSON 5

A Riddle Wrapped in a Mystery

Inverses of Linear Functions

KEY TERMS

inverse of a function

one-to-one function

Learning Goals

- Determine the inverse of a given situation using words.
- Determine the inverse of a function numerically using a table, an equation, and a graph.
- Determine whether given functions are one-to-one functions.

REVIEW (1–2 minutes)

> Solve each equation.

1. $2x - 5 = 97$

2. $\frac{1}{3}x + 40 = 280$

3. $-4x - 10 = -26$

You know that a function takes a set of inputs and maps them to a set of outputs.

What happens when you reverse the outputs and inputs?

Inside an Enigma

One of the simplest methods of creating a code is called a substitution cipher. For a substitution cipher, you can take each letter of the alphabet in numeric order and assign it to a different number using a mathematical rule.

1	2	3	4	5	6	7	8	9	10	11	12	13	14	15	16	17	18	19	20	21	22	23	24	25	26
A	B	C	D	E	F	G	H	I	J	K	L	M	N	O	P	Q	R	S	T	U	V	W	X	Y	Z

For example, if the cipher were written as $x + 4$, then *L*, which is currently assigned to 12, would be assigned to $12 + 4 = 16$, or *P*, in the code. The letter *Y*, which is currently assigned to 25, would be assigned to 3, or *C*, in the code.

Cipher: $x + 4$

Word	**Code**
inverse	mrzivwi

1. Write a substitution cipher rule. Then write a short note to a classmate in code. Give your rule and coded note to a classmate to decode.

2. Use mathematical notation to write the rule you used to decode your classmate's note.

3. Why is it important that the substitution cipher rule be a function?

4. Compare the inputs and outputs of the cipher rule you created and the rule used to decode your note. **What do you notice?**

The Inverse of a Function

To break the code in the Getting Started, you likely used the inverse of the rule that was used to create the code. Let's explore inverses as they relate to functions.

HABITS OF MIND
- Reason abstractly and quantitatively.
- Construct viable arguments and critique the reasoning of others.

Miguel is planning a trip to Turkey. Before he leaves, he wants to exchange his money to the Turkish lira, the official currency of Turkey. The exchange rate at the time of his trip is 4 lira per 1 U.S. dollar.

1. Complete the table of values to show the currency conversion for U.S. dollars to Turkish lira.

U.S. Currency (dollars)	Turkish Currency (lira)
100	
250	
400	
650	
1000	

2. Write an equation to represent the number of lira in terms of the number of U.S. dollars.

Suppose at the end of his trip, Miguel needs to convert any remaining lira to dollars. This situation is the inverse of the original situation.

3. What are the independent and dependent quantities of the inverse of the problem situation? **How do these quantities compare to the quantities in Question 1?**

4 Complete the table of values to show the inverse of the problem situation.

Turkish Currency (lira)	U.S. Currency (dollars)

5 Compare the tables in Questions 1 and 4. **What do you notice?**

6 Use the table to write an equation for the inverse of the problem situation. Does this equation represent a function? **Explain your answer.**

Recall that a function takes an input value, performs some operation(s) on this value, and creates an output value. The **inverse of a function** takes the output value, performs some operation(s) on this value, and arrives back at the original function's input value.

WORKED EXAMPLE

Given a function, $f(x)$, you can determine the inverse algebraically by following these steps.

STEP 1 Replace the function $f(x)$ with another variable, generally y.

STEP 2 Switch the x and y variables in the equation.

STEP 3 Solve for y.

7 Use function notation to represent the number of lira $f(x)$ in terms of the number of U.S. dollars, x. Then complete the steps shown in the worked example to represent the number of U.S. dollars in terms of the number of lira. Compare the inverse to the equation you wrote in Question 6. **What do you notice?**

Graphing Inverses of Functions

In the previous activity, you wrote the inverse of a function using algebra. Let's consider how to show the inverse of a function using its graph.

HABITS OF MIND

- Model with mathematics.
- Use appropriate tools strategically.

WORKED EXAMPLE

Given a function, $f(x)$, you can determine the inverse of a function graphically by following these steps.

STEP 1 Copy the coordinate plane and graph $f(x)$ and the line $y = x$ onto patty paper.

STEP 2 Heavily trace the graph of $f(x)$ with a pencil.

STEP 3 Reflect the patty paper across the line $y = x$, and rub the paper so that the image of the graph of its inverse appears.

1 Consider the graph of the function $f(x) = 4x$ from the previous activity. Complete the steps in the worked example to graph the inverse using patty paper.

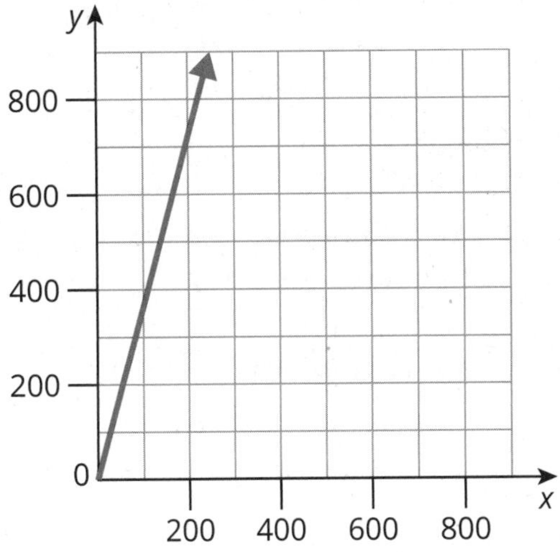

THINK ABOUT...

How do the algebraic process and the graphical process to determine an inverse compare?

2 Compare the image you created and the graph of the inverse.

(a) What do you notice about the image and the graph of the inverse?

(b) What does this tell you about the graph of a function and its inverse and about the line $y = x$?

3 For each function and a given point on the graph of the function, determine the corresponding point on the graph of the inverse of the function.

ⓐ Given that (3, 2) is a point on the graph of $g(x)$, what is the corresponding point on the graph of the inverse of $g(x)$?

ⓑ Given that (−1, 0) is a point on the graph of $h(x)$, what is the corresponding point on the graph of the inverse of $h(x)$?

ⓒ Given that (a, b) is a point on the graph of $f(x)$, what is the corresponding point on the graph of the inverse of $f(x)$?

One-to-One Functions

In this activity, you will determine the inverse of a function using multiple representations.

HABITS OF MIND
- Look for and make use of structure.
- Look for and express regularity in repeated reasoning.

1 For each given function, determine the inverse using each representation.

- Complete a table of values for the function and its inverse.
- Sketch the graph of the function using a solid line. Then sketch the inverse of the function on the same coordinate plane using a dashed line.
- Write an equation for the inverse.
- Determine whether the function is a *one-to-one function*. **Explain your reasoning.**

TAKE NOTE...
A function is a **one-to-one function** when both the function and its inverse are functions.

(a) $f(x) = 3x - 6$

x	$f(x)$
−2	
−1	
0	
1	
2	

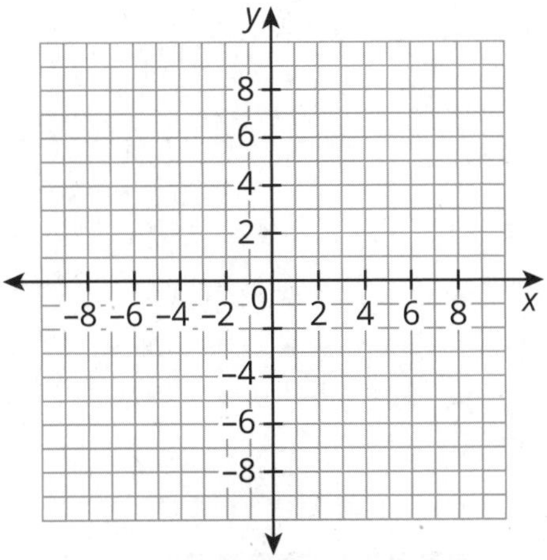

REMEMBER...
Use a straightedge to draw your lines.

Inverse of $f(x)$	
x	y
	−2
	−1
	0
	1
	2

(b) $g(x) = -x + 4$

x	$g(x)$
−2	
−1	
0	
1	
2	

Inverse of $g(x)$	
x	y
	−2
	−1
	0
	1
	2

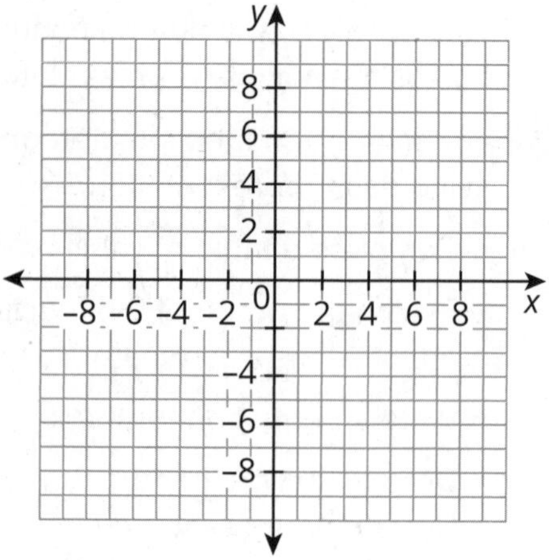

(c) $h(x) = 2$

x	$h(x)$
−2	
−1	
0	
1	
2	

Inverse of $h(x)$	
x	y
	−2
	−1
	0
	1
	2

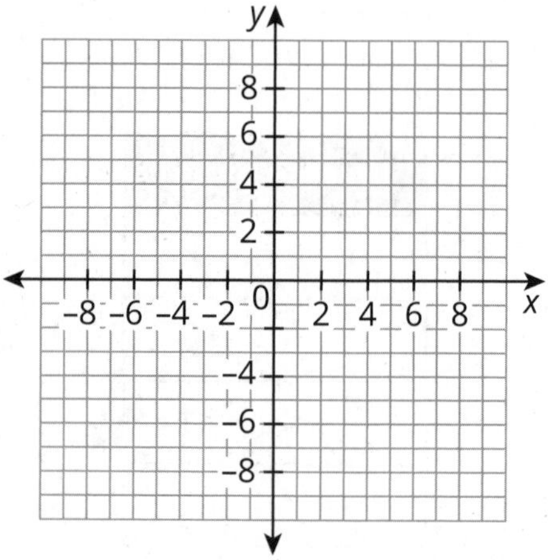

ⓓ $r(x) = |x|$

x	$r(x)$
−2	
−1	
0	
1	
2	

Inverse of $r(x)$

x	y
	2
	1
	0
	1
	2

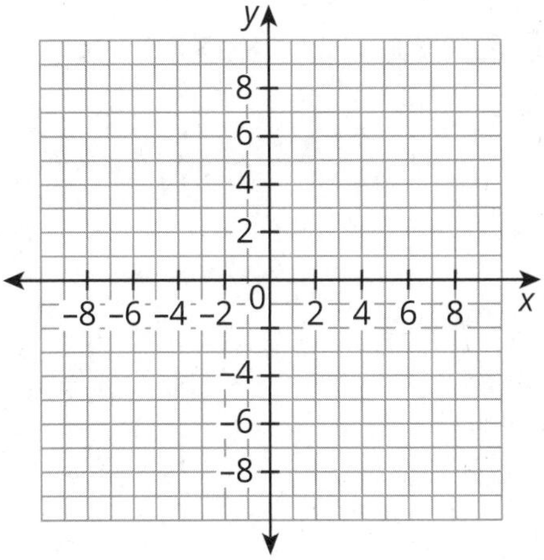

2 Adam and Stacey are working on a homework assignment in which they must identify all functions that are one-to-one functions.

- Adam says that all linear functions are one-to-one functions, so they don't even need to look at the linear functions.
- Stacey disagrees, and says that not all linear functions are one-to-one functions.

Who is correct? **Explain how you determined which student is correct.**

TOPIC 4

3 How can you determine whether an inverse exists given a linear function?

4 Can a linear function and its inverse be the same function? If so, provide an example. If not, explain why not.

TAKE NOTE...
For a one-to-one function $f(x)$, the notation for its inverse is $f^{-1}(x)$. The notation for inverse, $f^{-1}(x)$, does not mean the same thing as x^{-1}. You can rewrite the expression x^{-1} as $\frac{1}{x}$; however, you cannot rewrite $f^{-1}(x)$, because it is only used as notation. In other words, $f^{-1}(x) \neq \frac{1}{f(x)}$.

5 Complete the graphic organizer located on page 451. Write the definition for the inverse of a linear function. Then describe how to determine the inverse of a function algebraically, graphically, and numerically.

Inverses of Linear Functions

Definition	Algebraic Description

Graphical Description	Numeric Description (Table of Values)

Strike That. Invert It.

> Consider the linear function $y = ax + b$, where $a \neq 0$.

1 Use algebra to show that the inverse of this function is also a function.

2 Identify the slope and y-intercept of $f(x)$ and its inverse.

3 Given $y = 4x + 10$, identify the slope and y-intercept of $f(x)$ and its inverse.

4 Given $y = -3x + 6$, identify the slope and y-intercept of $f(x)$ and its inverse.

5 What happens to the slope and y-intercept of a linear function $y = ax + b$, where $a \neq 0$, when you take its inverse?

LESSON 5 ASSIGNMENT

> Use a separate piece of paper for your Journal entry.

JOURNAL

Describe how to use a graph to prove two relationships are inverses of each other.

REMEMBER

An inverse of a function "undoes" the function. You algebraically determine the inverse of a function by replacing $f(x)$ with y, switching the x and y variables, and solving for y.

A one-to-one function is a function in which its inverse is also a function.

PRACTICE

1. Clothing and shoe sizes typically vary from country to country. Kalinda is going to be spending a year in Italy and plans on shopping for dresses while she's there. While investigating the differences in sizing, she determines that to change the U.S. dress size to an Italian dress size, she must add 12 to the U.S. dress size and then double the sum.

(a) Complete the table of values to show the dress size conversion for U.S. dresses to Italian dresses.

U.S. Dress Size	Italian Dress Size
4	
6	
10	
14	
18	

(b) Write a function, $f(x)$, to represent the Italian dress size in terms of x, the U.S. dress size.

(c) Determine the inverse of this problem situation using words.

(d) Determine the inverse of the function algebraically. What does the inverse function represent in terms of the problem situation?

Go to LiveHint.com for help on the PRACTICE questions.

2 Determine the inverse of each function. Is the inverse also a function? Explain why or why not.

(a) $f(x) = 0.6x - 2$

(b) $g(x) = \frac{8}{3}x + 12$

3 Determine whether the functions $j(x) = 3 - 1.5x$ and $k(x) = -\frac{2}{3}x + 2$ are inverses. If so, explain how you know. If not, determine each function's inverse.

4 Sketch the inverse of the given function on the same graph as the function. Is the inverse also a function? Explain why or why not.

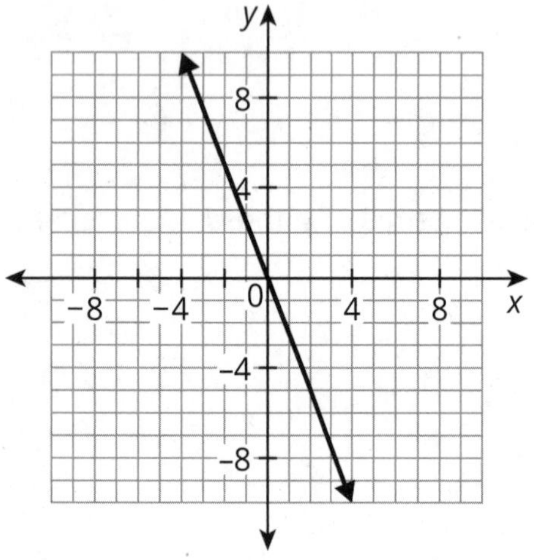

STRETCH Optional

> For the function $f(x) = x + 1$, the inverse function is $f^{-1}(x) = x - 1$.

1 Evaluate the function $f(x)$ by replacing x with $x - 1$. What do you notice? How does this relate to the process of using a graph to determine an inverse?

MIXED PRACTICE

> This Mixed Practice worksheet includes two sections: Spaced Review and End-of-Topic Review. **Use a separate piece of paper to show your work.**

Spaced Review

> Practice concepts from previous topics.

1 Declan is moving and needs to rent a truck for a day. Company A charges \$70 a day and \$0.99 per mile. Company B charges \$100 a day and \$0.75 per mile after the first 20 miles.

(a) Create a system of equations to model the situation.

(b) For what amount of miles does Company A make more sense? Company B?

2 Tessa has three daughters. Her 8-year-old weighs 60 pounds, her 6-year-old weighs 45 pounds, and her 2-year-old weighs 25 pounds.

(a) Write the equation of the regression line for the data.

(b) Use the equation to predict how much Tessa's 4-year-old niece weighs.

3 Consider the equation $6x - 2y = -12$.

(a) What is the slope of the equation?

(b) What are the intercepts of the equation?

4 The equation to calculate the area of a trapezoid is $A = \frac{1}{2}(a + b)h$. Rewrite the equation to solve for h.

5 Write the equation of the line that has the given slope and passes through the point given.

(a) $m = \frac{2}{3}$
$(2, -4)$

(b) $m = -4$
$(0.5, 7)$

6 Evaluate each function for the given value of x.

(a) $f(x) = 3x + 2(8 - x)$ for $x = -2$

(b) $f(x) = -\frac{2}{9}x - 4\left(\frac{1}{8}x + 3\right)$ for $x = 3$

End-of-Topic Review

AVAILABLE ONLINE

1. A **Topic Summary** reviews the main concepts for the topic.
2. A video of the **Worked Example** is provided.

> Practice concepts you learned in **Functions Derived from Linear Relationships.**

7 Given the function $f(x) = |x|$. Sketch a graph of each new function.

(a) $g(x) = -|x + 1| - 3$

(b) $h(x) = \frac{3}{4}|x - 2| + 1$

8 Solve each equation.

(a) $|x - 4| = 7$

(b) $|3x + 5| = 11$

9 Graph the piecewise function.

$$f(x) = \begin{cases} x + 2, & -5 < x \leq -1 \\ 1, & -1 < x < 3 \\ -x + 4, & 3 \leq x < 5 \end{cases}$$

10 Determine the inverse of each function. Is the inverse also a function? Explain why or why not.

(a) $y = -4$

(b) $y = \left(\frac{1}{4}\right)x + \frac{3}{2}$

11 The Me-OW Company sells cat food in bags labeled 13 pounds. The quality control manager is in charge of making sure the bags get filled properly. To be labeled 13 pounds, a difference of no more than 0.15 pound is acceptable.

(a) Write an absolute value inequality to represent the restrictions on the difference in the weight of the bag.

(b) Determine the greatest and least amount of cat food a bag can contain and still fall within the required specifications. Write your answer as an inequality.

12 Write the absolute value function for the graph shown.

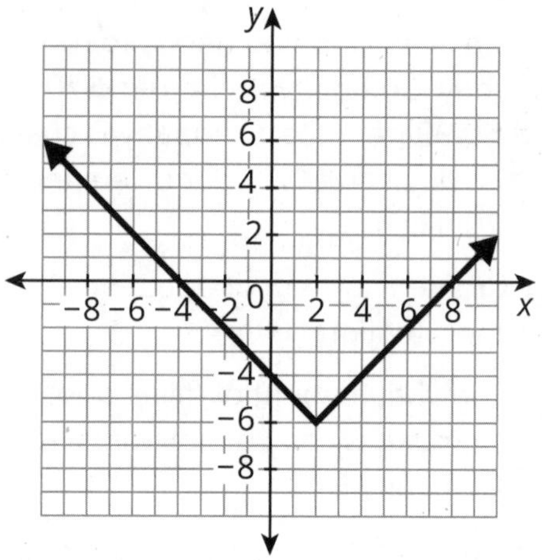

13 A school P.T.A. is organizing a Fun Run to benefit the school. A local business has agreed to donate cases of lemonade, with the following conditions.

- For less than 50 runners, they will donate two cases.
- For at least 50 but less than 100 runners they will donate five cases.
- For at least 100 but less than 150 runners they will donate twelve cases.
- For at least 150 runners they will donate twenty cases.

(a) Write a piecewise function $f(x)$ for the number of cases the business will donate, x.

(b) Is this piecewise function a step function? Explain your reasoning.

(c) Graph the function. Be sure to label the axes.

14 Arnav is saving money to buy a used car in six months, or 24 weeks. He already has \$550 saved. For four weeks in a row, he is able to put \$100 into the account. He goes through a period of three weeks during which he is unable to add to the account. The next seven weeks after that, he is able to put in \$75 each week. For the next four weeks, he has to take out \$50 a week to pay some bills. For the remaining weeks he is able to once again put \$100 a week into the account.

(a) Write a piecewise function to model the problem situation and graph on a coordinate plane. Be sure to label the axes.

(b) Determine how much money he will have in his account after 15 weeks. Identify the function you used and explain the reason.

Appendix

Getting Ready for Module 1

Review Answers

Searching for Patterns

1. $7 - 15 = -8$
2. $2(7) + 3.1 = 14 + 3.1$
   $= 17.1$
3. $-3(7 - 5) = -3(2)$
   $= -6$
4. $\frac{2}{3}(7 + 2) - 2(7)$
   $\frac{2}{3}(9) - 14$
   $6 - 14 = -8$

Getting Ready for Module 2

Review Answers

Exploring Constant Change

1. $x = -17$
2. $x = -3$
3. $x = -14$
4. $x = \frac{15}{8} = 1\frac{7}{8}$

Getting Ready for Module 3

Review Answers

Investigating Growth and Decay

1. 7
2. 11
3. 3
4. 5

Getting Ready for Module 4

Review Answers

Describing Distributions

1. 57%
2. 7%
3. 72.1%
4. 25%

Getting Ready for Module 5

Review Answers

Maximizing and Minimizing

1. $x = \pm 9$
2. $x = \pm 5$
3. $x = \pm 11$
4. $x = \pm 7$
5. $x + 5 = 0$
   $x = -5$
6. $2x = -5$
   $x = -\frac{5}{2}$

Glossary

A

absolute maximum

A function has an absolute maximum when there is a point that has a y-coordinate that is greater than the y-coordinates of every other point on the graph.

EXAMPLE

The absolute maximum of the graph of the function $f(x) = -\frac{1}{2}x^2 + 4x - 6$ is $y = 2$.

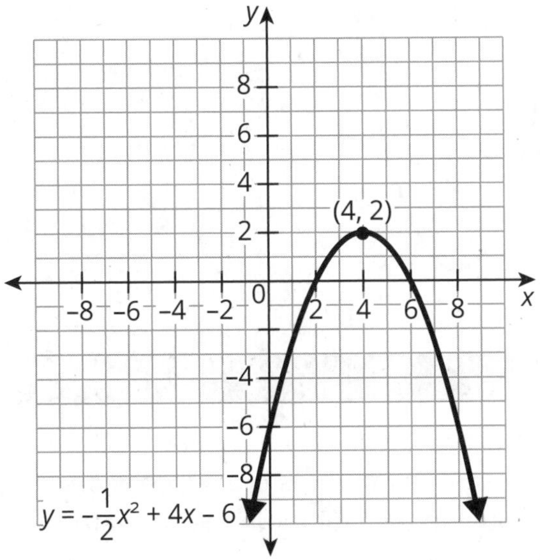

absolute minimum

A function has an absolute minimum when there is a point that has a y-coordinate that is less than the y-coordinates of every other point on the graph.

EXAMPLE

The absolute minimum of the graph of the function $y = \frac{2}{3}x^2 - \frac{4}{3}x - \frac{10}{3}$ is $y = -4$.

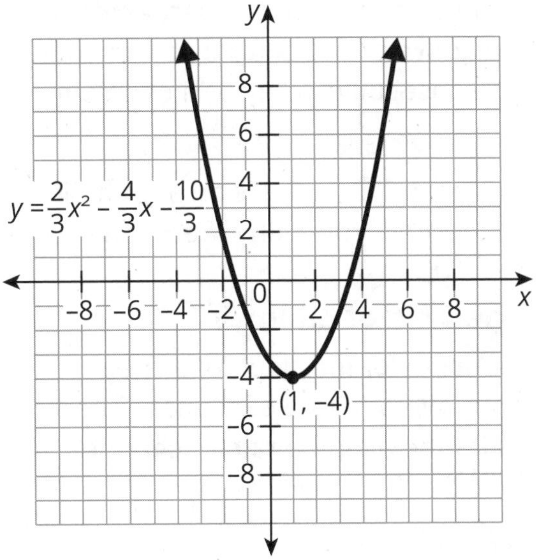

absolute value

The absolute value of a number is its distance from zero on the number line.

EXAMPLE

$|5| = 5$ because 5 is 5 units from 0 on the number line.
$|-3| = 3$ because -3 is 3 units from 0 on the number line.

additive inverses

You call two numbers with the sum of zero additive inverses.

EXAMPLE

$-19 + 19 = 0 \qquad a + -a = a$

argument of a function

The argument of a function is the variable on which the function operates.

EXAMPLE

In the function $f(x + 5) = 32$, the argument is $x + 5$.

arithmetic sequence

An arithmetic sequence is a sequence of numbers in which the difference between any two consecutive terms is a constant.

EXAMPLE

The sequence 1, 3, 5, 7,... is an arithmetic sequence with a common difference of 2.

average rate of change

Another name for the slope of a linear function is average rate of change. The formula for the average rate of change is $\frac{f(t) - f(s)}{t - s}$.

EXAMPLE

The average rate of change of the function shown is 3.

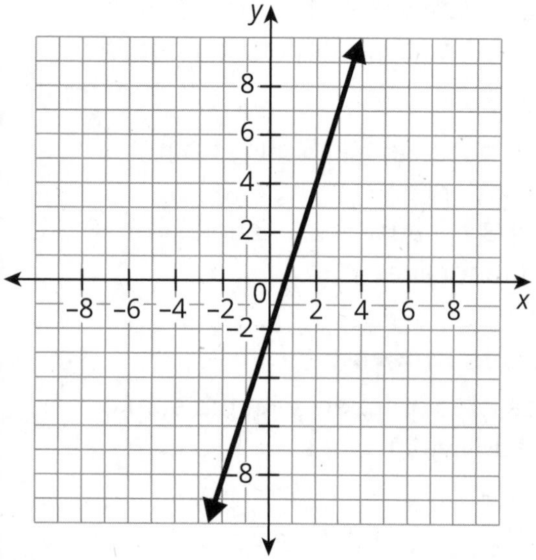

axis of symmetry

The axis of symmetry of a parabola is the vertical line that passes through the vertex and divides the parabola into two mirror images.

EXAMPLE

Line K is the axis of symmetry of this parabola.

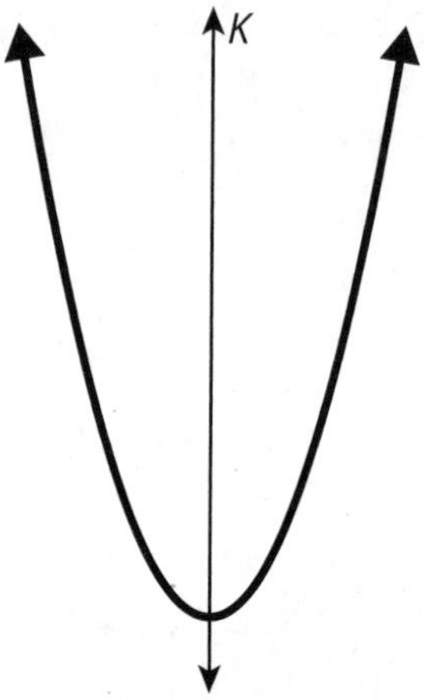

B

base

The base of a power is the expression that you use as a factor in the repeated multiplication.

EXAMPLES

$2^3 = 2 \times 2 \times 2 = 8$ — ↑ base

$8^0 = 1$ — ↑ base

basic function

A basic function is the simplest function of its type.

EXAMPLE

The basic linear function is $f(x) = x$.
The basic exponential function is $g(x) = 2^x$.
The basic quadratic function is $h(x) = x^2$.

bin

The width of a bar in a histogram is a bin and it represents an interval of data.

binomial

Polynomials with exactly two terms are binomials.

EXAMPLE

The polynomial $3x + 5$ is a binomial.

boundary line

A boundary line, determined by the inequality in a linear inequality, divides the plane into two half-planes and the inequality symbol indicates which half-plane contains all the solutions.

EXAMPLE

For the linear inequality $y > -x + 8$, the boundary line is a dashed line because no point on that line is a solution.

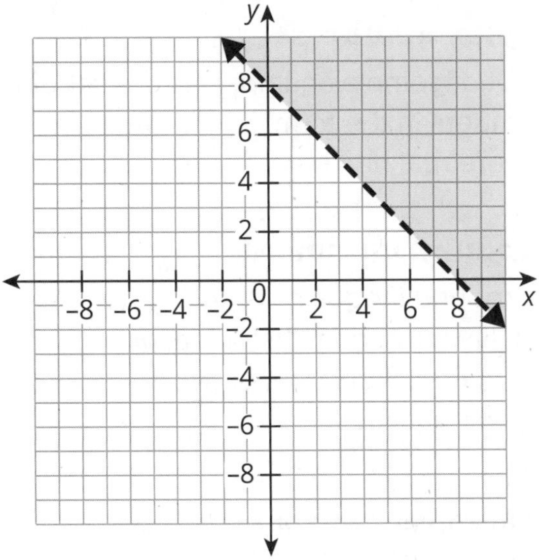

box-and-whisker plot

A box-and-whisker plot displays a data distribution based on a five-number summary.

EXAMPLE

The box-and-whisker plots compare the test scores from two algebra classes.

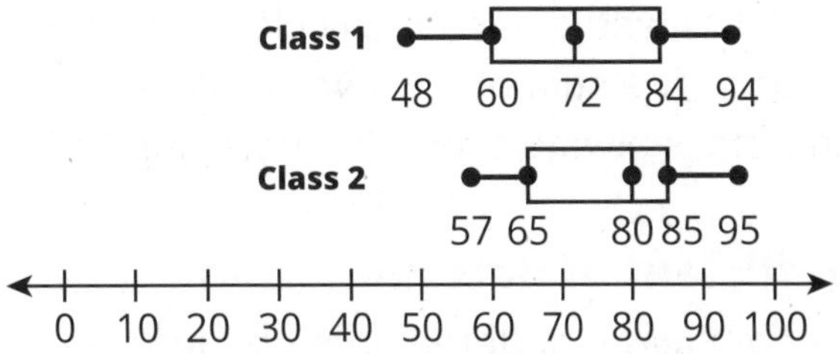

C

categorical data

Data that you can group into categories are categorical data.

causation

Causation is when one event affects the outcome of a second event.

centroid

The centroid is a point whose *x*-value is the mean of all the *x*-values of the points on the scatter plot and its *y*-value is the mean of all the *y*-values of the points on the scatter plot.

EXAMPLE

For the data points (1, 3), (1, 7), (2, 6), (3, 5), and (3, 4), the centroid is (2, 5).

closed (closure)

When you perform an operation on any of the numbers in a set and the result is a number that is also in the same set, the set is closed (or has closure) under that operation.

EXAMPLE

The set of whole numbers is closed under addition. The sum of any two whole numbers is always another whole number.

coefficient of determination

The coefficient of determination measures how well the graph of a regression fits the data. It is calculated by squaring the correlation coefficient and represents the percentage of variation of the observed values of the data points from their predicted values.

EXAMPLE

The correlation coefficient for a data set is -0.9935. The coefficient of determination for the same data set is approximately 0.987, which means 98.7% of the data values should fall within graph of the regression equation.

common difference

The difference between any two consecutive terms in an arithmetic sequence is the common difference. It is typically represented by the variable d.

EXAMPLE

The sequence 1, 3, 5, 7,... is an arithmetic sequence with a common difference of 2.

common ratio

The ratio between any two consecutive terms in a geometric sequence is the common ratio. It is typically represented by the variable r.

EXAMPLE

The sequence 2, 4, 8, 16,... is a geometric sequence with a common ratio of 2.

common response

A common response is when a variable other than the ones measured cause the same result as the one observed in the experiment.

completing the square

Completing the square is a process for writing a quadratic expression in vertex form which then allows you to solve for the zeros.

complex numbers

The set of complex numbers is the set of all numbers in the form $a + bi$, where a and b are real numbers.

compound inequality

A compound inequality is an inequality formed by the union, *or*, or the intersection, *and*, of two simple inequalities.

EXAMPLE

The statement $x > 5$ or $x < -5$ is a compound inequality.

compound interest

In a compound interest account, the balance is multiplied by the same amount at each interval.

EXAMPLE

Sonya opens a savings account with \$100. She earns \$4 in compound interest the first year. You calculate the compound interest y using the equation $y = 100(1 + 0.04)^t$, where t is the time in years.

concave down

A graph that opens downward is concave down.

EXAMPLE

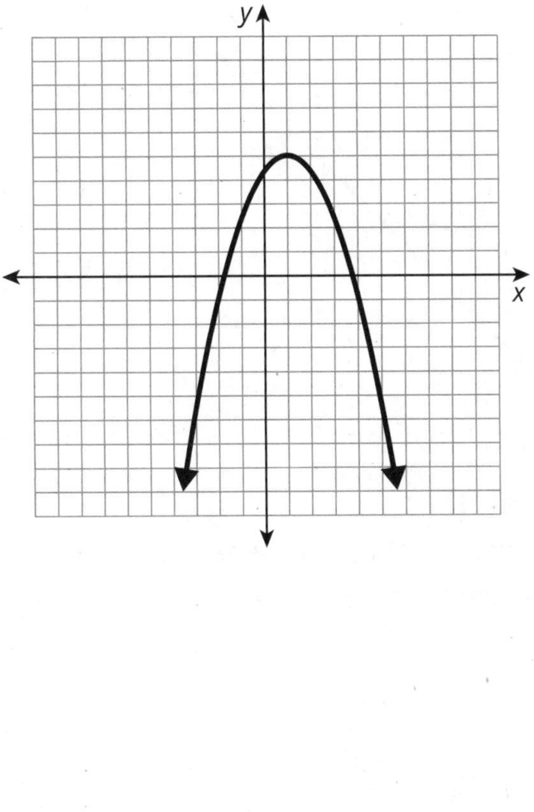

concave up

A graph that opens upward is concave down.

EXAMPLE

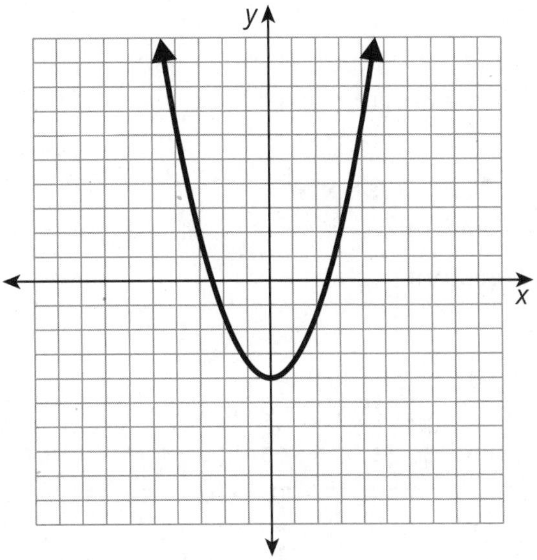

conditional relative frequency distribution

A conditional relative frequency distribution is the percent or proportion of occurrences of a category given the specific value of another category.

confounding variable

A confounding variable is when there are other variables in an experiment that are unknown or unobserved.

conjecture

A conjecture is a mathematical statement that appears to be true, but you still need to prove.

conjunction

A compound inequality in the form $a < x < b$, where a and b are any real numbers, is a conjunction.

EXAMPLE

The compound inequality $x \leq 1$ and $x > -3$ is a conjunction.

consistent systems

Systems that have one or many solutions are consistent systems.

constant function

If the dependent variable of a function does not change or remains constant over the entire domain, then the function is a constant function.

EXAMPLE

The function shown is a constant function.

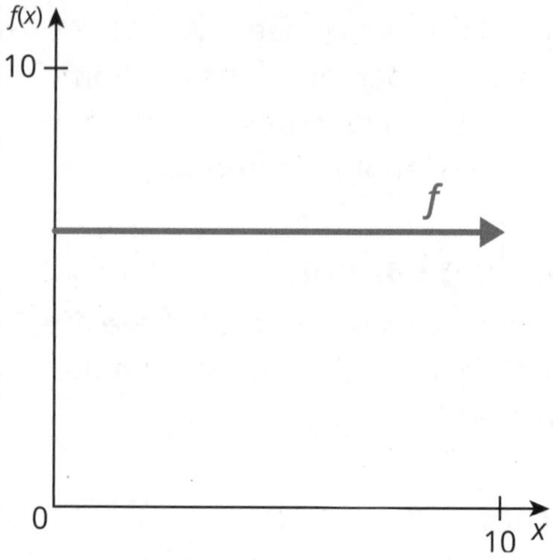

constraints

In a system of linear inequalities, the inequalities are known as constraints because the values of the expressions are "constrained" to lie within a certain region on the graph.

continuous graph

A continuous graph is a graph of points connected by a line or smooth curve. Continuous graphs have no breaks.

EXAMPLE

The graph shown is a continuous graph.

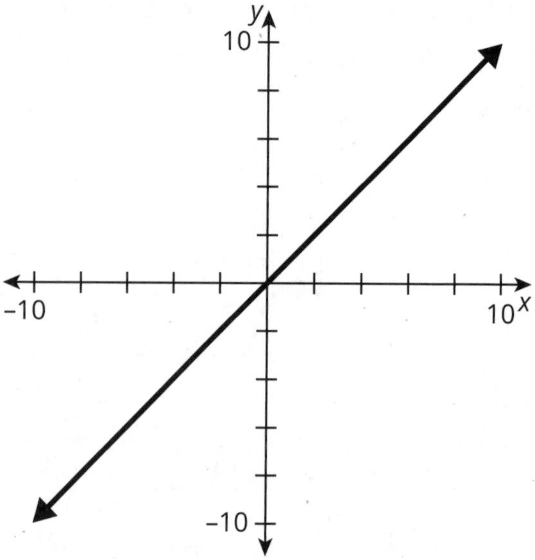

correlation

A measure of how well a regression fits a set of data is a correlation.

correlation coefficient

The correlation coefficient is a value between −1 and 1, which indicates how close the data are to the graph of the regression equation. The closer the correlation coefficient is to −1 or 1, the stronger the relationship is between the two variables. The variable *r* represents the correlation coefficient.

EXAMPLE

The correlation coefficient for these data is −0.9935. The value is negative because the equation has a negative slope. The value is close to −1 because the data are very close to the graph of the equation of the line.

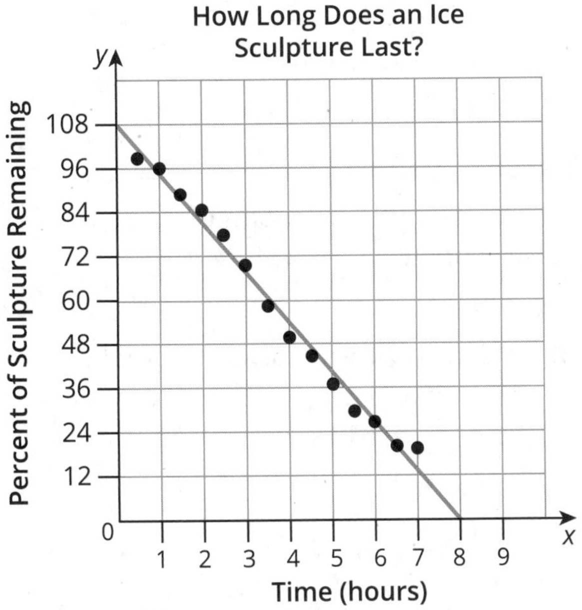

cube root

A cube root is one of 3 equal factors of a number.

EXAMPLE

The cube root of 125, $\sqrt[3]{125}$, is 5, because $5 \times 5 \times 5 = 125$.

D

data distribution

The overall shape of a data display is the data distribution.

EXAMPLE

There are three common data distributions: skewed left, skewed right, and symmetric.

decreasing function

If a function decreases across the entire domain, then the function is a decreasing function.

EXAMPLE

The function shown is a decreasing function.

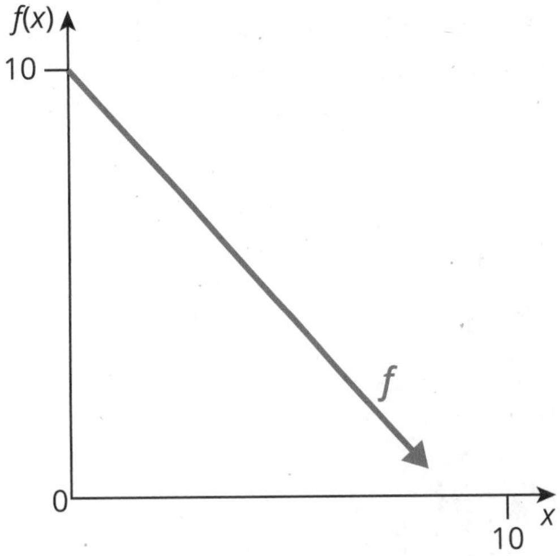

degree of a polynomial

The greatest exponent for any variable term in a polynomial determines the degree of the polynomial.

EXAMPLE

The polynomial $2x^3 + 5x^2 - 6x + 1$ has a degree of 3.

dependent quantity

When one quantity depends on another in a problem situation, it is the dependent quantity.

EXAMPLE

In the relationship between driving time and distance traveled, distance is the dependent quantity, because distance depends on the driving time.

difference of two squares

The difference of two squares is an expression in the form $a^2 - b^2$ that you can factor as $(a + b)(a - b)$.

dilation

A dilation is a transformation that produces a figure that is the same shape as the original figure, but not necessarily the same size.

EXAMPLE

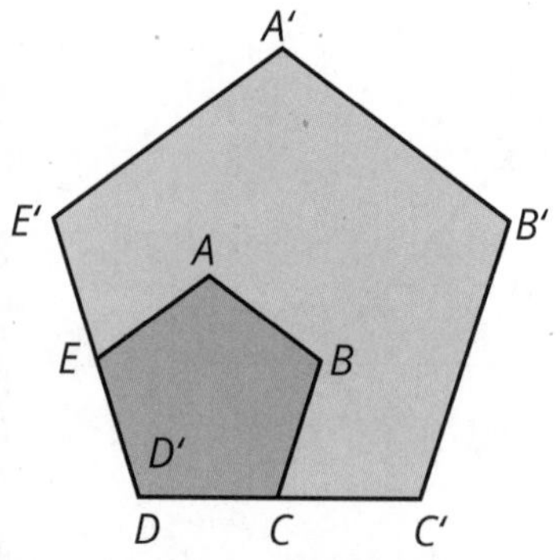

Pentagon $A'B'C'D'E'$ is a dilation of Pentagon $ABCDE$.

discontinuous graph

A discontinuous graph is a graph that is continuous for some values of the domain with at least one disjoint area between consecutive *x*-values.

EXAMPLE

The graph shown is a discontinuous graph.

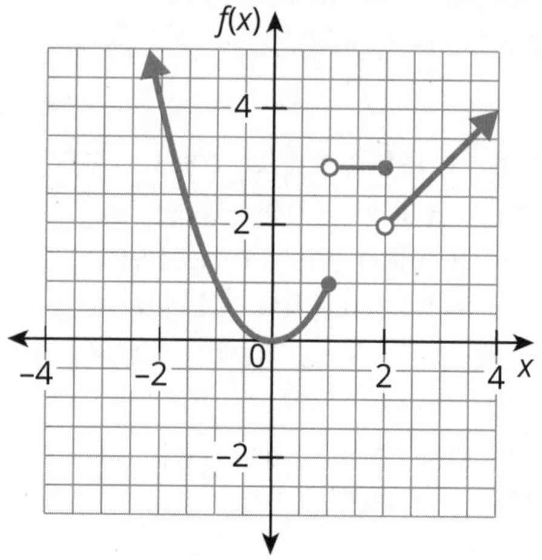

discrete graph

A discrete graph is a graph of isolated points.

EXAMPLE

The graph shown is a discrete graph.

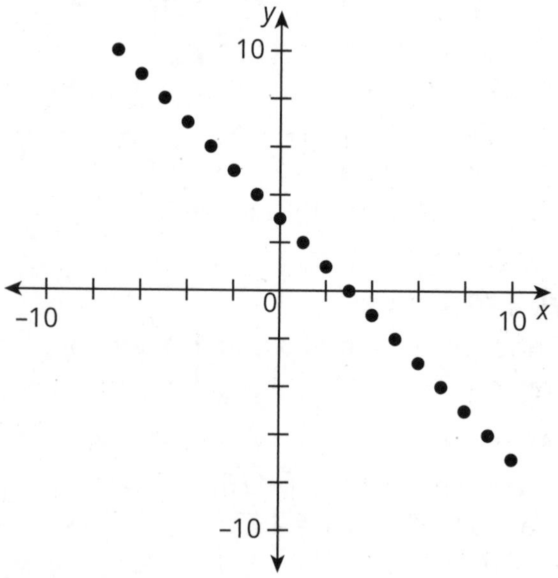

discriminant

The discriminant is the radicand expression in the Quadratic Formula that "discriminates" the number of real roots of a quadratic equation.

EXAMPLE

The discriminant in the Quadratic Formula is the expression $b^2 - 4ac$.

disjunction

A compound inequality in the form $x < a$ or $x > b$, where a and b are any real numbers, is a disjunction.

EXAMPLE

The compound inequality $x < -2$ or $x > 1$ is a disjunction.

domain

The domain is the set of input values in a relation.

EXAMPLE

The domain of the function $y = 2x$ is the set of all real numbers.

dot plot

A dot plot is a graph that shows the distribution of discrete data on a number line.

EXAMPLE

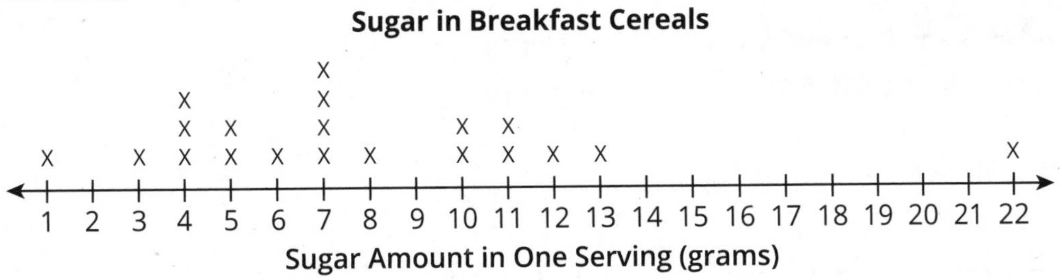

double root

The root of an equation indicates where the graph of the equation crosses the x-axis.
A double root occurs when the graph just touches the x-axis but does not cross it.

EXAMPLE

The quadratic equation $y = (x - 2)^2$ has a double root at $x = 2$.

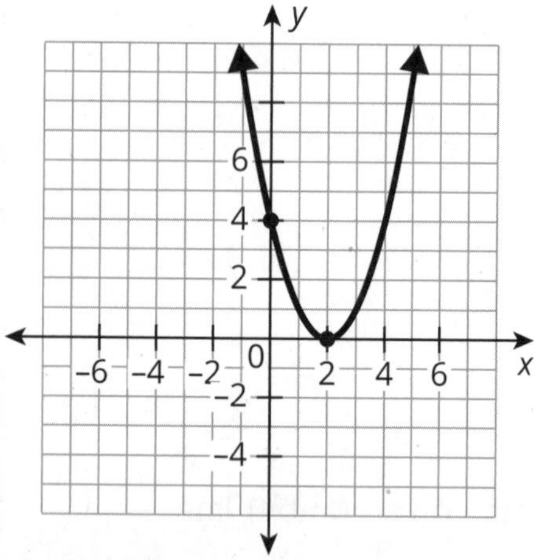

E

equivalent compound inequality

A compound inequality that is the equivalent of an absolute value inequality.

EXAMPLE

Absolute Value Inequality	Equivalent Compound Inequality
$\lvert ax + b \rvert < c$	$-c < ax + b < c$
$\lvert ax + b \rvert \leq c$	$-c \leq ax + b \leq c$
$\lvert ax + b \rvert > c$	$ax + b < -c$ or $ax + b > c$
$\lvert ax + b \rvert \geq c$	$ax + b \leq -c$ or $ax + b \geq c$

equivalent expressions

Equivalent expressions are two expressions that have the same value.

explicit formula

An explicit formula of a sequence is a formula for calculating the value of each term of a sequence using the term's position in the sequence. The explicit formula for an arithmetic sequence is $a_n = a_1 + d(n - 1)$. The explicit formula for a geometric sequence is $g_n = g_1 \cdot r^{n-1}$.

EXAMPLE

You can describe the sequence 1, 3, 5, 7, 9,... by the rule $a_n = 2n - 1$, where n is the position of the term. The fourth term of the sequence a_4 is $2(4) - 1$, or 7.

exponent

The exponent of the power is the number of times you use the base as a factor.

EXAMPLES

exponent

$2^3 = 2 \times 2 \times 2 = 8$

exponential decay function

An exponential decay function is an exponential function with a b-value greater than 0 and less than 1 and is of the form $y = a \cdot (1 - r)^x$, where r is the rate of decay.

EXAMPLE

Greenville has a population of 7000. Its population is decreasing at a rate of 1.75%. The exponential decay function that models this situation is $f(x) = 7000 \cdot 0.9825^x$.

exponential functions

The family of exponential functions includes functions of the form $f(x) = a \cdot b^x + c$, where a, b, and c are real numbers, and b is greater than 0 but is not equal to 1.

EXAMPLE

The function $f(x) = 2^x$ is an exponential function.

exponential growth function

An exponential growth function is an exponential function with a b-value greater than 1 and is of the form $y = a \cdot (1 + r)^x$, where r is the rate of growth.

EXAMPLE

Blueville has a population of 7000. Its population is increasing at a rate of 1.4%. The exponential growth function that models this situation is $f(x) = 7000 \cdot 1.014^x$.

extract the square root

To extract a square root, solve an equation of the form $a^2 = b$ for a.

extrapolation

To make predictions for values of x that are outside of the data set is extrapolation.

F

factored form

A quadratic function in the form $f(x) = a(x - r_1)(x - r_2)$, where $a \neq 0$, is in factored form.

EXAMPLE

The function $h(x) = x^2 - 8x + 12$ in factored form is $h(x) = (x - 6)(x - 2)$.

finite sequence

If a sequence terminates, it is a finite sequence.

EXAMPLE

The sequence 22, 26, 30 is a finite sequence.

first differences

First differences are the values determined by subtracting consecutive output values in a table when the input values have an interval of 1.

EXAMPLE

	Time (minutes)	Height (feet)	First Differences
	0	0	
$1 - 0 = 1$	1	1800	$1800 - 0 = 1800$
$2 - 1 = 1$	2	3600	$3600 - 1800 = 1800$
$3 - 2 = 1$	3	5400	$5400 - 3600 = 1800$

five-number summary

The five-number summary consists of the minimum value, the first quartile (Q1), the median, the third quartile (Q3), and the maximum value.

EXAMPLE

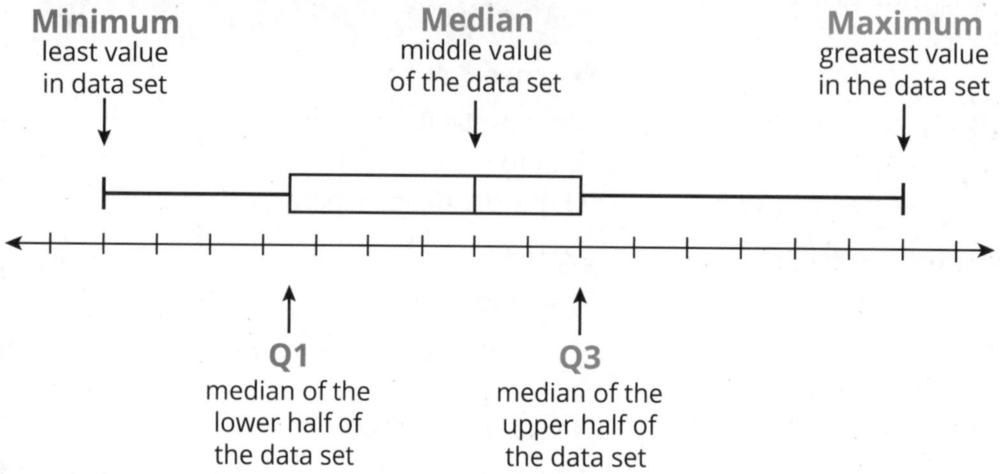

frequency

The height of each bar in a histogram indicates the frequency, which is the number of data values included in any given bin.

frequency distribution

A frequency distribution displays the frequencies for categorical data in a two-way table.

EXAMPLE

Favorite Meals of Students

Grade Level	Burgers	Chicken Nuggets	Pizza	Salad Bar	Total
9th grade	4	1	3	5	13
10th grade	3	7	3	4	17
Total	7	8	6	9	30

function

A function is a relation that assigns to each element of the domain exactly one element of the range.

EXAMPLE

The equation $y = 2x$ is a function. Every value of x has exactly one corresponding y-value.

function family

A function family is a group of functions that share certain characteristics.

EXAMPLE

Linear functions and exponential functions are examples of function families.

function notation

Function notation is a way of representing functions algebraically.

EXAMPLE

In the function $f(x) = 0.75x$, f is the name of the function, x represents the domain, and $f(x)$ represents the range.

G

general form (standard form) of a quadratic function

A quadratic function in the form $f(x) = ax^2 + bx + c$, where $a \neq 0$, is in general form, or standard form.

EXAMPLE

The function $f(x) = -5x^2 - 10x + 1$ is in general form.

geometric sequence

A geometric sequence is a sequence of numbers in which the ratio between any two consecutive terms is a constant.

EXAMPLE

The sequence 2, 4, 8, 16,... is a geometric sequence with a common ratio of 2.

greatest common factor (GCF)

The greatest common factor, or GCF, is the largest factor two or more numbers have in common.

EXAMPLE

factors of 16: **1**, **2**, **4**, 8, 16

factors of 12: **1**, **2**, 3, **4**, 6, 12

common factors: 1, 2, 4

greatest common factor: 4

greatest integer function (floor function)

The greatest integer function, also known as a floor function, is the greatest integer less than or equal to x.

EXAMPLE

For $f(x) = \lfloor x \rfloor$, if $x = 3.16$, $f(x) = 3$.

H

half-plane

The graph of a linear inequality is a half-plane, or half of a coordinate plane.

EXAMPLE

The shaded portion of the graph is a half-plane.

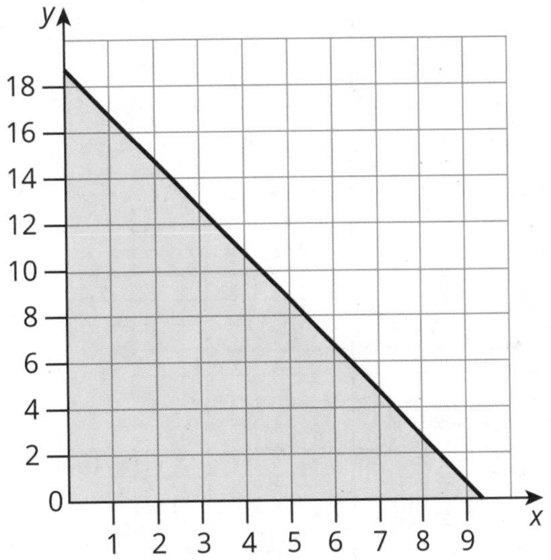

histogram

A histogram is a graphical way to display quantitative data using vertical bars.

EXAMPLE

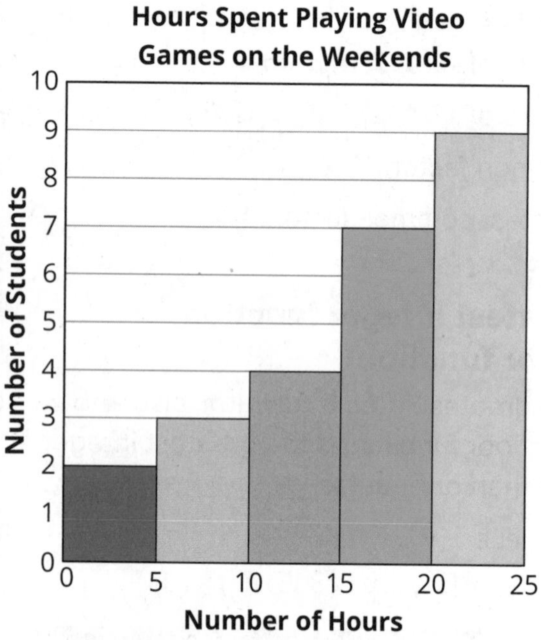

horizontal asymptote

A horizontal asymptote is a horizontal line that a function gets closer and closer to.

EXAMPLE

The graph shows a horizontal asymptote at $y = -1$.

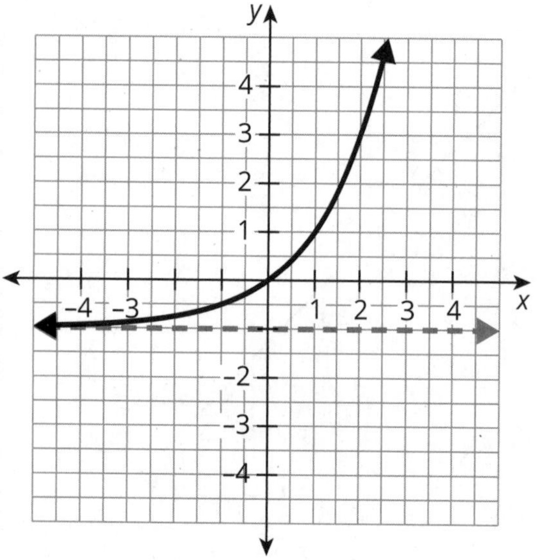

I

imaginary numbers

The set of imaginary numbers is the set of all numbers in the form $a + bi$, where a and b are real numbers and b is not equal to 0.

imaginary part of a complex number

In a complex number of the form $a + bi$, the term bi is the imaginary part of a complex number.

imaginary roots/imaginary zeros

Imaginary roots are imaginary solutions to equations. Quadratic functions that do not cross the x-axis have imaginary zeros.

inconsistent systems

Systems with no solution are inconsistent systems.

increasing function

If a function increases across the entire domain, then the function is an increasing function.

EXAMPLE

The function shown is an increasing function.

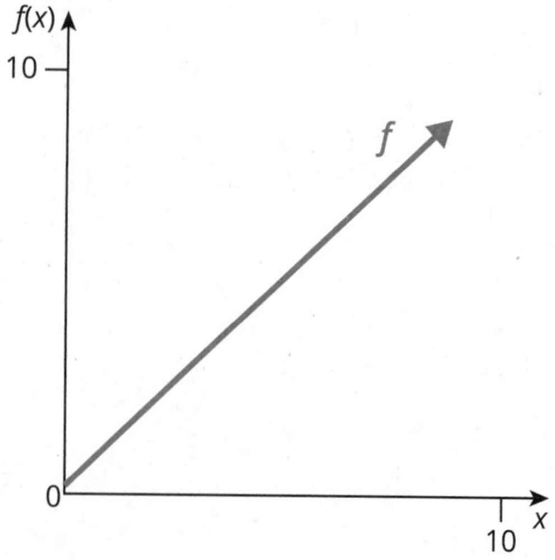

inequality

An inequality is a comparison of two values that shows that one value is greater than (>), less than (<), or not equal to (≠) the second value.

EXAMPLES

$0.3 > 0.28$	0.3 is greater than 0.28.
$\frac{3}{8} < \frac{3}{4}$	$\frac{3}{8}$ is less than $\frac{3}{4}$.
$7 \neq 11$	7 is not equal to 11.

independent quantity

The quantity that the dependent quantity depends upon is the independent quantity.

EXAMPLE

In the relationship between driving time and distance traveled, driving time is the independent quantity, because it does not depend on any other quantity.

infinite sequence

If a sequence continues on forever, it is an infinite sequence.

EXAMPLE

The sequence 22, 26, 30, 34,... is an infinite sequence.

infinite solutions

An equation with infinite solutions means that any value for the variable makes the equation true.

EXAMPLE

The equation $2x + 1 = 2x + 1$ has infinite solutions.

interpolation

Using a linear regression to make predictions within the data set is interpolation.

interquartile range (IQR)

The interquartile range, IQR, measures how far the data are spread out from the median.

EXAMPLE

In the data set 13, 17, 23, 24, 25, 29, 31, 45, 46, 53, 60, the median, 29, divides the data into two halves. The first quartile, 23, is the median of the lower half of the data. The third quartile, 46, is the median of the upper half of the data. The interquartile range is $46 - 23$, or 23.

inverse of a function

An inverse of a function takes the output value, performs some operation(s) on this value, and arrives back at the original function's input value.

EXAMPLE

The inverse of the function $y = 2x$ is the function $x = 2y$, or $y = \frac{x}{2}$.

J

joint frequency

Any frequency recorded within the body of a two-way frequency table is a joint frequency.

L

leading coefficient

The leading coefficient of a polynomial is the numeric coefficient of the term with the greatest power.

EXAMPLE

In the polynomial $-7x^2 + x + 25$, the value -7 is the leading coefficient.

least integer function (ceiling function)

The least integer function, also known as the ceiling function, is the least integer greater than or equal to *x*.

EXAMPLE

For $f(x) = \lceil x \rceil$, if $x = 3.16$, $f(x) = 4$.

Least Squares Method

The Least Squares Method is a method that creates a regression line for a scatter plot that has two basic requirements:
1) the line must contain the centroid of the data set, and 2) the sum of the squares of the vertical distances from each given data point is at a minimum with the line.

EXAMPLE

The regression line shown was created using the Least Squares Method.

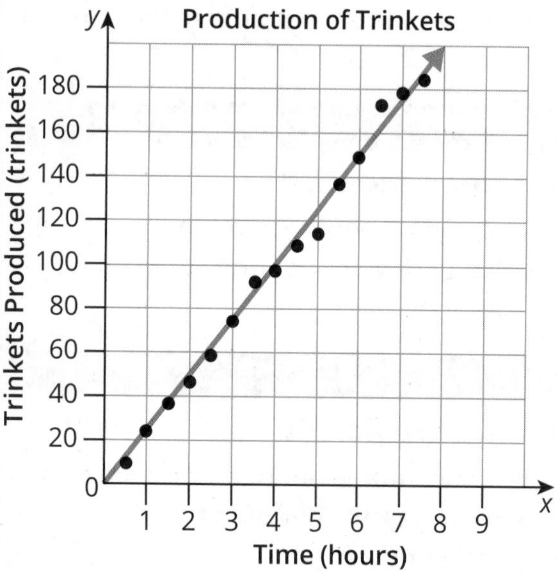

line of best fit

A line of best fit is a line that is as close to as many points as possible but doesn't have to go through all of the points.

EXAMPLE

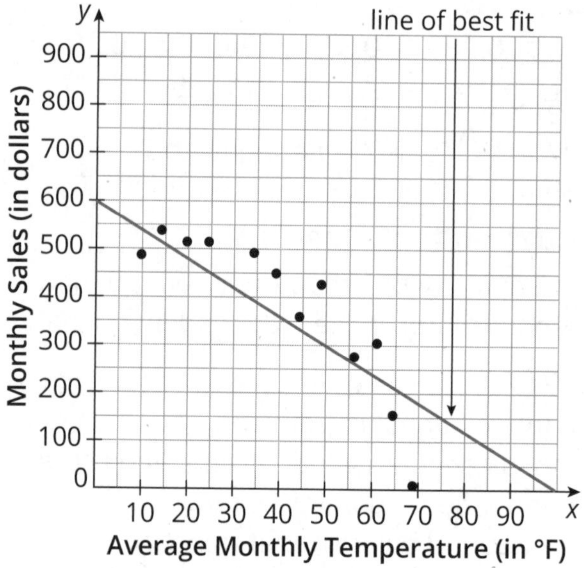

line of reflection

A line of reflection is the line that the graph is reflected across.

EXAMPLE

The graph of $y = |x| + 2$ is a reflection across the line of reflection, $y = 0$.

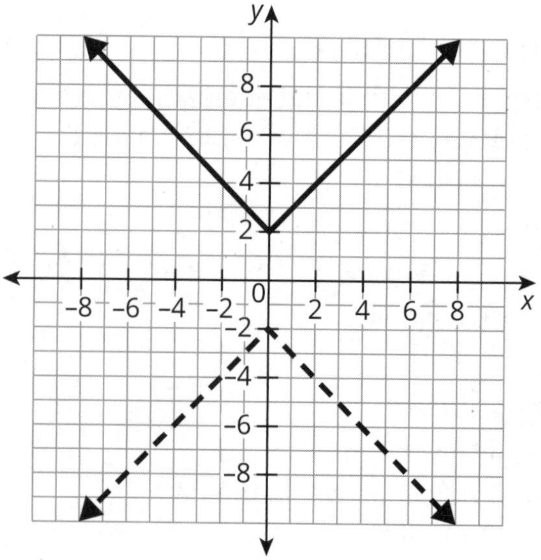

line of symmetry

A line of symmetry is an imaginary line that passes through a shape or object and divides it into two identical halves.

EXAMPLE

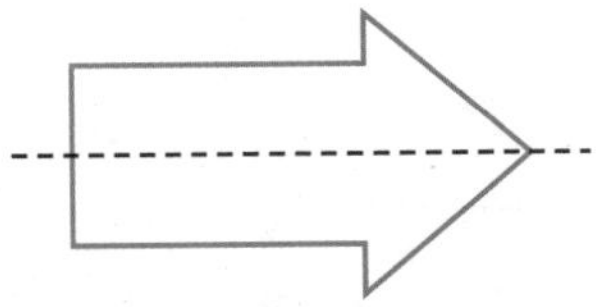

linear absolute value equation

An equation in the form $|x + a| = c$ is a linear absolute value equation.

EXAMPLE

The equation $|x - 1| = 6$ is a linear absolute value equation.

linear absolute value functions

The family of linear absolute value functions includes functions of the form $f(x) = a|x + b| + c$, where a, b, and c are real numbers, and a is not equal to 0.

EXAMPLE

The function $f(x) = |x - 3| - 2$ is a linear absolute value function.

linear absolute value inequality

An inequality in the form $|x + a| < c$ is a linear absolute value inequality.

EXAMPLE

The inequality $|w - 145.045| \leq 3.295$ is a linear absolute value inequality.

linear combinations method

The linear combinations method is a process used to solve a system of equations by adding two equations together, resulting in an equation with one variable.

EXAMPLE

Solve the following system of equations by using the linear combinations method:

$$\begin{cases} 6x - 5y = 3 \\ 2x + 2y = 12 \end{cases}$$

First, multiply the second equation by -3. Then, add the equations and solve for the remaining variable. Finally, substitute $y = 3$ into the first equation and solve for x. The solution of the system is (3, 3).

linear functions

The family of linear functions includes functions of the form $f(x) = ax + b$, where a and b are real numbers.

EXAMPLE

The function $f(x) = 3x + 2$ is a linear function.

linear piecewise functions

Linear piecewise functions include linear functions that have equation changes for different parts, or pieces, of the domain.

EXAMPLE

The function $f(x)$ is a linear piecewise function.

$$f(x) = \begin{cases} x + 5, & x \leq -2 \\ -2x + 1, & -2 < x \leq 2 \\ 2x - 9, & x > 2 \end{cases}$$

linear programming

Linear programming is a branch of mathematics that determines the maximum and minimum value of linear expressions on a region produced by a system of linear inequalities.

literal equation

Literal equations are equations in which the variables represent specific measures.

EXAMPLE

The equations $I = Prt$ and $A = lw$ are literal equations.

lower fence

The value of Q1 − (IQR · 1.5) is the lower fence.

M

marginal frequency distribution

A marginal frequency distribution displays the total of the frequencies of the rows or columns of a frequency distribution.

marginal relative frequency distribution

Displaying the relative frequencies for the rows or columns in a two-way table is a marginal relative frequency distribution. The marginal relative frequency distribution provides the ratio of total occurrences for each category to the total number of occurrences.

mathematical modeling

Mathematical modeling is explaining patterns in the real world based on mathematical ideas.

mean

The mean is the arithmetic average of the numbers in a data set.

EXAMPLE

Number of Pets

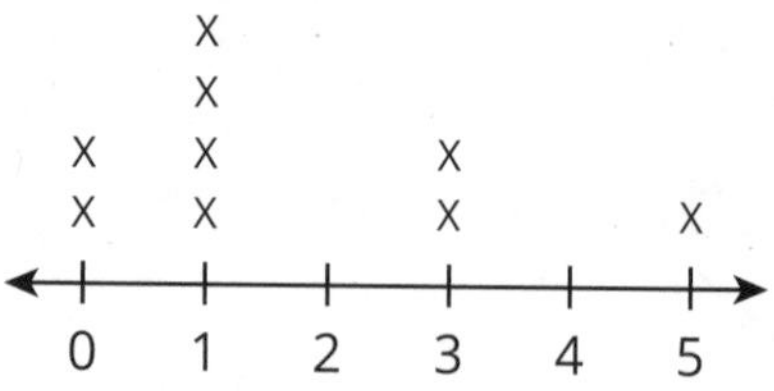

$$\text{Mean} = \frac{0+0+1+1+1+1+3+3+5}{9}$$
$$= \frac{15}{9} = 1\frac{2}{3} \text{ pets}$$

measure of center

A measure of center tells you how data values cluster, or the location of the center of the data.

EXAMPLES

Mean, median, and mode are each a measure of center for data.

measure of variation

A measure of variation describes the spread of data values.

EXAMPLE

Range is a measure of variation for data.

measure of central tendency

A measure of central tendency is a numeric value used to describe the overall clustering of data in a set.

EXAMPLE

The mean, median, and mode are the most common measures of central tendency.

monomial

Polynomials with only one term are monomials.

EXAMPLE

The expressions $5x$, 7, $-2xy$, and $13x^3$ are monomials.

N

no solution

An equation with no solution means that there is no value for the variable that makes the equation true.

EXAMPLE

The equation $2x + 1 = 2x + 3$ has no solution.

the number *i*

The number i is a number such that $i^2 = -1$.

numeric pattern

A numeric pattern is a sequence, or ordered set, of numbers that is created by following a given rule.

EXAMPLE

Rule: Multiply by 2.

Input	1	2	3	4
Output	2	4	6	8

O

one-to-one function

A function is a one-to-one function when both the function and its inverse are functions.

EXAMPLE

The equation $y = x^3$ is a one-to-one function because its inverse, $\sqrt[3]{x} = y$, is a function. The equation $y = x^2$ is not a one-to-one function because its inverse, $\pm\sqrt{x} = y$, is not a function.

outlier

An outlier is a data value that is significantly greater or lesser than other data values in a data set.

EXAMPLE

In the data set 1, 1, 3, 3, 4, 4, 5, 1000, the outlier is 1000.

P

parabola

The shape that a quadratic function forms when graphed is a parabola. A parabola is a smooth curve with reflectional symmetry.

EXAMPLE

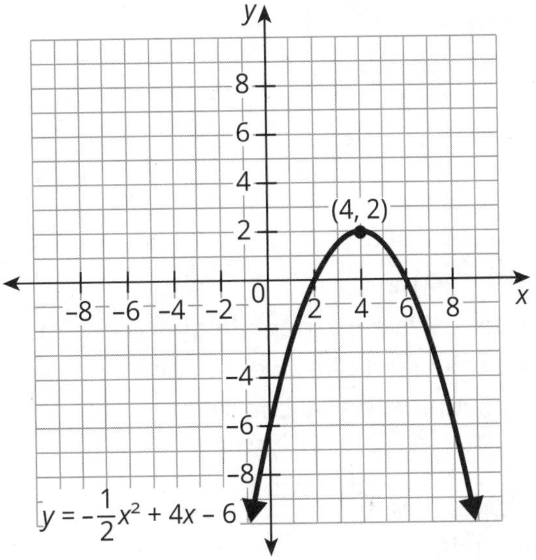

perfect square

A perfect square is the product of two equal integers.

EXAMPLES

9 is a perfect square: $3 \cdot 3 = 9$

25 is a perfect square: $5 \cdot 5 = 25$

perfect square trinomial

A perfect square trinomial is an expression in the form $a^2 + 2ab + b^2$ or in the form $a^2 - 2ab + b^2$.

piecewise function

A piecewise function is a function that you can represent using more than one function, each which corresponds to a part of the domain.

EXAMPLE

The graph represents a piecewise function.

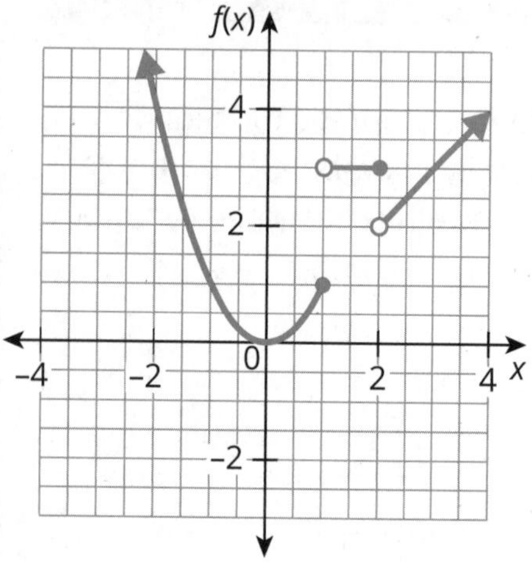

polynomial

A polynomial is a mathematical expression involving the sum of powers in one or more variables multiplied by coefficients.

EXAMPLE

The expression $3x^3 + 5x - 6x + 1$ is a polynomial.

prime factorization

Prime factorization is the process of writing numbers as the product of prime factors. You can use a factor tree to determine prime factors.

EXAMPLES

The factor tree shows the prime factorization of 30.

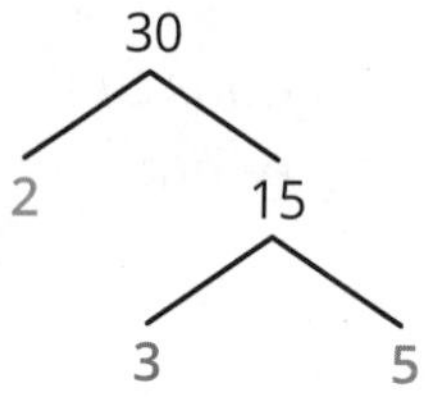

principal square root

The positive square root of a number.

pure imaginary number

A pure imaginary number is a number of the form bi, where b is not equal to 0.

Q

Quadratic Formula

The Quadratic Formula is $x = \frac{-b \pm \sqrt{b^2 - 4ac}}{2a}$, and you can use it to calculate the solutions to any quadratic equation of the form $ax^2 + bx + c$, where a, b, and c represent real numbers and $a \neq 0$.

quadratic functions

The family of quadratic functions includes functions of the form $f(x) = ax^2 + bx + c$, where a, b, and c are real numbers, and a is not equal to 0.

EXAMPLES

The equations $y = x^2 + 2x + 5$ and $y = -4x^2 - 7x + 1$ are quadratic functions.

R

range

The range is the set of output values in a relation.

EXAMPLE

The range of the function $y = x^2$ is the set of all numbers greater than or equal to zero.

rate of change

The rate of change for a situation describes the amount that the dependent variable changes compared to the amount the independent variable changes.

real part of a complex number

In a complex number of the form $a + bi$, the term a is the real part of a complex number.

recursive formula

A recursive formula expresses each new term of a sequence based on the preceding term in the sequence. The recursive formula for an arithmetic sequence is $a_n = a_{n-1} + d$. The recursive formula for a geometric sequence is $g_n = g_{n-1} \cdot r$.

EXAMPLE

The formula $a_n = a_{n-1} + 2$ is a recursive formula. Each successive term is calculated by adding 2 to the previous term. If $a_1 = 1$, then $a_2 = 1 + 2 = 3$.

reflection

A reflection of a graph is a mirror image of the graph about a line of reflection.

EXAMPLE

The triangle on the right is a reflection of the triangle on the left.

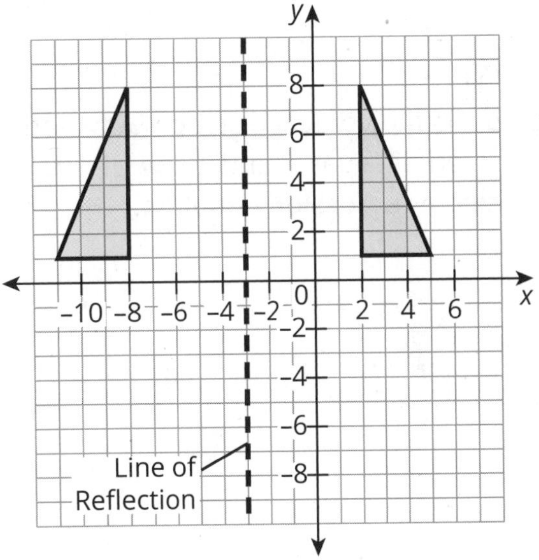

regression line

On a scatter plot, a regression line is a mathematical model you can use to predict the values of a dependent variable based upon the values of an independent variable.

relation

A relation is the mapping between a set of input values called the domain and a set of output values called the range.

EXAMPLE

The set of points {(0, 1), (1, 8), (2, 5), (3, 7)} is a relation.

relative frequency distribution

Representing the relative frequencies for joint data displayed in a two-way table is a relative frequency distribution. The relative frequency distribution provides the ratio of occurrences in each category to the total number of occurrences.

residual

A residual is the vertical distance between an observed data value and its predicted value using a regression equation.

residual plot

A residual plot is a scatter plot of the independent variable on the *x*-axis and the residuals on the *y*-axis.

EXAMPLE

The graph on the right shows a residual plot of the braking distance data.

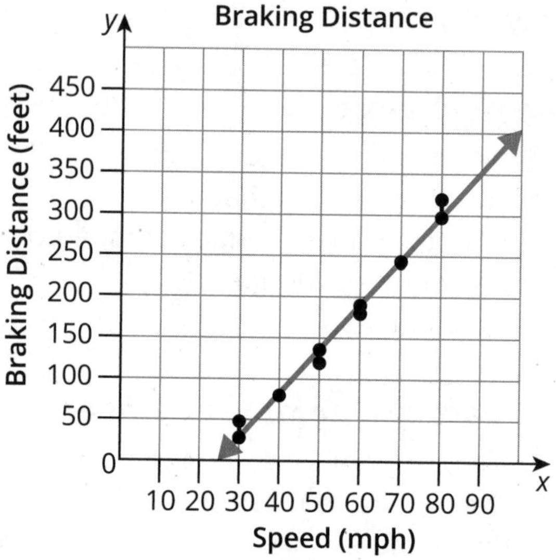

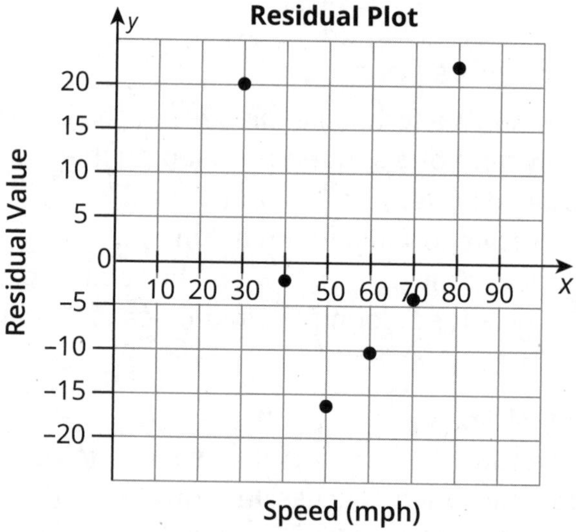

restrict the domain

To restrict the domain of a function means to define a new domain for the function that is a subset of the original domain.

root (roots)

The root or roots of an equation indicate where the graph of the equation crosses the *x*-axis.

EXAMPLE

The roots of the quadratic equation $x^2 - 4x + 3 = 0$ are $x = 3$ and $x = 1$.

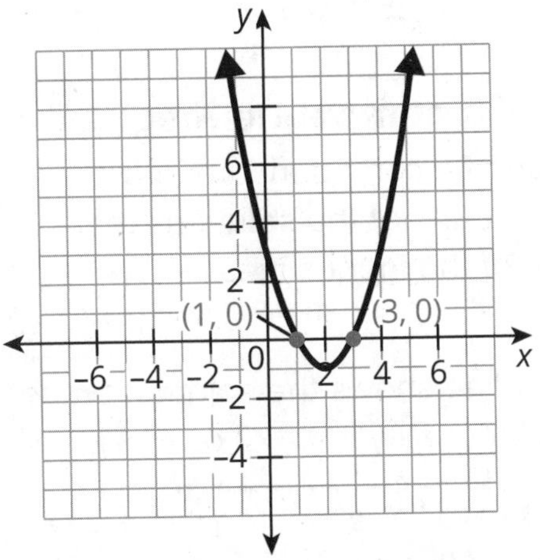

S

second differences

Second differences are the differences between consecutive values of the first differences.

EXAMPLE

x	y	First Differences	Second Differences
−3	−5		
−2	0	5	
−1	3	3	−2
0	4	1	−2
1	3	−1	−2
2	0	−3	−2
3	−5	−5	−2

sequence

A sequence is a pattern involving an ordered arrangement of numbers, geometric figures, letters, or other objects.

EXAMPLE

The numbers 1, 1, 2, 3, 5, 8, 13,... form a sequence.

simple interest

In a simple interest account, the interest earned at the end of each interval is a percent of the starting balance (also known as the principal).

EXAMPLE

Tonya deposits \$200 in a 3-year certificate of deposit that earns 4% simple interest. You calculate the amount of interest that Tonya earns using the simple interest formula.

$$I = (200)(0.04)(3)$$

$$I = 24$$

Tonya earns \$24 in interest.

skewed distribution

In a skewed distribution, the peak of the data is to the left or the right side of the graph.

EXAMPLE

The data in the dot plot have a skewed distribution.

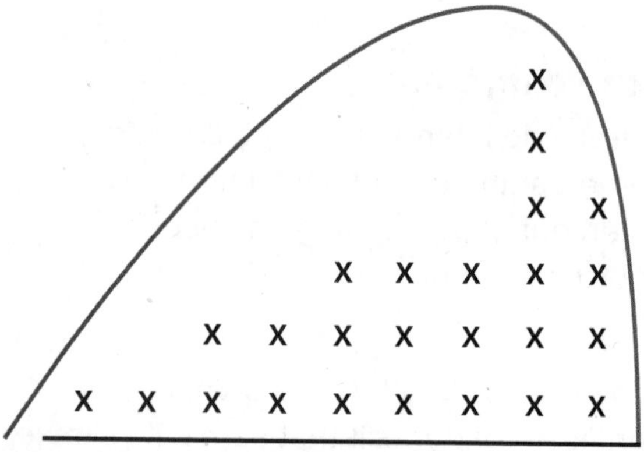

slope

In any linear relationship, slope describes the direction and steepness of a line and you usually represent it with the variable *m*. Slope is another name for rate of change. (See *rate of change*.)

EXAMPLE

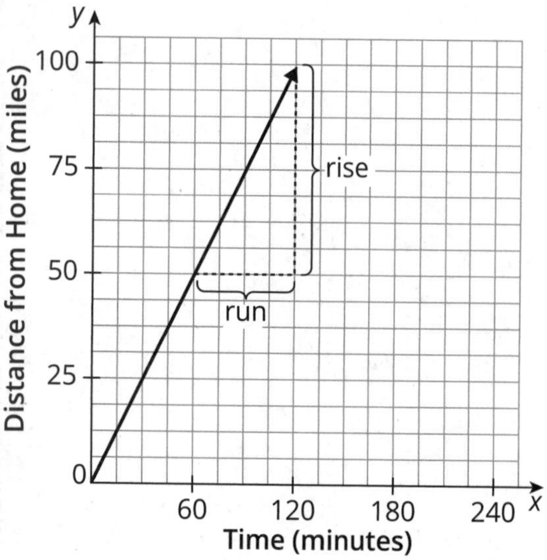

The slope of the line is $\frac{50}{60}$, or $\frac{5}{6}$.

solution

The solution to an equation is any value for the variable that makes the equation a true statement.

EXAMPLE

The solution of the equation $3x + 4 = 25$ is 7 because 7 makes the equation true: $3(7) + 4 = 25$, or $25 = 25$.

solution of a compound inequality

The solution of a compound inequality is the part or parts of the solutions that satisfy both of the inequalities.

EXAMPLE

The number line shows the solution of the compound inequality $x < -2$ or $x > 1$.

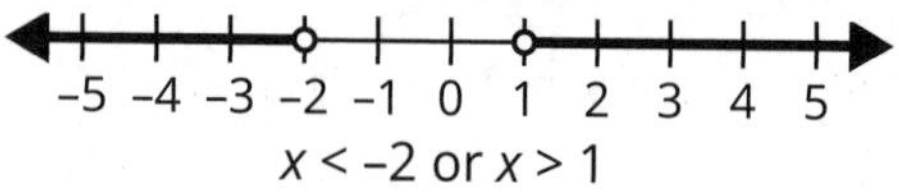

solution of a system of linear inequalities

The solution of a system of linear inequalities is the intersection of the solutions to each inequality. Every point in the intersection region satisfies all inequalities in the system.

EXAMPLE

$$\begin{cases} 200a + 100c \leq 800 \\ 75(a-1) + 50c \geq 150 \end{cases}$$

The solution of this system of linear inequalities is shown by the shaded region, which represents the intersection of the solutions to each inequality.

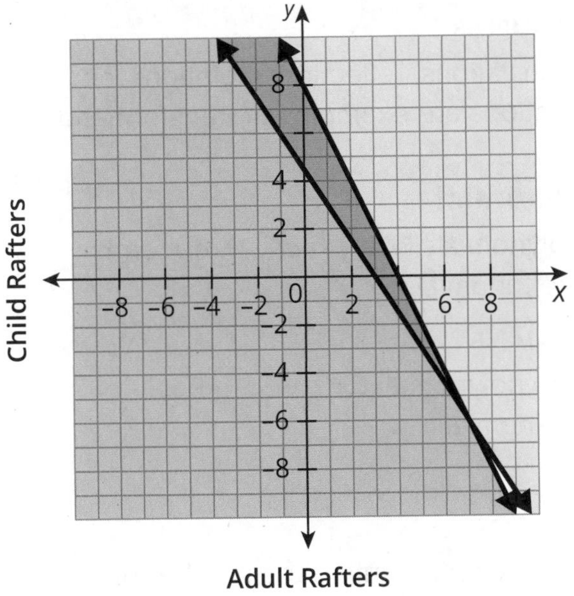

solve an inequality

To solve an inequality means to determine the values of the variable that make the inequality true.

EXAMPLE

You can solve the inequality $x + 5 > 6$ by subtracting 5 from each side of the inequality. The solution is $x > 1$. Any number greater than 1 will make the inequality $x + 5 > 6$ true.

square root

A square root is one of two equal factors of a number.

EXAMPLE

The square root of 36, $\sqrt{36}$, is 6, because $6 \cdot 6 = 36$.

standard deviation

Standard deviation is a measure of how spread out the data are from the mean.

statistics

Statistics are numeric characteristics of data.

step function

A step function is a piecewise function on a given interval whose pieces are discontinuous constant functions.

EXAMPLE

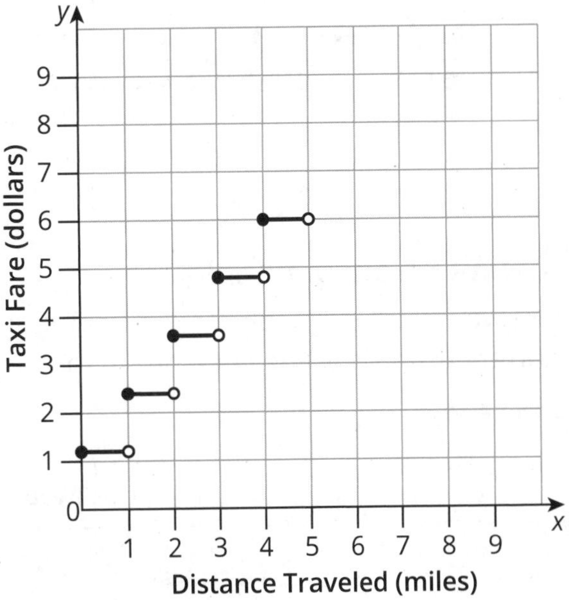

system of linear equations

When two or more linear equations define a relationship between quantities, they form a system of linear equations.

EXAMPLE

The equations $y = 3x + 7$ and $y = -4x$ are a system of linear equations.

$$\begin{cases} y = 3x + 7 \\ y = -4x \end{cases}$$

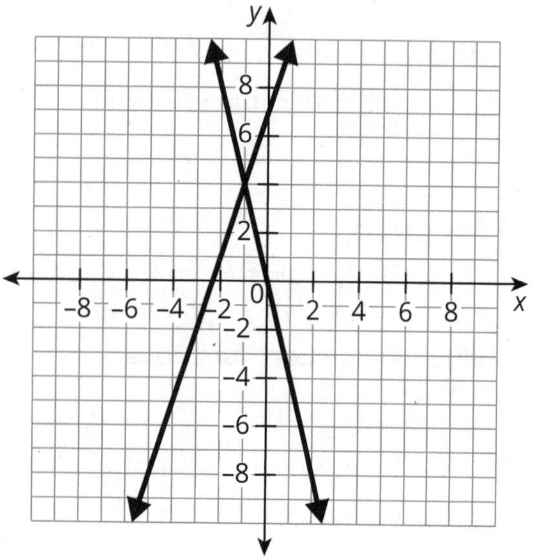

T

term of a sequence

A term of a sequence is an individual number, figure, or letter in the sequence.

EXAMPLE

In the sequence 2, 4, 6, 8, 10,... the first term is 2, the second term is 4, and the third term is 6.

transformation

A transformation is the mapping, or movement, of a plane and all the points of a figure on a plane according to a common action or operation.

EXAMPLES

Translations, reflections, rotations, and dilations are examples of transformations.

trinomial

Polynomials with exactly three terms are trinomials.

EXAMPLE

The polynomial $5x^2 - 6x + 9$ is a trinomial.

two-way frequency table

A two-way frequency table displays categorical data by representing the number of occurrences that fall into each group for two variables.

EXAMPLE

Favorite Meals of Students

		Burgers	Chicken Nuggets	Pizza	Salad Bar
Grade Level	9th grade	//// 4	/ 1	/// 3	~~////~~ 5
	10th grade	/// 3	~~////~~ // 7	/// 3	//// 4

U

upper fence

The value of Q3 + (IQR • 1.5) is the upper fence.

V

vertex form

A quadratic function in the form $f(x) = a(x - h)^2 + k$, where $a \neq 0$, is in vertex form.

EXAMPLE

The equation $y = 2(x - 5)^2 + 10$ is in vertex form. The vertex of the graph is the point (5, 10).

vertex of a parabola

The vertex of a parabola is the lowest or highest point on the graph of the quadratic function.

EXAMPLE

The vertex of the graph of $f(x)$ is the point (1, −4).

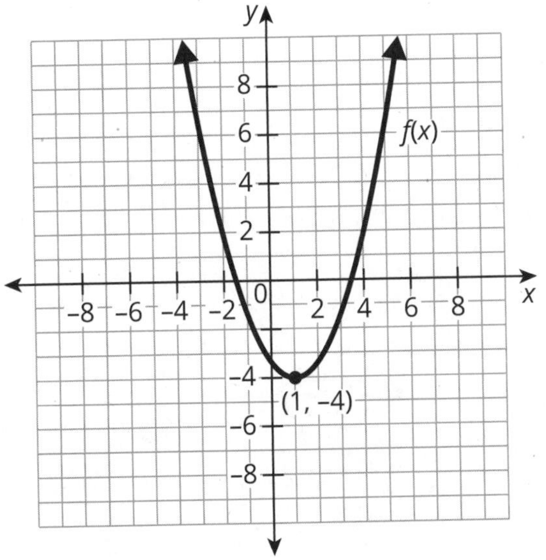

vertical line test

The vertical line test is a visual method used to determine whether a relation represented as a graph is a function.

EXAMPLE

The equation $y = 3x^2$ is a function. The graph passes the vertical line test because there are no vertical lines you can draw that would intersect the graph at more than one point.

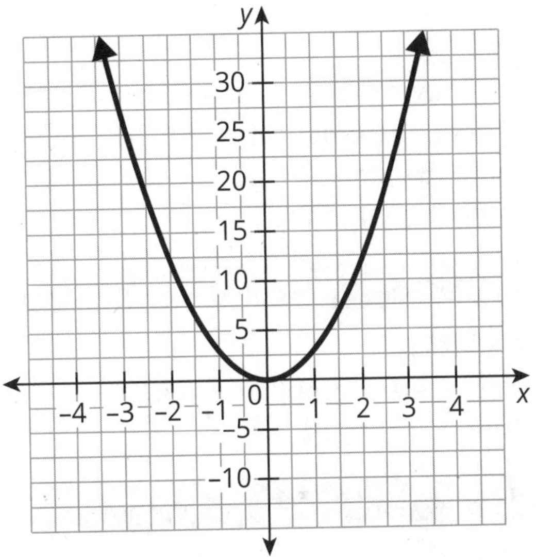

The equation $x^2 + y^2 = 9$ is not a function. The graph fails the vertical line test because you can draw a vertical line that intersects the graph at more than one point.

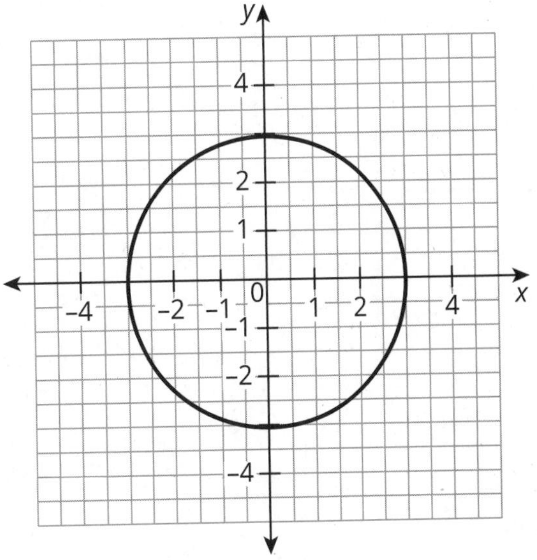

vertical motion model

A vertical motion model is a quadratic equation that models the height of an object at a given time. The equation is of the form $g(t) = -16t^2 + v_0t + h_0$, where $g(t)$ represents the height of the object in feet, t represents the time in seconds that the object has been moving, v_0 represents the initial velocity (speed) of the object in feet per second, and h_0 represents the initial height of the object in feet.

EXAMPLE

A rock is thrown in the air at a velocity of 10 feet per second from a cliff that is 100 feet high. The equation $y = -16t^2 + 10t + 100$ models the height of the rock.

X

x-intercept

The point where a graph crosses the *x*-axis is an *x*-intercept.

Y

y-intercept

The point where a graph crosses the *y*-axis is a *y*-intercept.

Z

zero of a function

A zero of a function is a real number that makes the value of the function equal to zero, or $f(x) = 0$.

EXAMPLE

The zero of the linear function $f(x) = 2(x - 4)$ is (4, 0).

The zeros of the quadratic function $f(x) = -2x^2 + 4x$ are (0, 0) and (2, 0).

Zero Product Property

The Zero Product Property states that if the product of two or more factors is equal to zero, then at least one factor must be equal to zero.

Index

D

E

M

N

O

P

S

T

U

V

X

Y

Z

Photo Credits

All images obtained via Getty Images: 3 sukanya sitthikongsak/Moment; 17 Marc Romanelli/Royalty-free; 31 drnadig/E+; 53 View Pictures/Contributor/Universal Images Group; 65 MirageC/Moment; 79 feellife/Plant; 109 cmannphoto/E+; 121 Kameleon007/E+; 135 Eugene4873/Garment; 147 Shanna Baker/Moment; 161 mikkelwilliam/Composition; 173 artisteer/Arts Culture and Entertainment; 189 simarik/Concepts; 203 Inna Giliarova/Symbol; 221 harpazo_hope/Moment; 237 Irina274/Small Group Of Objects; 247 Barcin/E+; 259 SimpleImages/Moment; 271 Yevgen Romanenko/Moment; 285 Photography Aubrey Stoll/Moment; 301 retales botijero/Moment; 317 cmannphoto/Household Fixture; 331 eugenesergeev/Building Feature; 347 Alaska Photography/Moment; 359 Travis Wolfe/EyeEm/EyeEm; 369 gregepperson/Climbing; 381 Fraser McAlister/Moment Open; 399 cmannphoto/E+; 413 undefined undefined/Geographical Locations; 429 Mint Images/Mint Images RF; 441 Pachai-Leknettip/Concepts; 461 Maren Winter/Food Staple; 477 GK Hart/Vikki Hart/Stone; 497 jayk7/Moment; 523 Richard T. Nowitz/The Image Bank; 535 zhaojiankang/Topics; 545 cmannphoto/Hot Drink; 557 Kameleon007/Key; 571 xphiyya sx hnxngbaw/EyeEm/EyeEm; 581 Ignacio Palacios/Stone; 599 PLAINVIEW/Fish Tank; 609 Viktoryia Vinnikava/EyeEm/EyeEm; 625 Kevin Trimmer/Moment; 635 krisanapong detraphiphat/Moment; 643 trekandshoot/Residential Building; 657 Rudy Malmquist/Moment; 673 omersukrugox/Commercial Activity; 697 Hans Strand/Corbis Documentary; 723 Toshiro Shimada/Moment; 741 Peter Dazeley/The Image Bank; 765 Bill Ross/The Image Bank; 779 coldsnowstorm/Lepidoptera; 791 marekuliasz/Leisure Games; 813 sturti/Entertainment Event; 841 peepo/Domestic Car; 851 3DSculptor/Spaceship; 863 kunst-mp/Container;